GCSE Health & Social Care for OCR

Double Award Student's Book

Angela Fisher, Stephen Seamons,
Richard Cresswell and Mike Ancil

Acknowledgements

Photos:

p.iv 2009 © elenathewise. Image from BigStockPhoto.com; p.v © Andrey Mirzoyants/Fotolia; p.2 © iStockphoto.com/Rich Legg; p.3 © photoconcepts1/Fotolia; p.4 © deanm1974/Fotolia; p.8 © Monika Adamczyk/Fotolia; p.11 © Aramanda/Fotolia; p.12 © Pavel Losevsky/Fotolia; p.17 © iStockphoto.com/Winston Davidian; p.21 2009 © vgstudio. Image from BigStockPhoto.com; p.22 © Margo Harrison/Fotolia; p.27 © iStockphoto.com/Roman Milert; p.32 © Imagenatural/Fotolia; p.38 © John Edward Linden/archaid.co.uk; p.42 © John Birdsall/John Birdsall/PA Photos; p.44 © David Hoffman www.hoffmanphotos.com; p.50 © iStockphoto.com/Rich Legg; p.51 © deanm1974/Fotolia; p.58 © photoconcepts1/Fotolia; p.60 © iStockphoto.com/Eliza Snow; p.61 (top) © Monkey Business/Fotolia, (bottom) © Paula Solloway/Photofusion; p.64 © Monkey Business/Fotolia; p.66 © iStockphoto.com/Chris Schmidt; p.70 © Lisa F. Young/Fotolia; p.75 © Roman Milert/Fotolia; p.78 © iStockphoto.com/Damir Cudic; p.79 © Galina Barskaya/Fotolia; p.80 © erwinova/Fotolia; p.84 © Vladimir Mucibabic/Fotolia; p.87 © Adam Przezak/Fotolia; p.88 © Kurhan/Fotolia; p.90 © moodboard/Fotolia; p.92 © PCmi/Fotolia; p.94 © iStockphoto.com/Mara Radeva; p.95 © ACE STOCK LIMITED/Alamy; p.96 © Monkey Business/Fotolia; p.98 © Stephen Coburn/Fotolia.com; p.100 © iStockphoto.com/Frances Twitty; p.103 © iStockphoto.com/Tomaz Levstek; p.106 © Yuri Arcurs/Fotolia; p.108 © iStockphoto.com/Murat Koc; p.110 (top) © iStockphoto.com/Stephanie Horrocks, (bottom) © Monkey Business/Fotolia; p.112 © Coka/Fotolia; p.115 (left) © Monkey Business/Fotolia, (right) © Renata Osinska/Fotolia; p.117 © Monkey Business/Fotolia; p.119 © iStockphoto.com/dra_schwartz; p.120 © iStockphoto.com/Manuela Krause; p.121 © Joe Gough/Fotolia; p.124 (left) © iStockphoto.com/fotoVoyager, (right) © Stephen Finn/Fotolia; p.133 © Kristian Sekulic/Fotolia; p.135 © iStockphoto.com/Ian Hamilton; p.136 © iStockphoto.com/Karen Town; p.138 (top) © Jason Stitt/Fotolia, (bottom) © Ki Price/Rex Features; p.139 © moodboard/Fotolia; p.142 © iStockphoto.com/Nikolay Mamluke; p.143 © Eddie Mulholland/Rex Features; p.145 (left) 2009 © elenathewise. Image from BigStockPhoto.com, (right) © Monkey Business/Fotolia; p.146 © Monkey Business/Fotolia; p.150 © Thomas Perkins/Fotolia; p.151 © Monkey Business/Fotolia; p.152 © iStockphoto.com/Jennifer Trenchard; p.154 © endostock/Fotolia; p.160 © iStockphoto.com/Rich Legg; p.162 © Geoff A Howard/Alamy; p.163 © iStockphoto.com/James Pauls; p.165 © iStockphoto.com/Yarinca; p.168 © Monkey Business/Fotolia; p.172 2009 © andres. Image from BigStockPhoto.com; p.173 © Fotolia IV/Fotolia; p.174 2009 © andres. Image from BigStockPhoto.com; p.176 © iStockphoto.com/Michael DeLeon; p.183 © George Chamberlain/Fotolia; p.185 © iStockphoto.com/Michael Krinke; p.190 2009 © danabeth555. Image from BigStockPhoto.com; p.191 © Burger/Phanie/Rex Features; p.196 © Fotolia V/Fotolia; p.198 © iStockphoto.com/Michel de Nijs; p.202 © iStockphoto.com/ZoneCreative; p.204 © iStockphoto.com/vndrpttn; p.205 © iStockphoto.com/technotr; p.206 © iStockphoto.com/Leigh Schindler; p.207 © iStockphoto.com/Ethan Myerson; p.208 © iStockphoto.com/Eliza Snow; p.210 (top) © iStockphoto.com/Joseph C. Justice Jr., (bottom) © poco_bw/Fotolia; p.212 (top) © iStockphoto.com/Catherine Yeulet, (bottom) © iStockphoto.com/Christian Wheatley; p.219 © Allstar Picture Library/Alamy; p.221 (top) Reproduced with permission of the Department of Health, (bottom) © ITV/Rex Features; p.223 © Manuela Cifra/Newspix/Rex Features; p.225 © Ian Miles-Flashpoint Pictures/Alamy; p.227 © iStockphoto.com/Patricia Nelson; p.229 © Janine Wiedel Photolibrary/Alamy; p.231 © iStockphoto.com/Jorgen Udvang; p.234 © Alex Segre/Alamy; p.235 © Tim Ireland/PA Archive/PA Photos; p.236 © iStockphoto.com/Ernesto Solla; p.239 © iStockphoto.com/Eric Hood; p.244 © John Birdsall/John Birdsall/PA Photos; p.246 © iStockphoto.com/Fred Goldstein; p.247 © Andrey Mirzoyants/Fotolia; p.248 © iStockphoto.com/Andrew Howe Photography; p.251 © deanm1974/Fotolia; p.258 © Monkey Business/Fotolia; p.263 © iStockphoto.com/Vasiliki Varvaki; p.266 © Rex Features; p.274 © iStockphoto.com/Curt Pickens; p.275 © iStockphoto.com/Nilgun Bostanci; p.276 © beerkoff/Fotolia; p.278 © iStockphoto.com/Tomas Bercic; p.281 © David Grossman/Alamy; p.290 © iStockphoto.com/Dawn Hudson; p.291 © iStockphoto.com/Matjaz Boncina; p.297 © Photofusion Picture Library/Alamy; p.309 © iStockphoto.com/Huchen Lu; p.312 © iStockphoto.com/Alex Hinds; p.313 © Icon Digital Featurepix/Alamy; p.314 © SHOUT/Alamy; p.320 2009 © radhoose. Image from BigStockPhoto.com; p.322 © cegli/Fotolia.

Other:

p.33 *New hope for Alzheimer's sufferers after new treatment 'restores memory in minutes'*, by Jenny Hope: Reproduced with permission of the Daily Mail/Mail Online.
p.39 The Strategic Health Authorities objectives: Crown copyright material is reproduced with the permission of the Controller Office of Public Sector Information (OPSI). Reproduced under the terms of the Click-Use Licence.
p.179 World Health Organization logo: Reproduced with permission of the World Health Organization.
p.233 The eatwell plate: Crown copyright material is reproduced with the permission of the Controller Office of Public Sector Information (OPSI). Reproduced under the terms of the Click-Use Licence.

United Kingdom: Folens Publishers, Waterslade House, Thame Road, Haddenham, Buckinghamshire, HP17 8NT.
Email: folens@folens.com Website: www.folens.com

Ireland: Folens Publishers, Greenhills Road, Tallaght, Dublin 24.
Email: info@folens.ie Website: www.folens.ie

Editor: Geoff Tuttle
Text design and page layout: Neil Sutton at Pumpkin House
Cover design: Jump To!
Cover images: (left) © moodboard/Fotolia; (centre left) © Monkey Business/Fotolia; (centre right) © Marzanna Syncerz/Fotolia; (right) © Monkey Business/Fotolia
Illustrations: Debbie Hinks and Tony Randell

The websites recommended in this publication were correct at the time of going to press, however websites may have been removed or web addresses changed since that time. Folens has made every attempt to suggest websites that are reliable and appropriate for student's use. It is not unknown for unscrupulous individuals to put unsuitable material on websites that may be accessed by students. Teachers should check all websites before allowing students to access them. Folens is not responsible for the content of external websites.

For general spellings Folens adheres to Oxford Dictionary of English, Second Edition (Revised), 2005.

First published 2009 by Folens Limited.

British Library Cataloguing in Publication Data. A catalogue record for this publication is available from the British Library.

ISBN 978-1-85008-424-2 Folens code FD4242

Contents

Introduction to the course

You will need to decide whether to follow the Single Award (A406) or the Double Award (A412) in Health and Social Care. If following the Single Award you will be learning about the health, social care and early years sectors, and about personal development and relationships. When moving to the Double Award, the two additional units will focus on making sure that you understand how to maintain health and well-being, as well as considering how to safeguard and protect individuals who seek support from different types of care settings.

The Single Award is made up of **two** units. These are:

Unit	Title	Type of assessment
1 (A911)	Health, Social Care and Early Years Provision	Controlled assessment
2 (A912)	Understanding Personal Development and Relationships	Externally tested

If you are following the Double Award the additional units will be:

Unit	Title	Type of assessment
3 (A913)	Promoting Health and Well-being	Controlled assessment
4 (A914)	Safeguarding and Protecting Individuals	Externally tested

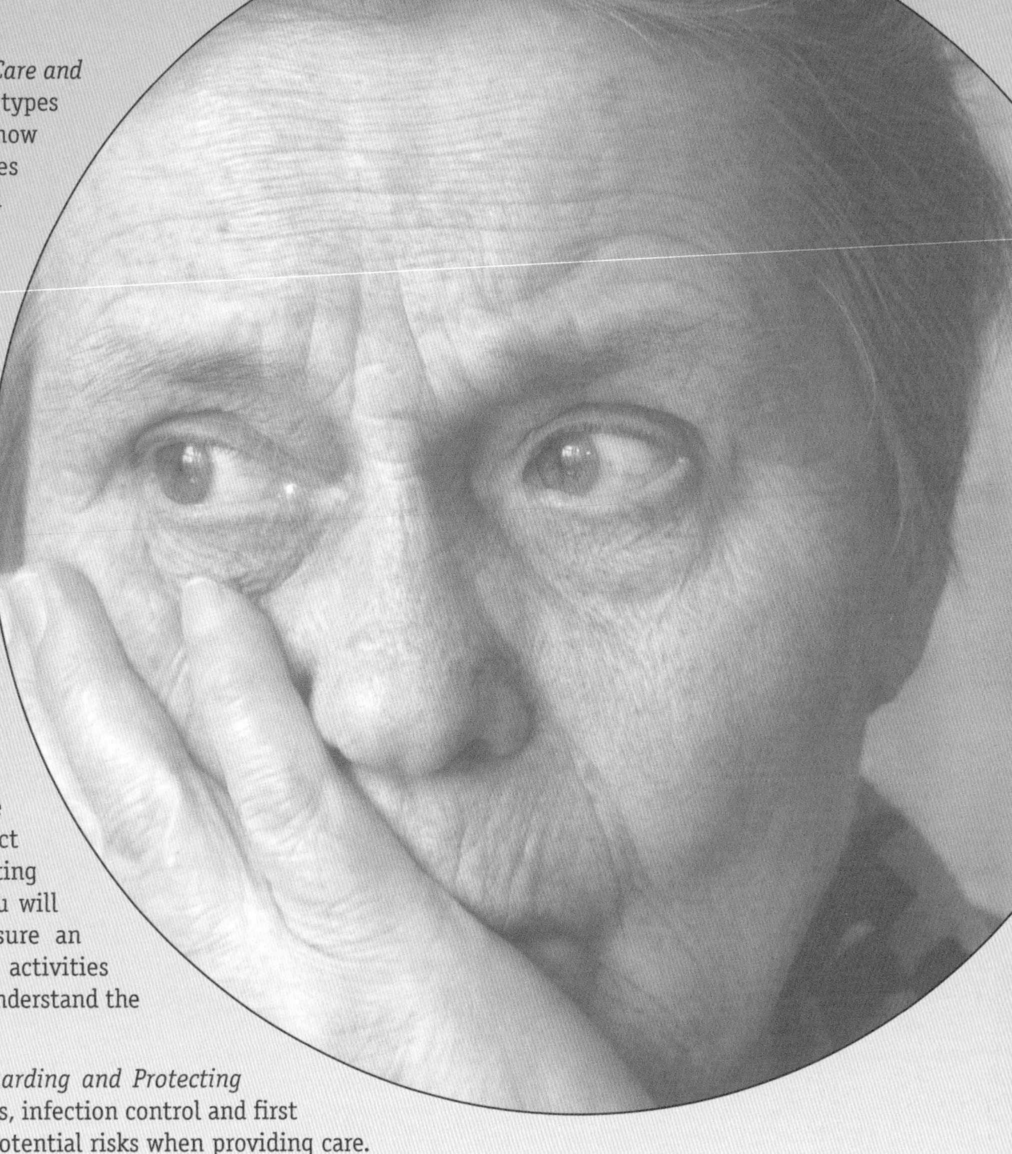

In this book, *Unit 1 (A911): Health, Social Care and Early Years Provision* considers the different types of services available to individuals and how these are organized. Some of the job roles available in the sector, and the skills and qualifications needed to do these jobs will be considered. You will also find out about the different types of clients who use the services and the barriers that can prevent people from accessing the services.

Unit 2 (A912): Understanding Personal Development and Relationships provides information about characteristics of growth and development, the factors that can influence the development of individuals and major life changes, showing how individuals can be supported and how such support will help them to cope.

When looking at *Unit 3 (A913): Promoting Health and Well-Being* you will give consideration to factors that can affect health and well-being, and ways of promoting and supporting health improvements. You will also be asked to use methods to measure an individual's health status. Some practical activities will be incorporated, which will help you understand the topics in your student's book.

The topics within *Unit 4 (A914): Safeguarding and Protecting Individuals* include how to safeguard clients, infection control and first aid, as well as learning how to recognize potential risks when providing care.

You may, as part of your course, be asked to visit health, social care and early years settings, or you may have visits from specialists from the care sector. Such visits will be very useful for your coursework but you must remember that confidentiality will be very important. For example, you must change the names of the people and the care setting so that they cannot be recognized.

Working through the topics within each unit will help you to gain knowledge, skills and understanding, as well as helping you to prepare for the controlled assignments and external tests.

It will be important to follow the specifications for each of the units, the grading requirements and the guidance given in order to achieve successful outcomes.

We hope you will enjoy using this book and that it helps you to have a broad knowledge of the care sector, as well as being successful in achieving the qualification.

How to use this book

The book is divided into units. These are shown in the contents.

Each unit has sections. These are shown in the contents.

Unit 1 Health, Social Care and Early Years Provision

Unit 2 Understanding Personal Development and Relationships

At the beginning of each section is a Getting started page. This shows you what you will know when you have completed the section.

1 Health, Social Care and Early Years Provision

The range of care needs of major client groups

The range of care needs of major client groups

Who needs care services and why?

Getting started

You need to understand how care services are designed to meet the health, developmental and social needs of major client groups. Major client groups are:

- babies and children
- adolescents
- adults
- older adults
- people with disabilities

Services are designed to meet the physical, intellectual, emotional and social care needs of individuals. In this section you will find out who the major client groups are by conducting a survey or client interviews.

Key words are shown in **bold type.** The word check boxes tell you what they mean.

Extra material for those working at a higher level is shown with a yellow tint behind it.

Answering theses questions will check your understanding of what you have read.

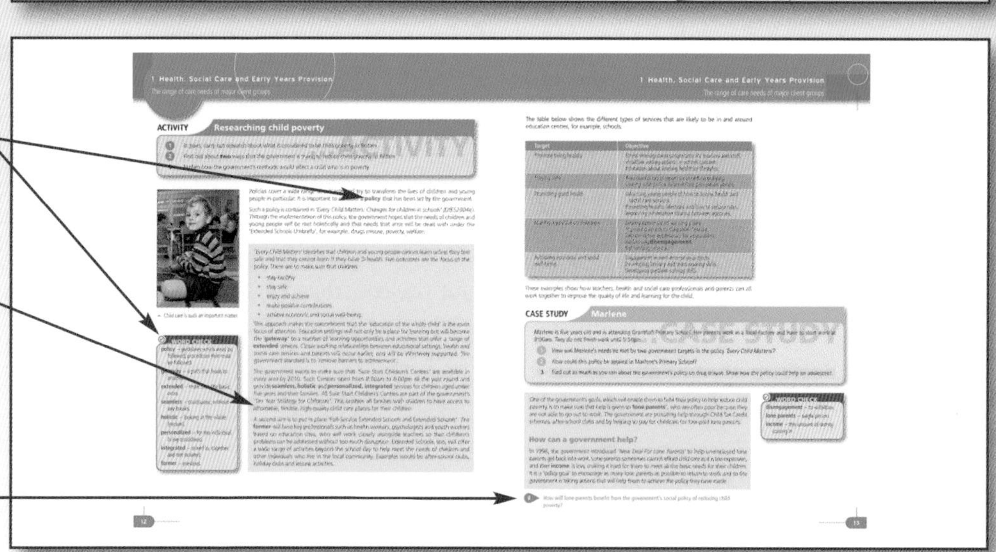
1 Health, Social Care and Early Years Provision

ACTIVITY Researching child poverty

CASE STUDY Marlene

How can a government help?

relevant – appropriate to.
positively – a good effect or influence.
diversity – being different from others.

under the Act, for modifications to improve the access for disabled people onto trains and buses. A number of other changes have been made to improve the quality of life for disabled people.

ACTIVITY How can legislation help?

1. Work in pairs to produce a quiz that checks the knowledge of others in the group about **one** of the following:
   - The Human Rights Act
   - The Mental Health Act
   - The Disability Discrimination Act

   Make sure you work out the answers before asking other people in the group the questions.
2. Working in pairs, write a short scenario about someone who has become disabled as a result of an accident. Exchange your scenario with a different pair and discuss how legislation could help the person. Share your answers.

Doing these activities will help you to develop knowledge, skills and understanding.

CASE STUDY Fion

Fion, who is four years old, attends playgroup three times each week. The assistant at the playgroup becomes very worried as Fion has bruises on her legs and on her tummy. She notices these when she takes Fion to the toilet. The assistant reports the bruising to the 'named person' at the playgroup.

Two weeks later, Fion is found to have more bruises and she seems to be very sad and cries a lot. The named person at the playgroup telephones social services to report their concerns.

1. Why did the assistant report to the 'named person'?
2. Why do settings that provide care and education for children have a 'named' person?
3. Produce your own short case study to include a different third-party referral.
4. Exchange your scenario with another group and check whether it is a third-party referral.

This is a 'third-party' referral because the playgroup named person has telephoned the social worker. It is not a self-referral because the child or her parent has not done the referring. It is not a professional referral because a professional care worker has not referred the child. Instead, another adult has done the referring and so this is a 'third-party referral'.

Case studies show different health and social care situations. Some show people working in health and social care. Others show clients with health and social care needs.

Group Activity

Try to visit a nursery and a residential home or day-care centre to find out the different methods of referral that have been used. You may wish to do this during work experience. Alternatively your tutor may arrange for two professional care workers to visit your centre

The third way in which clients can be referred to health, social care or early years services is called 'third-party referral'. This is when another person, who is not a professional care worker, refers or draws attention to an individual. The person who makes the referral could be a relative, another professional, a neighbour, an employer or a friend.

In all educational and care settings for children and young people, there has to be a 'named person' who will take responsibility for reporting suspected cases of child abuse. This is a legal requirement and the instructions given within the legislation state that a 'named person' must be in place and should have undertaken the required training. Any suspicions by staff must be reported to the named person, who, after considering the facts, will probably contact a social worker or key worker, who will investigate the concerns further.

Other examples of third-party referral could include:

- a teacher telephoning a social worker because they have concerns about a child

Group activities are for more than one person or the whole class to join in with.

The ways people can obtain services and the possible barriers

ASSESSMENT PRACTICE: PREPARATION

Continued from previous page

3. Produce a questionnaire for a short survey that could be used to find out about some of the possible barriers the Fry family could meet when using services. When you have completed the survey and had it checked either:
   - visit a setting to obtain some answers

   OR

   - invite a specialist from a care setting to your centre to ask them about the survey you are carrying out.
4. Evaluate your findings from the survey. Try to present them in the form of a pie chart or graph, as well as explaining the results.
5. Explain the possible effects of barriers on the different members of the Fry family.
6. Explain how the removal of possible barriers could empower the members of the Fry family.
7. Choose one piece of legislation and show the impact this has had on the service researched above.
8. Explain how the postcode lottery, poor integration of services and rationing could affect the services required by the Fry family.

Assessment practices allow you to prepare for your exam or portfolio assignment.

1 Health, Social Care and Early Years Provision

Contents

About this unit

For your portfolio you will choose **ONE sector** from:

- Health services, for example, health centre or hospital (private or NHS)
- Social care services, for example, day centre for older people, residential homes
- Early years services – focusing on 0–8 years, for example, nursery, paediatric service, children's centre.

You will need to focus on services that are from one sector in the local community. All of your investigation within the unit will relate to the one sector you have chosen, to include:

- the range of care needs of major client groups and why they may need the services
- the ways people can obtain services in the sector chosen and the possible barriers that could prevent people from gaining access to the services
- the different types of services in the sector that exist to meet different needs of individuals and how they are developed and organized
- the principles of care that underpin all care work with clients
- the main work roles and skills of people who provide health, social care and early years services.

You must also present your work in an appropriate format using evidence that is relevant to the investigation you have decided to carry out. You must include:

- A plan or checklist
- Improvements that could be made
- An evaluation:
  - aim
  - objectives
  - effectiveness
  - conclusions
- A bibliography

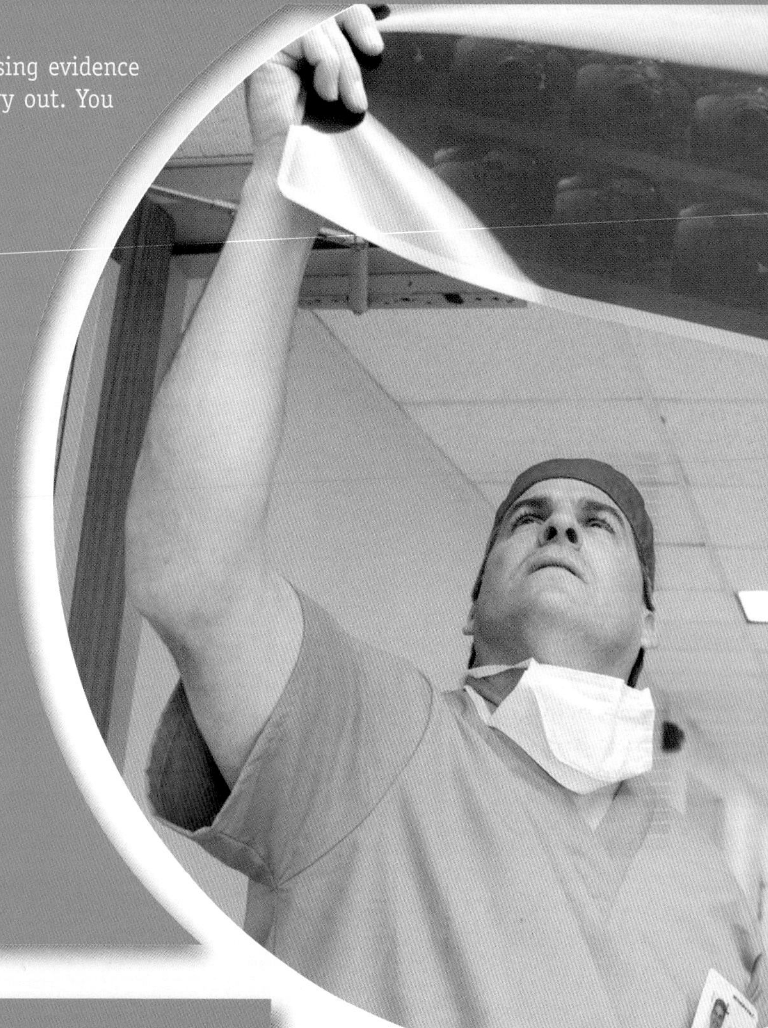

Start your plan

You will need to start a plan for the investigation of the sector you have chosen. You will need to follow this plan after the teaching has been completed and before starting the controlled assignment. You should include:

- the dates when you propose to investigate and write up the information
- the actions you propose to take
- the reasons for the actions to be taken.

TO DO...

Draw up the outline plan you intend to use for your investigation.
Begin your bibliography – a record of some of the books and websites that you intend to use. It is recommended that your plan is in 'landscape' format as this will help to provide the space you will need. A sample outline plan is given below:

Date	Actions to be taken	Reason for actions
15 Jan	Research the structure of the health sector	To find out how it is organized at national and local levels

This is only a sample to show the possible layout. Your plan will need to be larger than this.

Introducing this unit

Services in the local community provide for the needs of individuals. Examples are:

- health care: health centres, hospitals, GP surgeries, dentists
- social care: day-care centres for older people (local authority and private), residential homes (private)
- early years: nursery classes or schools, playgroups, crèches, focusing on 0–8 years.

At some time in our lives we will all need support and care from at least one of these types of services.

TO DO...

Work with another person and write down three services that you or your family have used. Produce a table with three columns headed 'Health Care', 'Social Care' and 'Early Years'. Place the services that each of you have used under the correct heading. Why did you use the services?
Compare your table with that of a different pair within your group.
Are they similar or different?

In this unit you will find out who uses services, why they are used and the different types of treatment that the services can provide.

Was it easy to use the services you have listed or did you have any difficulty accessing them? While studying this unit you will explore the different types of barriers that can make it difficult for some people to use them.

TO DO...

With another person in the group, discuss how an individual with a health need might feel if they were prevented from using the service they needed because of lack of money or being unable to reach it.
Discuss your thoughts as a whole group.

Providing care for the local community takes a great deal of planning and those who are involved in this process have to think about national targets and standards as well as the needs of individual clients. Planning has to consider all who live in the local community, not just one section of the population. In this unit you will find out how services need to work together in order to provide for the needs of different client groups.

Once services have been established, those who work in them, the professional practitioners, have to respond to the individual needs of clients. These are not just the client's physical needs, but the intellectual, emotional and social needs of individuals. Practitioners have to set targets, maintain standards and use different approaches in order to meet the individual needs of those who require care. While studying this unit you will find out about the ways in which professional care workers apply the care values in their day-to-day tasks and about their job roles. You will also think about the skills they need to carry out their work.

TO DO...

How did the professional care workers apply the care values in the services you used? How did this make you feel? It is the quality of service that we receive when we are in need of health and social care that will influence how we 'rate' the service. How well did the service meet your needs? Make some notes and then discuss this with the rest of the group.

The range of care needs of major client groups

Who needs care services and why?

Getting started

You need to understand how care services are designed to meet the health, developmental and social needs of major client groups. Major client groups are:

- babies and children
- adolescents
- adults
- older adults
- people with disabilities

Services are designed to meet the physical, intellectual, emotional and social care needs of individuals. In this section you will find out who the major client groups are by conducting a survey or client interviews.

You will have to:

- understand how universal services are developed and targeted to provide and meet social policy goals, such as reducing child poverty, homelessness, drug misuse in the population, transforming the lives of children and young people in care
- know that health authorities and local authorities assess the needs of the local population in order to identify likely service demand in a local area
- know why individuals may require and seek to use health, social care and early years services
- understand how services provide equality and meet the needs of a diverse cultural population.

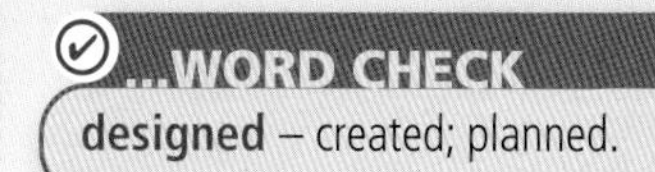

HOW SERVICES ARE DESIGNED TO MEET THE NEEDS OF MAJOR CLIENT GROUPS

Services will not be appropriate if they do not meet the needs of the individuals who use them; therefore, they must be planned or **designed** so that they do meet these needs. We all have the same basic needs. Maslow represented these needs in the form of a pyramid showing which needs must be met first before other needs can be satisfied. On the right is a diagram showing Maslow's pyramid of needs.

Abraham Maslow included five levels of need. He placed the levels that he thought were most important at the base of the pyramid, supporting all the rest. Only when the basic needs have been met at level 1, can levels 2, 3, 4 and 5 be met.

1. What needs are met at levels 2, 3, 4 and 5?
2. How are these needs met for you?

LEVEL 5
Intellectual needs
personal growth and fulfilment

LEVEL 4
Emotional needs
love, companionship, respect

LEVEL 3
Social needs
friendship, communication, mixing with others

LEVEL 2
Safety needs
protection from dangers

LEVEL 1
Physical needs
food and water, shelter and warmth

Maslow's pyramid of needs.

People who work in care services consider clients as 'whole people'. They try to work out the client's individual needs and then provide a service that will meet those needs. This is called an **holistic** approach, which is used to meet all the individual needs of a person.

Our individual needs include:

- physical needs
- intellectual needs
- emotional needs
- social needs.

3 What basic needs do you have in order to keep you alive?
How are these needs met by a GP practice?

A GP (doctor) meets the needs of all individuals. Below is a table that shows how some of the needs of different individuals are met by a GP practice:

Clients	How needs are met
Infants	Immunizations Vaccinations
Children	Diagnosing illness Prescribing medication
Adults	Health promotion Monitoring health, for example, blood pressure Counselling
Older people	Giving advice Diabetes clinics Chiropractors
People with disabilities	Liaising with specialists Recommending aids

...WORD CHECK

holistic – looking at the whole (person).

service providers – those who provide services to meet the needs of individuals.

All of the services provided could be used by different people in different life stages. The organizations providing care are called **service providers**. Some service providers will meet more than one of our needs, while others may provide for one particular need. You may have visited your GP, the dentist or spent some time in hospital? Perhaps you attended a playgroup? All of these are services that meet our needs, whether they are health, social care or early years needs.

Different services will provide for our needs in a variety of ways. For example, a nurse will provide for physical needs when cleaning a wound and putting on a protective dressing.

The nurse will also satisfy emotional, social and intellectual needs by:

- reassuring the patient and helping to stop them from worrying
- explaining what he/she is going to do and why by answering questions
- being with the patient and talking about things of interest.

4 Look at the three bullet points above: which meet social, which meet emotional and which meet intellectual needs?
Compare your answers with someone else in the group.

A primary school meets the needs of children from five to eleven years, although these ages can vary if there is a 'middle school' in the area. Who are the clients at an infant school? For the reception class they are children aged five to six years (sometimes four-and-a-half to six years). The parents of the children attending the primary school are also clients, as they will want to know how well their child is achieving, the ways in which they are being cared for and any issues that might arise while their child is in the care of these professionals who are caring for the child.

...WORD CHECK

stimulate – help a person think.

challenge – an interesting task.

A reception class at a primary school will provide for a child's intellectual, emotional and social needs. Encouraging the child to take part in activities such as painting, word games and doing simple sums will **stimulate** and offer a **challenge**. In this way the child's intellectual needs are met. Helping to make them feel secure by providing a happy and safe environment in the reception class, where they can mix with other children, will meet their emotional and social needs. The child's physical needs will be met by providing healthy snacks and lunch while they are at school.

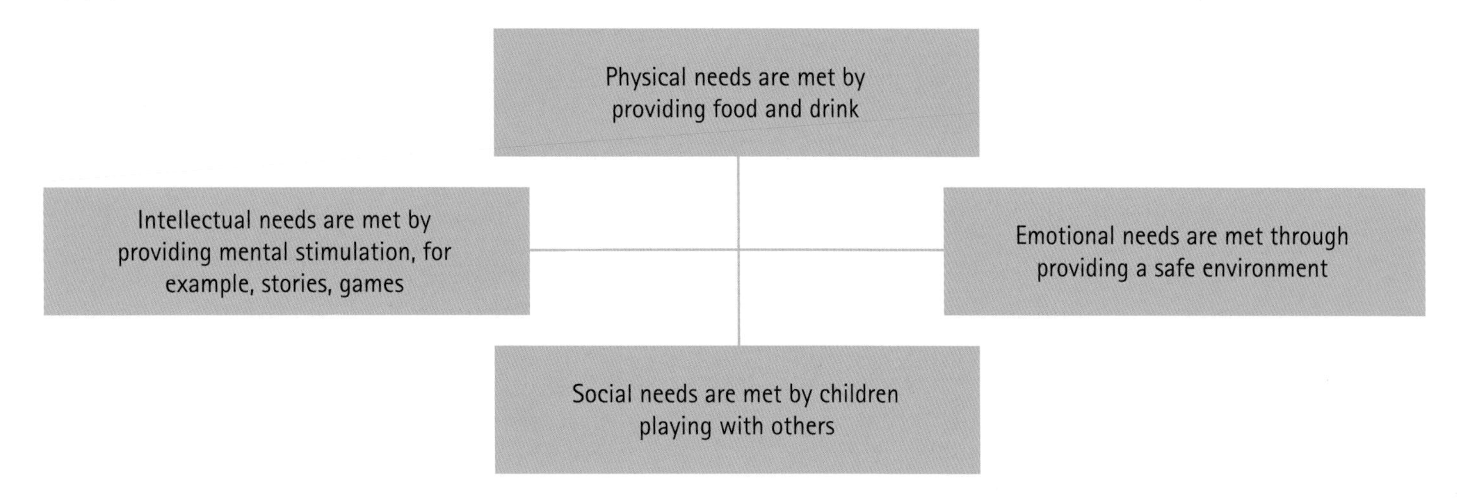

A day-care centre for older people will meet physical needs. An example is by providing lunch for them. Their intellectual needs will be met through the different activities such as bingo or community singing. Emotional and social support will be provided by making sure older people can talk to friends and to professional care workers about their interests and problems.

CASE STUDY Hebbi and James

Hebbi is five years old. She lives with her mum, who is divorced, and with her brother, James, who is three years old. They have moved away from their family home and into a small house many miles away. This means that both Hebbi and James have to start at a new school.

Hebbi is very upset that she is no longer living with her father. She cries a lot and does not want to go out and play with others of her own age. She tells her mother that she does not want to start at a new school.

James has made friends with a little boy who lives next door. They play in the garden and enjoy talking with one another. James is looking forward to going to the same nursery school as his new friend, Benjamin.

1. How could a GP practice meet Hebbi's physical needs?
2. How could the reception class meet Hebbi's intellectual needs?
3. How are the emotional needs of James being met?
4. Look at Maslow's pyramid of needs. How could Hebbi and James' Level 3 needs be met?

Major client groups

People with disabilities/special needs
Age range: All age groups

Infants (babies)
Age range: 0–3

Older adults
Age range: women 60+ and men 65+

Major client groups

Children and young people
Age range: 4–10

Adults
Age range: 19+

Adolescents
Age range: 11–18

...WORD CHECK

stimulating – to help a person to think.

intellect – the mind; the brain's activity.

self-esteem – how a person feels about themselves.

communicate – to share information either verbally, in writing, by signal or electronically.

Physical needs

Physical needs are most important as without them we would not be able to live. Physical needs include food, drink, warmth and shelter. To be healthy we all need to eat five daily portions of fruit and vegetables, and other foods that contain all the nutrients to help the body to function properly. We need water to drink and clothing to keep us warm. Housing also provides shelter to protect us from the cold, from rain and from too much sun. Safety is a need common to all of us, as we need to be protected from danger.

Intellectual needs

The children in the picture opposite are involved in a **stimulating** task. They are meeting needs for the part of the mind which does our thinking. The brain is used to solve problems that occur in our day-to-day lives, in our work, and during leisure and recreational activities. We also use our brains to help us develop new skills and knowledge. We all have our own interests and like different things and so as individuals we think in different ways. To make the best use of all our abilities, we need to use our **intellect** to set ourselves goals and targets. In doing this we will help to develop our **self-esteem**. When we **communicate** with others, our intellectual needs are also being met, and doing so helps us to develop and have a good self-image. For example, if we use our brain to help us solve a problem, we will feel a sense of achievement.

5 How do you like to be intellectually stimulated? Share your thinking with someone else in the group.

Stimulating the mind.

Emotional needs

How do we feel about ourselves and others? How we feel is linked to our emotions. Sometimes we will feel happy because we have friends who understand us and have the same interests or because we have achieved a good grade in an examination. On other occasions we may feel sad because we have had a disagreement with a member of our family or we have to move away from our friends. Being accepted by our family, our friends and by others is very important to us. We all need to be loved and wanted, and when this happens our emotional needs are being met. Being treated with **respect** and **dignity**, and being given privacy and independence also contribute to meeting our emotional needs.

...WORD CHECK

respect – to treat a person with kindness and with value.

dignity – to value a person.

valued – to hold dear; to show respect.

6 How has your own emotional health been affected? How is your emotional health likely to affect people that you live with or your friends?

Social needs

How often do you meet with friends to share interests? Sometimes you will just want to talk to one person about the things you have done rather than being with a group of people. Being able to join in activities and communicate with other people is a way of meeting our social needs. Usually we take part in activities and communicate with people who share the same interests as ourselves. Social needs also include being **valued** as an individual, having friends, feeling a sense of belonging and enjoying being with other people.

CASE STUDY Greg

Greg is three years old. He lives with his mum and dad but both have to work each day, so Greg attends the local nursery school. Before going to the nursery, Greg has breakfast at home. He likes to have a toasted sandwich, which is cut up and dipped into marmite. He also has a fruit drink and an apple.

Greg enjoys going to the nursery as he has a special friend who he likes to play with on the large equipment. He enjoys painting and story time, as well as making things with play dough.

His mum collects Greg at 5:00pm and they visit the public play area on the way home. After tea, Greg has a bath and likes his mum or dad to read him a story before he goes to sleep. They both give him a big hug and a kiss before turning off the light.

1. How are Greg's mum and dad meeting his physical, intellectual, emotional and social needs?
2. How are staff at the nursery school meeting Greg's physical, intellectual and social needs?
3. How could the staff at the nursery school meet Greg's emotional needs?
4. Think about your own physical, intellectual, emotional and social needs. How are these being met by your family and your leisure activities?

How services are shaped to meet individual needs

…WORD CHECK

isolate – to separate; to be considered on its own.

assessment – to make decisions about what is required.

care management process – making an assessment of needs and managing the process.

assess – to make decisions about what is required.

implemented – to put into place; to carry out.

deficiencies – lacking in something; not to have enough.

In order to accurately **isolate** individual needs, an individual **assessment** is required. The **care management process** is a system for assessing and organizing the provision of care for an individual. Even when a client appears to have the same condition as another, their needs will be different because of their circumstances.

When an assessment is sought, a referral will be made to the Social Services Department. Such a referral could come from a GP, a hospital or from another care professional. A person, for example, a social worker or an occupational therapist, will be allocated to **assess** the client's needs.

During the initial assessment a practitioner will:

- talk with and listen to the client
- talk with and listen to informal carers
- provide information about what is available
- possibly observe the client carrying out a variety of tasks
- record information observed or discussed
- discuss with the clients their preferences regarding services that may be needed
- write a report about the outcomes of the assessment.

When carrying out an assessment, it will be important to find out what is the least that it is necessary to know. This will be done by either a social worker or an occupational therapist but, if a complex assessment is to be carried out, several professional care workers may be involved. For example, an occupational therapist or a physiotherapist may also need to be involved. Assessment is between the person(s) carrying out the assessment and the individual, making it a two-way process that involves a great deal of trust. If other professionals are involved in the assessment, consent will need to be obtained from the client.

Care planning is identifying the most appropriate ways of meeting the needs of the client to find the best type of resources available. Responsibility for ensuring that the care plan is **implemented** at the correct pace will be that of the key worker. Implementing means carrying out the plan or contributing the services. While the plan is being implemented, it is important to set out the arrangements for monitoring it. This is essential to make sure that the plan is still meeting the client's needs.

The services supplying care must be carefully monitored to ensure that:

- the expected quality of care is being provided
- the care being provided meets the objectives that were agreed
- the care being provided meets the cost agreed
- the timing of the service provision is suitable for the client and the main carer
- any changes from the agreed plan and the reasons for such changes are recorded
- whether there are any **deficiencies** within the plan is checked.

Monitoring a care plan is important because it ensures that the client's needs continue to be met. A review of a care plan must be made within the first six weeks of the starting date.

Evaluation involves:

- looking at the objectives
- considering the nature of the interventions
- assessing the effectiveness of what has taken place
- considering if there is a need for improvement.

It is essential that a balanced view is taken when reviewing/evaluating. Those involved will need to reflect and to make informed judgements about what has taken place. They will need to analyse and make judgements about whether the care plan could have been improved, and whether the outcomes actually match with the objectives set.

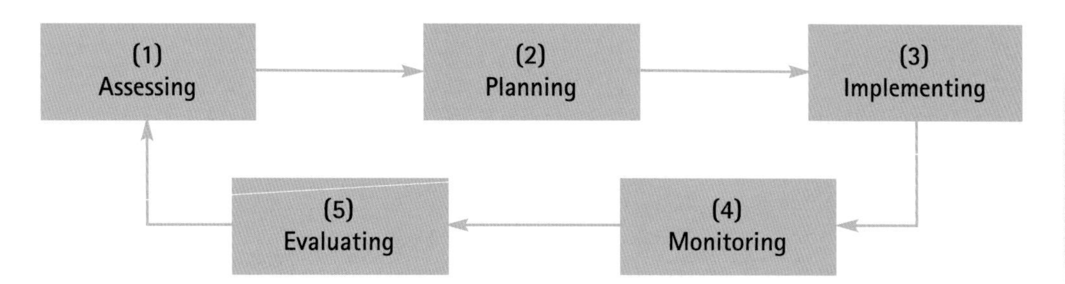

...WORD CHECK

aims – the overall target or purpose.

policy – guidelines which must be followed; procedures that must be followed.

approach – the method used.

CASE STUDY Maggi

Maggi is 75 years of age. She is recovering from a broken arm and leg in hospital but is now ready to return to her own home. An assessment of her needs is to be carried out in her own home before she finally leaves hospital.

1. Identify who is likely to attend Maggi's assessment. Explain the role of each person.
2. Explain how the care management process will be applied to Maggi.
3. Explain how Maggi's individual needs will have been isolated.
4. Draw up a list of services that could meet Maggi's needs and describe how each could help.

Policies

Before making decisions about which services to provide, there is discussion between different members of the government and other people in the local area, to decide what are to be their **aims** for health, social care and early years services. The group of people make their decisions and then use these to form a **policy** that will guide them when they make other decisions. Often there is no 'right way' to make sure that people get the best health care, social care or early years services that they need. A policy will provide 'broad ideas' or an **approach** that will be the basis on which other decisions will be made.

Reducing child poverty and improving quality of life for children.

What is the purpose of having a policy?

A government will have a large number of targets or **goals**. Each will be formed to try to deal with a particular problem or issue that needs to be solved. They will form a policy about how to deal with the issue. For example, one policy the present government has is to 'reduce child **poverty**'. The idea of this approach or policy is to try and make sure that fewer children, in this country, are poor. Having made this decision, the government will then set goals. These are **targets** that they want to meet.

One of the government's goals, which will enable them to fulfil their policy to help reduce child poverty, is to provide help through Child Tax Credit schemes, after-school clubs and by helping to pay for child care for low-paid, lone parents.

...WORD CHECK

goals – the outcomes to be achieved.

poverty – to not have sufficient money to meet basic needs; to be very poor.

targets – goals; points that must be achieved.

ACTIVITY Researching child poverty

1. In pairs, carry out research about what is considered to be child poverty in Britain.
2. Find out about **two** ways that the government is trying to reduce child poverty in Britain.
3. Explain how the government's methods would affect a child who is in poverty.

Child care is such an important matter.

...WORD CHECK

policy – guidelines which must be followed; procedures that must be followed.

gateway – a path that leads to another.

extended – more than the basic; extra.

seamless – continuous; without any breaks.

holistic – looking at the whole (person).

personalized – for the individual being considered.

integrated – mixed in; together and not isolated.

former – previous.

Policies cover a wide range of subjects and try to transform the lives of children and young people in particular. It is important to consider a **policy** that has been set by the government.

Such a policy is contained in *'Every Child Matters: Changes for children in schools' (DfES2004e)*. Through the implementation of this policy, the government hopes that the needs of children and young people will be met holistically and that needs that arise will be dealt with under the 'Extended Schools Umbrella', for example, drugs misuse, poverty, welfare.

'Every Child Matters' identifies that children and young people cannot learn unless they feel safe and that they cannot learn if they have ill-health. Five outcomes are the focus of the policy. These are to make sure that children:

- stay healthy
- stay safe
- enjoy and achieve
- make positive contributions
- achieve economic and social well-being.

This approach makes the commitment that the 'education of the whole child' is the main focus of attention. Education settings will not only be a place for learning but will become the '**gateway**' to a number of learning opportunities and activities that offer a range of **extended** services. Closer working relationships between educational settings, health and social care services and parents will occur earlier, and will be effectively supported. The government standard is to 'remove barriers to achievement'.

The government wants to make sure that 'Sure Start Children's Centres' are available in every area by 2010. Such Centres open from 8:00am to 6:00pm all the year round and provide **seamless, holistic** and **personalized, integrated** services for children aged under five years and their families. All Sure Start Children's Centres are part of the government's 'Ten Year Strategy for Childcare'. This enables all families with children to have access to affordable, flexible, high-quality child care places for their children.

A second aim is to put in place 'Full-Service Extended Schools and Extended Schools'. The **former** will have key professionals such as health workers, psychologists and youth workers based on education sites, who will work closely alongside teachers so that children's problems can be addressed without too much disruption. Extended Schools, too, will offer a wide range of activities beyond the school day to help meet the needs of children and other individuals who live in the local community. Examples would be after-school clubs, holiday clubs and leisure activities.

The table below shows the different types of services that are likely to be in and around education centres, for example, schools:

Target	Objective
Promote being healthy	Stress-management programme for learners and staff. Healthier eating options in school canteen. Education about leading healthier lifestyles.
Staying safe	Peer-mentoring programme to reduce bullying. Linking with police liaison/crime prevention panels.
Enjoy and achieve	Emphasizing the importance of and providing the opportunities for students to achieve a balance between education/work and leisure, for example, running after school clubs and activities.
Making a positive contribution	Setting personalized learning plans. Improving access to diagnostic testing. Improving the opportunity for assessment. Addressing **disengagement**. Befriending scheme.
Achieving economic and social well-being	Engagement in mini-enterprise projects. Developing literacy and teamworking skills. Developing problem-solving skills.

These examples show how teachers, health and social care professionals and parents can all work together to improve the quality of life and learning for the child.

CASE STUDY Marlene

Marlene is five years old and is attending Granthall Primary School. Her parents work in a local factory and have to start work at 8:00am. They do not finish work until 5:30pm.

1. How will Marlene's needs be met by **two** government targets in the policy *'Every Child Matters'*?
2. How could this policy be applied in Marlene's Primary School?
3. Find out as much as you can about the government's policy on drug misuse. Show how the policy could help an adolescent.

One of the government's goals, which will enable them to fulfil their policy to help reduce child poverty, is to make sure that help is given to '**lone parents**', who are often poor because they are not able to go out to work. The government are providing help through Child Tax Credit schemes, after-school clubs and by helping to pay for childcare for low-paid lone parents.

How can the government help?

In 1998, the government introduced *'New Deal For Lone Parents'* to help unemployed lone parents get back into work. Lone parents sometimes cannot afford child care as it is too expensive, and their **income** is low, making it hard for them to meet all the basic needs for their children. It is a 'policy goal' to encourage as many lone parents as possible to return to work and so the government is taking actions that will help them to achieve the policy they have made.

...WORD CHECK

disengagement – withdrawing from something.

lone parents – single person.

income – the amount of money coming in.

8 How will lone parents benefit from the government's social policy of reducing child poverty?

What other social policies are there?

Other social policies of our current government are to **reduce** homelessness and drug misuse. To help them do this they have set policy goals – targets they want to meet by a certain time.

Once a policy has been made, consideration is given to the services that will be needed to make the policy successful. For example, if the government has a policy to reduce drug misuse, they will need to make sure that there are sufficient services available to help clients to do this. They have to think about:

- Who will want to use the services?
- What type of services will be needed?
- Which type of health care workers will be required to run the services?
- Where in the country will the services be most needed?

They will **consult** those who are responsible for the provision of services in local areas, for example, **local authorities** and **health authorities**, and people who may have opinions about the social issue that is being considered. These people will look at the needs of their **population** and then give the government the information they need to make decisions about which services to provide. They will also think about where the services will need to be **located** and whether more people will need to be trained so they can run the services. There will be a lot of **debate** about how the goals will be achieved and who will be involved.

...WORD CHECK

reduce – to lower.

consult – to seek the opinion of others.

local authorities – those who are elected/employed to make decisions in the local area.

health authorities – those who make decisions about health care provided in a local area.

population – the people who live in an area.

located – where it is found.

debate – to discuss; to talk about.

pressure groups – an individual or a group of people who try to persuade someone that their way is the right or correct approach to use.

media – TV, daily newspapers, radio.

demographics – characteristics or groups of a population, for example, disabled, unemployed, single parents.

assess – to make decisions about what is required.

How do pressure groups affect decisions?

Some people may disagree with the ideas that are being put forward and they may try to form **pressure groups** to prevent or encourage the government in carrying out its goals. The **media** will discuss some of the points made by people and will put their ideas forward. When everyone has had the chance to make their views and opinions known, the government will make their decisions using all the information gathered. Look at the diagram below to see how the process works.

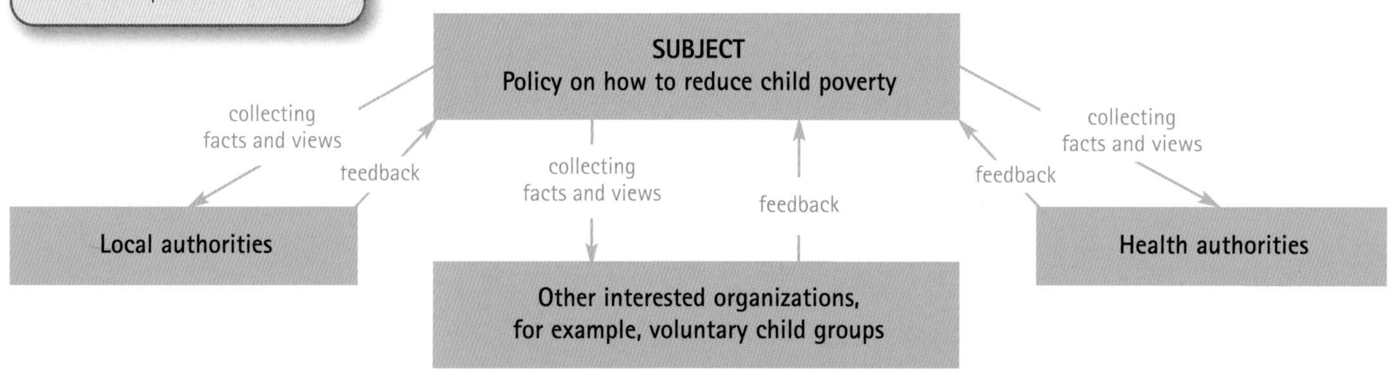

HOW DO LOCAL AUTHORITIES AND HEALTH AUTHORITIES ASSESS THE CARE NEEDS OF THE LOCAL POPULATION?

Local authorities and health authorities use **demographics** to help them **assess** the needs of the population in their community. Those who are planning health, social care and child care provision for their local communities must research and find out about the different types of people living in their area, taking their health needs into consideration. For example:

like health, social care and early years services to be delivered. Services try really hard to meet the needs of all their population by:

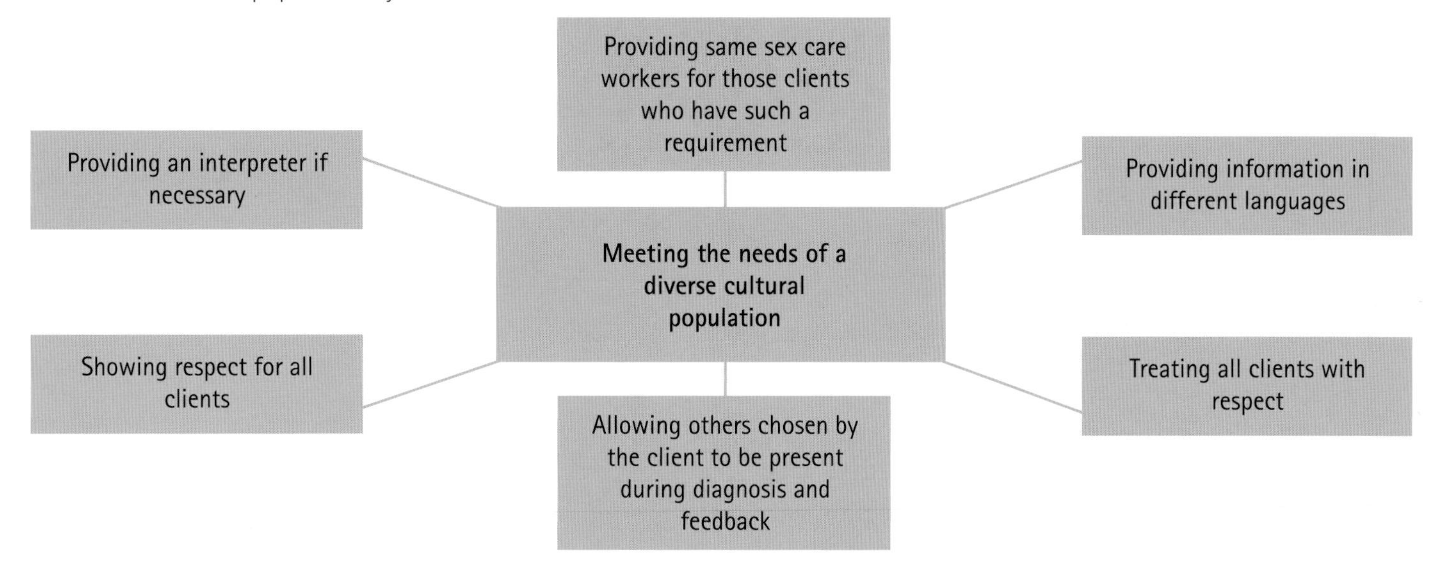

ASSESSMENT PRACTICE: PREPARATION

Porchester Local Authority and Health Authority want to find out about services needed in their local area. They also want to know who uses the services and how the services meet the needs of the clients. They have asked you to help them with this project.

1. Choose one health, social care or early years service. Name the sector it is in. It is this sector and the services within the sector that will be the focus of your investigation.
2. Draw up a plan to show:
   - timescales, the tasks, reasons for the tasks
   - the resources you will use, for example, the books, magazines, websites, and people you may talk to.
3. How do the local authority and health authorities use social policy goals to help them decide on the need of their population for the sector you have chosen?
4. Explain the planning process involved in producing services (this can be new or existing services).
5. Explain how the services meet the physical, intellectual, emotional and social needs of the individuals using them.
6. Explain the complexity of isolating the needs of individual clients.
7. How do services work together (have a multi-disciplinary approach) when meeting the needs of individuals? Use a case study to illustrate this.
8. For the service you have chosen, draw a diagram to show how they fit into the national framework. Explain the diagram.
9. How do the services you have chosen provide equality to meet the needs of a diverse cultural population?

Remember:

- Keep aims and objectives for your investigation.
- Make a plan that shows the order in which you will work, giving the dates, actions and the reasons for the actions to be taken.
- Keep a bibliography that shows primary and secondary sources of evidence, and any Internet or other material used.

The ways people can obtain services and the possible barriers

How can people gain access to care services and what can prevent people from being able to use the services they need?

Getting started

In this section you will learn about how people can gain access to care services in the sector you have chosen and what can prevent people from being able to use the services. You will need to include:

- self-referral
- professional referral
- third-party referral.

You will also learn about legislation that protects individual rights to the access of services they require to include:

- The Human Rights Act 1998 (updated 2000)
- Mental Health Act 1983 and 2007
- Children Act 1989 and 2004
- Disability Discrimination Act 1998 and 2005
- Residential Care Homes Regulation 1984 (amended 2002).

You should also understand that removing barriers empowers an individual to take control of his or her life instead of having to rely on other people.

You will need to be able to identify possible barriers that could prevent people from making use of the services that they need, for example:

- physical barriers, for example, stairs, a lack of lifts, lack of adapted toilets, which can prevent access to premises by people who have mobility problems
- psychological barriers, for example, fear of losing independence, the stigma associated with some services and not wanting to be looked after
- financial barriers, for example, charges and fees, which can deter people who do not have the money to pay for services
- geographical barriers, for example, in rural areas the location of an organization or practitioner, which may be a barrier if there is a lack of public transport
- cultural barriers, for example, cultural beliefs about who should provide care and how illness and social problems should be dealt with
- language barriers, as well as difficulties in using English, which could deter members of some communities from using care services
- resource barriers, for example, lack of staff, lack of information about services, lack of money to fund services or a large demand for services, which can prevent access to services when clients need or want them.

You will also be able to suggest ways in which services and individuals that they serve might be able to overcome these barriers. You should understand that poor integration of services, rationing and the postcode lottery may affect availability of services in the local area.

METHODS OF REFERRAL

Think about the number of times that you have used different services that provide health and social care or child care? You may have used a dentist, GP, hospital, nursery school or social services.

How have the services used been **accessed**?

> **...WORD CHECK**
> **accessed** – used or experienced.

ACTIVITY Methods of referral

Work with another person to decide which method was used by the following three people to access the services:

Person A: GP asked them to see a specialist heart consultant.

Person B: A teacher asked a social worker to visit a student

Person C: Gemma visited the dentist.

Compare your answers with another group.

Write a short definition of the three different ways of accessing the services.

Self-referral

Self-**referral** is when a person has gone straight to their GP, for example, and not approached him/her through another professional care worker. When wanting to see a GP, most of us will gain access by taking ourselves directly to the surgery.

When feeling unwell or where a prescription may be needed to help fight an illness, such as flu, an individual will probably go directly to their GP or telephone the GP to make an appointment. This is a **direct** approach.

> **...WORD CHECK**
> **referral** – the method by which a patient is put in contact with a medical specialist.
> **direct** – straight to the person/ openly; to be responsible for a person's care.
> **consultant** – a person who specializes in a medical field.

What is a professional referral?

The GP, however, may on some occasions want an individual to make an appointment with a professional who specializes in specific types of conditions or illnesses, or a person who deals with specific injuries. He/she will then either telephone or write to the specialist, who is usually known as a '**consultant**', to make an appointment on the individual's behalf.

This method of making an arrangement to see someone else is called a 'professional referral'. Perhaps you have had such an appointment made for you if you have hurt your arm or leg and the GP thinks an x-ray is necessary? Or maybe you have had an illness that the GP needs a second opinion about and they have made an arrangement for you to see the specialist at the local hospital?

GP telephoning consultant in a hospital.

Third-party referral

CASE STUDY Fion

Fion, who is four years old, attends playgroup three times each week. The assistant at the playgroup becomes very worried as Fion has bruises on her legs and on her tummy. She notices these when she takes Fion to the toilet. The assistant reports the bruising to the 'named person' at the playgroup.

Two weeks later, Fion is found to have more bruises and she seems to be very sad and cries a lot. The named person at the playgroup telephones social services to report their concerns.

1. Why did the assistant report to the 'named person'?
2. Why do settings that provide care and education for children have a 'named' person?
3. Produce your own short case study to include a different third-party referral.
4. Exchange your scenario with another group and check whether it is a third-party referral.

This is a 'third-party' referral because the playgroup named person has telephoned the social worker. It is not a self-referral because the child or her parent has not done the referring. It is not a professional referral because a professional care worker has not referred the child. Instead, another adult has done the referring and so this is a 'third-party referral'.

Group Activity

Try to visit a nursery and a residential home or day-care centre to find out the different methods of referral that have been used. You may wish to do this during work experience. Alternatively your tutor may arrange for two professional care workers to visit your centre to talk about the different methods they have experienced.

After the visit, discuss:

1 Which methods have been used to refer people?

2 What are the differences between the methods?

The third way in which clients can be referred to health, social care or early years services is called 'third-party referral'. This is when another person, who is not a professional care worker, refers or draws attention to an individual. The person who makes the referral could be a relative, another professional, a neighbour, an employer or a friend.

In all educational and care settings for children and young people, there has to be a 'named person' who will take responsibility for reporting suspected cases of child abuse. This is a legal requirement and the instructions given within the legislation state that a 'named person' must be in place and should have undertaken the required training. Any suspicions by staff must be reported to the named person, who, after considering the facts, will probably contact a social worker or key worker, who will investigate the concerns further.

Other examples of third-party referral could include:

- a teacher telephoning a social worker because they have concerns about a child
- a neighbour telephoning a social worker or GP because they have concerns about a child that lives next door
- a neighbour telephoning social services because an older person is wandering about in the garden at night or leaving the gas on
- an employer telephoning a GP about a young employee who seems to be very depressed as they think he may harm himself
- a person telephoning the emergency services for an ambulance to take an injured person to hospital.

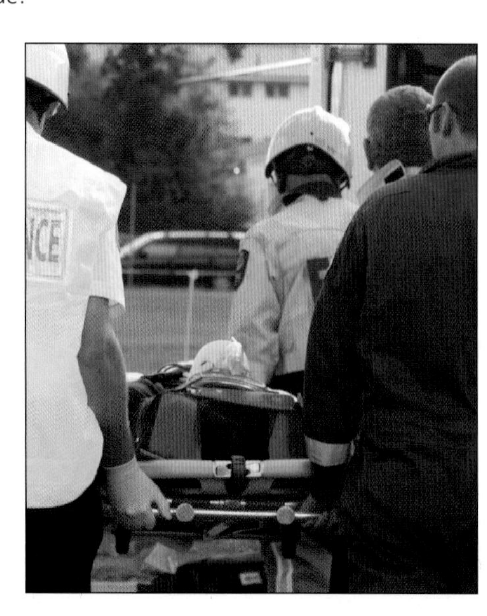

An ambulance crew collecting an injured person to take them to hospital.

Why is it important that people know how to access health, social care and early years services?

ACTIVITY The Bishop family

Russell and Heather Bishop have three children: Malcolm, who is thirteen, Naomi, who is nine years old, and Daniel, who is four. Heather's mum, Greta, lives with the family and she is 72 years old.

1. Daniel has a cold, a very bad cough and also has a high temperature. His mother takes him to the GP, as she is slightly worried about him.
   - Identify the type of referral this would be and explain why.
   - What type of needs does Daniel have?
   - How can these needs be met?
2. Greta is seen by a social worker as she does not meet many people of her own age. The social worker refers Greta to a social worker at the local day-care centre to try and encourage Greta to attend twice each week.
   - Identify the type of referral this would be and explain why.
   - What type of needs does Greta have?
   - How can these needs be met?

LEGISLATION

Legislation protects an individual's rights to access the services they need. It also protects individuals' human rights and helps to prevent discrimination from occurring.

Human Rights Act 1998

This Act covers a range of human rights that could affect health and care practice in the future. The Human Rights Act links directly to care values, which means treating others as you would like to be treated yourself. That is:

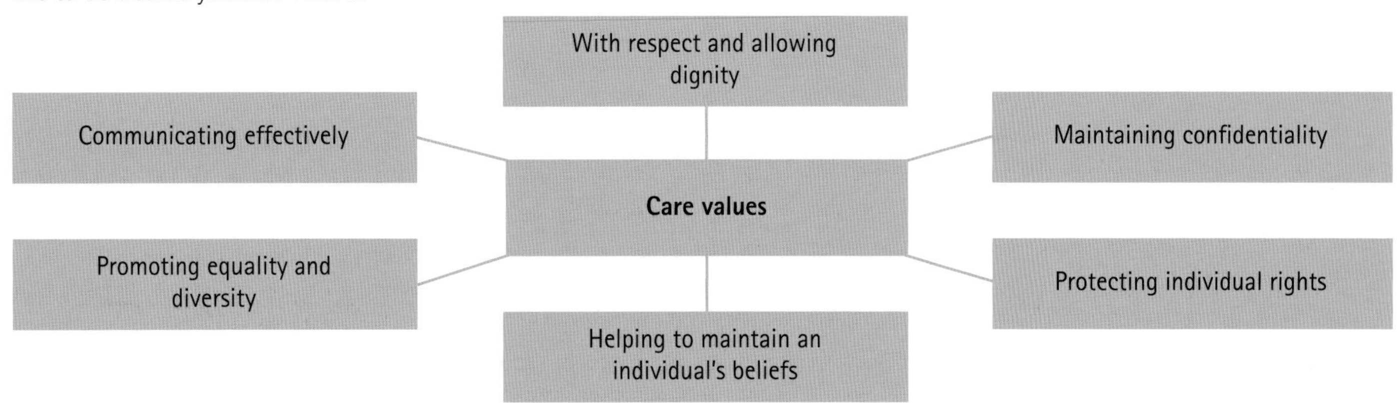

The Act brought the European Convention on Human Rights into UK law. The government must make sure that all new legislation meets the requirements of the Act. Anyone who feels their human rights have been **violated** by a public organization (for example, local or central government, the courts or police) can take them to court or a tribunal.

WORD CHECK
violated – broken or breached.

In the year 2000, the Human Rights Act was amended. The main revisions are given below:

Human Rights Act 2000

Group Activity

Article 2 within the Human Rights Act is about the 'right to life'. This means the state must protect life as well as preventing the taking of life. This means that patients could challenge their local authority if certain drugs are not available in their area.

Find newspaper articles that relate to the restriction of drugs. Read one article to the group. Discuss the implications as far as human rights are concerned.

...WORD CHECK

jurisdiction – area; under their control.

The Human Rights Act came into force on 2 October 2000 and incorporates into UK law certain rights and freedoms set out in the European Convention on Human Rights, such as:

- Right to life (article 2)
- Protection from torture and inhuman or degrading treatment or punishment (article 3)
- Protection from slavery and forced or compulsory labour (article 4)
- The right to liberty and security of person (article 5)
- The right to a fair trial (article 6)
- Protection from retrospective criminal offences (article 7)
- The protection of private and family life (article 8)
- Freedom of thought, conscience and religion (article 9)
- Freedom of expression (article 10)
- Freedom of association and assembly (article 11)
- The right to marry and found a family (article 12)
- Freedom from discrimination (article 13)
- The right to property (article 1 of the first protocol)
- The right to education (article 2 of the first protocol)
- The right to free and fair elections (article 3 of the first protocol)
- The abolition of the death penalty in peacetime (sixth protocol).

These rights are known as 'Convention rights'. They will therefore have an impact on areas such as criminal law, family law and housing. Countries who have signed up to the Convention must secure the above rights for everyone in their **jurisdiction** and individuals must also have an effective remedy to protect those rights in the country's courts without the need to go to the European Court of Human Rights. The role of the European Court of Human Rights will be to determine whether the domestic courts have been true to the Convention.

All national courts and tribunals must take into account the case law of the European Court of Human Rights. The Human Rights Act covers England, Wales, Scotland and Northern Ireland. The Act does not take away or restrict any existing human rights recognized in a country.

Children Act 1989

Local authority social services departments were required by the Children Act 1989 to work together to provide services and support for children and young people and their families, including disabled children. The Act covers children and young people under 18. Key features of this legislation are:

- to protect children who are at risk – the paramouncy principle
- all children have the right to be 'heard'
- the wishes of children must be taken into consideration, particularly where decisions affect them
- support must be provided to keep families together whenever this is possible.

▲ The child must be protected.

The services provided under the Children Act can include:

- social work
- help with housing and support
- equipment and adaptations
- occupational therapists or other specialists
- short-term breaks
- counselling
- interpreters
- an advocate or representative for individuals or families
- benefits advice.

The county court, as a result of this Act, has the ability to protect a child by making them a ward of court and placing them under the protection of the court and the Official Solicitor. They also have the ability to make orders that can move a child to safety or take other protective action.

The Children (Scotland) Act 1995 and the Children (Northern Ireland) Order 1995 have similar provisions for children's services in Scotland and Northern Ireland.

WORD CHECK

minimized – reducing the risk; to make as small as possible.

Children Act 2004

This Act came into being as a result of the *'Victoria Climbie Inquiry Report'* in 2003 and the green paper, *'Every Child Matters'* 2003.

10 Work with another person to find out what happened to Victoria Climbie. Why do you think there was an inquiry?

It was decided at this time that the risks to children and young people must be **minimized** and that the focus of regulations and legislation must be more on the needs of young people and their families. Services were required to work more closely with one another, sharing information, planning actions together, having joint funding arrangements and working together to deliver services. As a result, a 'Children's Commissioner' was appointed, whose main role was to represent the views of children. Other roles of the Children's Commissioner are:

- to find out the views of children and young people
- to investigate any matter that relates to the interests and well-being of children and young people
- to make enquiries on behalf of children and young people.

Group Activity

Work with another person and find out more about the role of the Children's Commissioner and the responsibilities of the local authority under the Children Act 2004.

Present the information found to others in the group.

CASE STUDY Bertha

Caroline is a social worker who specializes in working with children. She is asked to visit Headlands reception class to discuss some issues with the 'named person' about a little girl called Bertha.

Bertha has recently joined the reception class and often looks sullen and will not join in the activities. The staff try to talk to Bertha but she says 'mummy told me not to tell our business'. Bertha's mother is a single parent who often arrives quite late to collect her. On several occasions, Bertha has arrived at playgroup with bruises on her face, legs and arms. When asked, her mother says that she does not know how these happened, but the staff are not convinced.

1. Which piece of legislation would help the social worker?
2. How could the Children Act of 2004 help?
3. What action should be taken next?
4. How could the local authority help?

Mental Health Act 1983

...WORD CHECK

arrested – prevented from progressing.

psychopathic – an in-balance of the mind.

compulsory – to make an individual or group follow what is set out; to conform.

This Act gave a definition of 'mental disorder' and offered guidance and protection, through clearly set out procedures, for people who were mentally ill and required hospital admission and/or treatment. The Act stated that mental disorder is '**arrested** or incomplete development of mind, **psychopathic** disorder and any other disorder or disability of mind'. It covered informal patients (those who go into hospital voluntarily) and this accounts for approximately 90% of mental health admissions. It also dealt with **compulsory** admissions for people who were thought to be a danger to themselves and/or others. Patients could be detained, for varying lengths of time, for observation, diagnosis and treatment, and have the right to have the medical reasons for their detention reviewed by a Mental Health Review Tribunal. People with learning disabilities are also covered by some parts of this Act.

Mental Health Act 2007

Group Activity

Work with another person to find out the meaning of:

- mental disorder
- mental impairment
- psychopathic disorder.

Give an example of each.

Share your research and the examples with the rest of the group.

This legislation extends and amends the Mental Health Act 1983. The 1983 Act is largely concerned with the circumstances in which a person with a mental disorder can be detained for treatment for that disorder without his or her consent. It also sets out the processes that must be followed and the safeguards for patients, to ensure that they are not inappropriately detained or treated without their consent. The main purpose of the legislation is to ensure that people with serious mental disorders, which threaten their health or safety, or the safety of the public, can be treated irrespective of their consent, where it is necessary to prevent them from harming themselves or others.

The following are the main changes to the 1983 Act made by the 2007 Act:

- *Definition of mental disorder:* changes the way the 1983 Act defines mental disorder.
- *Criteria for detention:* gives a new 'appropriate medical treatment' test that will apply to all the longer-term powers of detention.
- *Professional roles:* broadens the group of practitioners who can take on the functions currently performed by the approved social worker (ASW) and responsible medical officer (RMO).
- *Nearest relative:* patients now have the right to make an application to the county court to displace their nearest relative to represent them.
- *Nearest relative:* the provisions for determining the nearest relative were amended to include civil partners amongst the list of relatives from 1 December 2007.
- *Supervised community treatment (SCT):* for patients following a period of detention in hospital. It is expected that this will allow a small number of patients with a mental disorder to be discharged from detention subject to the possibility of recall to hospital if necessary.
- *Electro-convulsive therapy:* new safeguards for patients have been given.
- *Tribunal:* this reduces the periods after which hospital managers must refer certain patients' cases to the Tribunal if they do not apply themselves.
- *Advocacy:* places a duty on the appropriate national authority to make arrangements for help to be provided by independent mental health advocates.
- *Age-appropriate services:* will require hospital managers to ensure that patients aged under 18 admitted to hospital for a mental disorder are accommodated in an environment that is suitable for their age (subject to their needs).

Other legislation and regulations that help to protect the individual are:

Disability Discrimination Act 1998

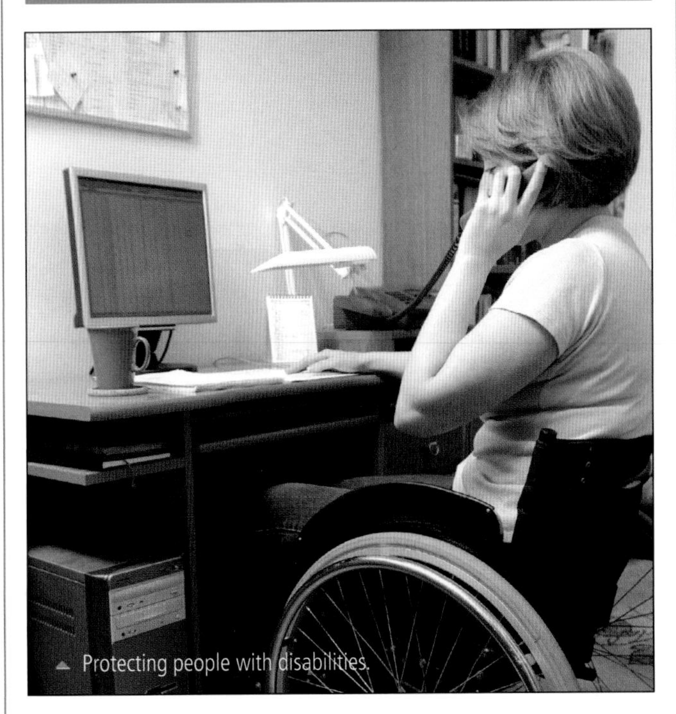

▲ Protecting people with disabilities.

This Act is concerned with preventing discrimination against people with disabilities. It covers housing, transport, employment, access to education and obtaining goods and services.

Employers must not discriminate against an employee (whether they are actually employed or could be employed in the future) with a disability or who has had a disability in the past. This includes ensuring that the interview and selection process, the practices and rules, and the premises of the employer do not put a disabled person at a disadvantage as compared to a person without a disability. This also includes promotion, training, pensions and other benefits, including equipment to meet a disabled employee's needs.

Other responsibilities an employer will have to a disabled employee are providing supervision, and modifying instructions or reference manuals so that they are, for example, in large print or Braille. Employers must allow absences from work/rehabilitation related to an employee's disability, and modify or purchase new equipment to enable them to work safely and appropriately.

Any employees who believe that they have been the subject of discrimination can apply to an Employment Tribunal within three months of the date of the discrimination.

Nursing and Residential Care Homes Regulation 1984 (amended 2002) – Registered Homes Act

This Act controls the registration, inspection and conditions for setting up or running residential care homes. It covers levels of staffing, facilities, safety and record keeping. All residential nursing and care homes must be registered with their local authority and are therefore subject to inspection by the local authority inspectorate.

In Northern Ireland it is the Registered Homes Order, 1992. In Scotland it is the Registered Establishments (Scotland) Act, 1987.

The Registered Homes Act 1984 has been subsumed by the Care Standards Act 2000, which covers inspections of residential and nursing homes.

Residential homes are expected to provide a level of care that one would expect from a **competent**, caring relative. In some residential homes, the professional care workers have to carry out tasks that border on the duty of nursing homes as more people are living into their 80s.

In 2002, some amendments were added to the Care Standards Act, particularly relating to the funding of individuals who live in residential homes.

11 Work with another person to find out more about the Care Standards Act 2000 and how it impacts on clients. Present your findings to others in the group.

...WORD CHECK

competent – being able to perform a task to show a high level of skills.

The Disability Discrimination Act 2005

...WORD CHECK

empowerment – to enable a client to be in control of their life and to make their own decisions.

relevant – appropriate to.

positively – a good effect or influence.

diversity – being different from others.

This Act updated the 1998 Act by widening the definition of disability to include people with progressive conditions, such as HIV, MS and cancers, from the point of diagnosis, together with removing the necessity for mental health conditions to be clinically well recognized. It requires all public bodies to promote positive attitudes towards disabled people and for identified organizations, like schools, to implement disability equality schemes. A completion date of 2020 has been set, under the Act, for modifications to improve the access for disabled people onto trains and buses. A number of other changes have been made to improve the quality of life for disabled people.

ACTIVITY How can legislation help?

1. Work in pairs to produce a quiz that checks the knowledge of others in the group about **one** of the following:
   - The Human Rights Act
   - The Mental Health Act
   - The Disability Discrimination Act

   Make sure you work out the answers before asking other people in the group the questions.
2. Working in pairs, write a short scenario about someone who has become disabled as a result of an accident. Exchange your scenario with a different pair and discuss how legislation could help the person. Share your answers.

EMPOWERING CLIENTS

'What would you like to wear today?'

What is **empowerment**? It is allowing the client to take control of their own lives. This means giving them all the **relevant** information and allowing them to make choices and decisions. A client who feels that their views and decisions are valued is more likely to respond **positively**. All individuals will need to feel that they are equal to others and not someone for whom 'things are done or arranged'. The aim is to form a good working relationship or partnership where each person is valued. This will mean:

- respecting the individual's rights
- maintaining confidentiality
- respecting the person's beliefs, cultural views and opinions
- allowing individuals to express their views and opinions
- tolerating **diversity** when clients do not act or have the same opinions as we do.

Empowerment enables the individual to retain their own identity and does not involve the care worker imposing their identity on them.

ACTIVITY Empowering individuals

Work with another person to see how a professional could empower one of the following individuals:

- a child who has arrived for the first time at a playgroup
- an older adult who is attending a day-care centre
- an older adult in a residential home, who is trying to decide which treatment to have.

Share your answer with others.

WHAT MIGHT PREVENT PEOPLE FROM USING THE SERVICES THAT THEY NEED?

Sometimes people do not use the health, social care and early years services that they need. This could be for a variety of reasons but mainly because barriers prevent them from doing so. Legislation has meant that barriers are not as common as they used to be, as organizations have removed some of the obstacles to access. Possible barriers are as follows:

Physical barriers

Imagine you are in your seventies and you suffer from rheumatism, so that you have to use a walking stick. You want to go to the dentist but the only way to get to the surgery is by going up some very steep steps.

You would know that you could not make it up those steps, so you would probably not go to the dentist in the first place! You would go without treatment or cleaning because of the **physical barrier** of the steps.

Quite a lot of people are prevented from using health, social care and early years services because they are unable to enter or leave a building. Or they may not be able to use the toilet because it is upstairs or the door is not wide enough for a wheelchair to enter.

Some people could be prevented from using a lift because they cannot access the control buttons or, if they are blind, they may be unable to read the instructions because they have not been given in Braille.

'How am I going to get to see the dentist?'

Psychological barriers

These affect the way we think. Some people are afraid of going to the dentist. They have a 'fear' of dentists. This is an example of a psychological barrier. Some older people will not agree to going into a residential home because they think they will become **dependent** on others or because they think people will not have any respect for them because they cannot cope. They think there is a '**stigma**' attached to it and will not accept the care offered even though they may know it is best for them.

Individuals who have mental health conditions are sometimes afraid to access the service they need. In their minds they could be afraid of meeting other people or they may think that the professional care worker will immediately make them go to a clinic for treatment. While such fears are unfounded, they still loom large in the mind of the individual.

...WORD CHECK

physical barrier – preventing someone from obtaining access, for example, a lift or operator buttons not in place in Braille for a person who cannot see.

dependent – to have to rely on others.

stigma – something that does not present a good image of the person.

Financial barriers

How often have you been prevented from doing something because it cost too much? Most of us have at some time or another. But, when people are unable to use a health, social care or early years service because of a lack of money, their health may suffer as a result. If someone lives some distance from health services, for example, the cost of travelling to them may be too much. If it is a private service, such as a playgroup, a family with several children may not be able to afford to send them all to the playgroup. Cost can stop people from getting their prescription, if they have to pay for it, and so they do not get the medication they may need.

Geographical barriers

Some people live in rural areas and may find that getting to the services they need is difficult because they do not have a car and buses may run at times that are not suitable. Older people may have difficulty getting on and off public transport and they may not be able to walk the distance to the service they require. They may put off going to see their GP because of this and, as a result, their condition could get worse. Some individuals and families may not be able to afford a car, particularly with fuel prices being so expensive, so they could be prevented from accessing the service they need because of the geographical location and the cost.

Cultural and language barriers

In order to find out about services it is most likely that you will need to read signs, leaflets or posters. If these are written in English and this is not the language that you usually use, it may be difficult to fully understand the information that is given and, thus, you may not know what services are available. Also, if a leaflet is provided by a GP or specialist to explain the treatment that is being proposed, the person may not be able to read or understand what is being said in the leaflet. This could cause them to become worried or frightened, creating a psychological barrier.

'I can't make sense of this!'

Resource barriers

Sometimes we are not able to get the services we want because there is a shortage of staff or money to pay for the service. The lack of such resources can prevent people from gaining access to services when they really need them. Also, if there is a large demand for a particular service, then people may have to wait as there may only be sufficient money to pay for some, and not all, who require the service.

Health care professionals often have to make very difficult decisions about who gets treatment and who does not. They may have one child that needs treatment that will cost a great deal of money. The same amount of money would perhaps cover 50 people who need hip replacement operations. They may not have the money for both – who should they treat?

The table below gives a summary of the possible barriers that can prevent people from getting the care they need.

Barrier	Examples
Physical barriers	• clients working shifts, therefore unable to access service, as the service is not available when they are not working • stairs • lack of adapted toilets • lift operating system being out of reach • lack of ramps • lack of lifts
Psychological barriers	• fear of losing independence • stigma associated with using some services • not wanting to be looked after by others • mental health problems
Financial barriers	• charges/fees • lack of money for transport • lack of money to provide the service
Geographical barriers	• living in a rural area where facilities are limited • living in a rural area where transport is not available when the services are open • a long bus/train journey may not be practical
Cultural and language barriers	• using English may deter some people from using services • not having professionals who are of the same sex, for example, women doctors/consultants for women • written information not in the person's own language • not knowing what is available • some treatments being considered unacceptable to certain cultures
Resource barriers	• lack of staff • lack of information about services • lack of money to fund services • a large demand for a particular service

CASE STUDY Remus and family

Remus has only been living in this country for a few months. He and his partner, Katrina, are trying to learn English but they are finding it very hard. Remus is unemployed and is finding it difficult to get work, but his partner has a part-time job in the local hotel. Remus and Katrina have two children, Kerry, who is four, and Brendon, who is two years old. It is difficult for the family to get transport into town, where the health, social care and early years services are. A bus leaves twice each day but the costs are high. Katrina and Remus would like Kerry to go to playgroup but there isn't one in the village. Brendon has to go to the hospital once a week as he has cystic fibrosis and needs treatment. He is waiting to have an operation to help clear his airways but the hospital has a long waiting list and staff shortages.

1. Katrina and Remus have a lot of barriers to cope with. Use the table above, which shows the different types of barriers that people face, to help you with this task. Draw up a table of your own, copying the main types of barriers shown on the left-hand side. Complete the examples by using the case study and describe how each barrier will affect the family.
2. Think about all the different types of barriers that can exist when clients want to use health, social care and early years services. Conduct a survey to find out how easy it is for clients to access **three** different services. Record the types of client that use the services, explain their needs and get information about the barriers that may prevent them from using the service. Clearly record your findings and draw some conclusions. You can use graphs, pie charts or other methods to help you do this.
3. How might an individual feel if they are not able to use a service they need?

HOW CAN BARRIERS TO ACCESSING SERVICES BE OVERCOME?

Group Activity

Work with another person to find newspaper cuttings about individuals who have complained about not being able to access the drugs they need.
Make a summary of their protest.
Discuss your findings with the rest of the group.

Getting past the 'barriers' and accessing health, social care and early years services is important for clients. Service providers, too, want to make sure that they reach all those who need their services.

When new services are developed, those responsible put a great deal of thought into how they can be made accessible to all. For example, if someone lives in a rural area and needs to get to the hospital, but the buses are not timetabled so that this can happen, or if the person who needs to go to the hospital is in a wheelchair and cannot get on a bus, how can this be overcome? In this situation the voluntary care sector will probably be able to help. They would organize a volunteer with transport to collect the person and take them to the hospital.

Lena's first language is not English and she cannot read the leaflet about health services.

Overcome by: having leaflets printed in other languages so that they are accessible to all.

Martin is in a wheelchair. He cannot use the lift because the control panel is too high.

Overcome by: moving the control panel so that it can be reached at wheelchair height.

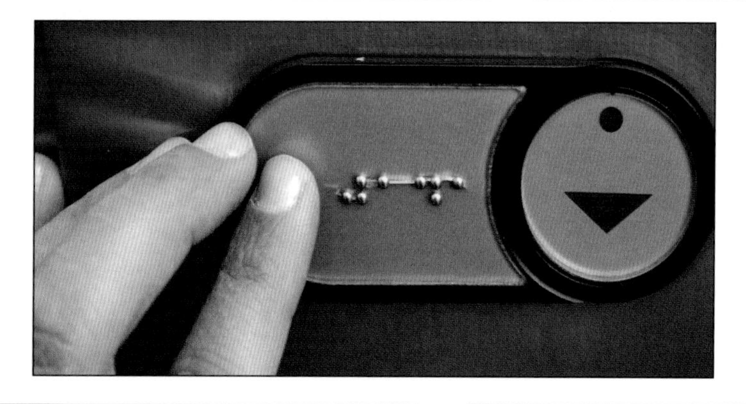

'Now I have access!'

Amy is blind and cannot use the lift at the hospital as she cannot use the control panel.

Overcome by: putting in a control panel that also uses braille.

Kelly has three children and lives on an estate that is two miles from the GP surgery. She finds it very hard to get to the surgery with three children, as it is a long way to walk and she cannot afford to take the bus.

Overcome by: having a mobile surgery to visit the estate twice each week so that mothers with young children and older people on the estate will not have to travel. This would also reduce the cost to the clients.

Ian works shifts. The GP surgery is not open when he is off work, so he can never go for his health checks.

Overcome by: holding some surgeries at the factory where Ian works or having early or late surgery appointments on one weekday or at weekends.

If clients were faced with the barriers given above or any other barrier, this is likely to affect their self-esteem/self-concept. They are very likely not to feel good about themselves and consider that they might not be as good as other people. The effects will not be the same for everyone but some of the effects could be:

- not feeling valued
- thinking that others do not care about their disability
- having a low self-esteem/self-concept
- being depressed
- feeling angry
- feeling unloved/unwanted
- becoming withdrawn
- feeling excluded

12 Work with another person. Think about a time when someone in your family was unable to access a service they needed. How did you feel?

ACTIVITY Overcoming the barriers

1. For each scenario on page 32, explain how the client would feel when faced with the barrier. Explain how it would affect the clients physically, intellectually, emotionally and socially.
2. How would overcoming each barrier help to empower clients?

The postcode lottery

Drugs and treatment are expensive. Decisions about which drugs and which treatments to provide in any area are made by the local Primary Care Trust or by a central organization called 'NICE', (the National Institute for Health and Clinical Excellence). This is an organization that decides whether a drug is too expensive for the health service to use.

On occasions, a certain drug is used or a treatment is made available in some areas, while it is not in other areas. This is known as the postcode lottery. This type of decision is considered to be unfair, particularly by those for whom the drug or treatment is not available. On other occasions NICE will decide that no one can access the drug or treatment because it is not good value for money. In either situation a client's life could be affected as their condition could get worse or they could even die

Group Activity

Work with another person to find newspaper cuttings about individuals who have complained about not being able to access the drugs they need.

Make a summary of their protests.

Discuss your findings with the rest of the group.

CASE STUDY New therapy could hold out hope for Britain's 400,000 Alzheimer's sufferers

New treatment for Alzheimer's disease

Doctors are calling for a clinical trial of an experimental drug treatment that it is claimed can reverse the symptoms of Alzheimer's disease 'in minutes'.

US researchers say the treatment allowed an 82-year-old sufferer to recognize his wife for the first time in years. In the UK, specialists believe the claims should be properly tested, as only a few patients have been treated so far. The treatment involves injecting a drug called Enbrel – which is normally used to treat arthritis – into the spine at the neck. Patients are then tilted to encourage blood flow into the brain, where the drug is designed to block a chemical responsible for inflammation. At least one Alzheimer's patient had his symptoms reversed 'in minutes' while others have shown some continuing improvement in problems such as forgetfulness and confusion after weekly injections. They needed less help from carers during treatment, which appears to reach a plateau at three months.
Around 50 people are being treated by the Institute of Neurological Research, a private clinic in California, with some having had injections for three years.

Continued on next page

Continued from previous page

In one case, the clinic has video evidence of Marvin Miller, 82, which showed he was unable to answer basic questions by a nurse, or identify everyday objects like a bracelet and a pencil. Shortly afterwards he is injected with the drug and it is claimed that five minutes later he could greet his shocked wife, who said he had not recognized her for years.
The experiment follows the discovery that levels of TNF (tumour necrosis factor) can be up to 25 times higher in the fluid surrounding the brain in sufferers of Alzheimer's disease. Enbrel, a biologic treatment licensed for rheumatoid arthritis, binds to excess TNF in the body and makes it inactive.
When used by arthritis sufferers, the drug is self-administered by injection and researchers had to develop a way of injecting the drug into the spine in order to get an effect in brain cells.
Enbrel is not approved for treating Alzheimer's in the US or in the UK and is regarded at this stage as a highly experimental therapy.
Rebecca Wood, chief executive of the Alzheimer's Research Trust, said: 'It is too early to speak of a miracle cure and we need to do more research into this'.

New hope for Alzheimer's sufferers after new treatment 'restores memory in minutes', by Jenny Hope, Mail Online (last updated 11 April 2008).

13 Discuss this article as a group. What are the likely effects if this treatment is a success? What effect will this have on the NHS? What effect could it have on clients?

Poor integration and rationing of services

...WORD CHECK

seamlessness of service – continuous; without any breaks.

continuity – without a break; continuous.

economic – saving money.

Currently the government is trying to persuade organizations within health, social care and early years services to work together rather than to operate individually. By working together there is more likely to be 'a **seamlessness of service**' and **continuity** of care. The individual's needs will be viewed holistically by a small team rather than having to be seen in different places by different specialists. By working in this way, those involved will need to work together, in a partnership, and it is hoped that this approach will bring better results for an individual, as well as being more **economic** to run. More information about this multi-disciplinary approach will be given later in the unit (see pages 45–46).

ASSESSMENT PRACTICE: PREPARATION

This assessment must be based on the same sector, and the services within that sector, chosen for the earlier Assessment Practice.

The Fry family consists of dad and mum, Jules and Jolene, and their four children, Jasper, aged fourteen, Joey, aged ten, Megan, aged six, and Hazel, who is three years old. Also living with the family are Jules' parents, Michael and Michelle, both of whom are in their seventies.

They live in a village and have a detached house with a large garden. It is only a small village and the family have to travel to the nearest town, which is seven miles away, for services and entertainment. Jolene does not drive but there is a bus service twice each day. The family use the Primary Care Trust quite a lot.

1. Draw the table given below. Complete the table to show the different types of referral methods.

Reason for referral	Type of referral
Jolene goes to the GP as she has found a lump in her breast	
The GP sends Jolene to see a specialist	
Jules rings the dentist at the hospital to make an appointment for the removal of wisdom teeth	
A social worker refers both of the grandparents to the hospital for checks on their heart	
The teacher refers Megan to the hospital as she has an eating disorder	
Hazel falls and hurts herself in the playground and another parent calls the ambulance	

2. Use the three main types of referral given in the above table to show your understanding of the different ways people can be referred to the service chosen. Use examples to help explain the points you make. You may wish to add others.
3. Produce a questionnaire for a short survey that could be used to find out about some of the possible barriers the Fry family could meet when using services. When you have completed the survey and had it checked either:
   - visit a setting to obtain some answers

   OR

   - invite a specialist from a care setting to your centre to ask them about the survey you are carrying out.
4. Evaluate your findings from the survey. Try to present them in the form of a pie chart or graph, as well as explaining the results.
5. Explain the possible effects of barriers on the different members of the Fry family.
6. Explain how the removal of possible barriers could empower the members of the Fry family.
7. Choose one piece of legislation and show the impact this has had on the service researched above.
8. Explain how the postcode lottery, poor integration of services and rationing could affect the services required by the Fry family.

Types of care services

What types of care services are provided to meet client group needs?

Getting started

In this section you will learn about which types of care services are provided to meet client group needs. This will include:

- finding out about organizations and private practitioners that deliver health, social care and early years services
- understanding the mainstream universal services that are offered to different client groups and the targeted services to support delivery
- knowing how these services are organized for the sector you have chosen
- understanding how different services work together to meet complex needs.

You must be able to identify local and national examples of service providers who operate in the:

- statutory sector, for example, trusts and local authority services
- private care sector, for example, private companies and self-employed practitioners
- third sector, for example, charities and local support groups using volunteers and not-for-profit organizations who may have paid employees.

You must also understand how different service providers work together to meet client group needs.

You must also know that informal carers (family, friends and neighbours) also provide care and understand the increasing importance of the third sector.

TYPES OF CARE SERVICE

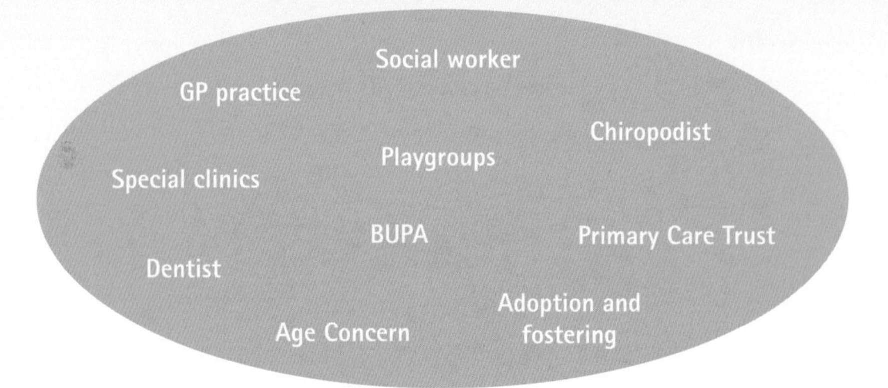

14 Work with another person. Think about two services that have given you some help, for example, a nursery school or GP surgery. To which sector did they belong? Share your information with others.

ACTIVITY Town trail

Follow a route organized by your tutor. Note down any health, social care or early years services that you come across. What services do they provide? Which clients do they provide for? When do they open and close?

When you have completed your walk, mark the services on a map. Make sure you colour code the different sectors to which the services belong. Make a 'Directory' of the services.

Alternatively, this activity can be carried out by using telephone directories, guides to health, social care and early years services and local city/town information packs.

This activity could be evidence for your portfolio building.

Services that are available to all individuals in England can be from:

- the statutory sector – provided through government legislation and usually free
- the private sector – paid for by the individual using the service, which provides a source of income to maintain the service
- the voluntary sector – not-for-profit organizations, who, on some occasions, have paid employees working for them, as well as voluntary workers. Some voluntary organizations will work alongside statutory organizations, for example, Meals on Wheels.

How are services organized?

Those responsible for statutory services can be:

- Primary Care Trusts
- Local authorities.

The structure of health and social care statutory services is currently as shown below:

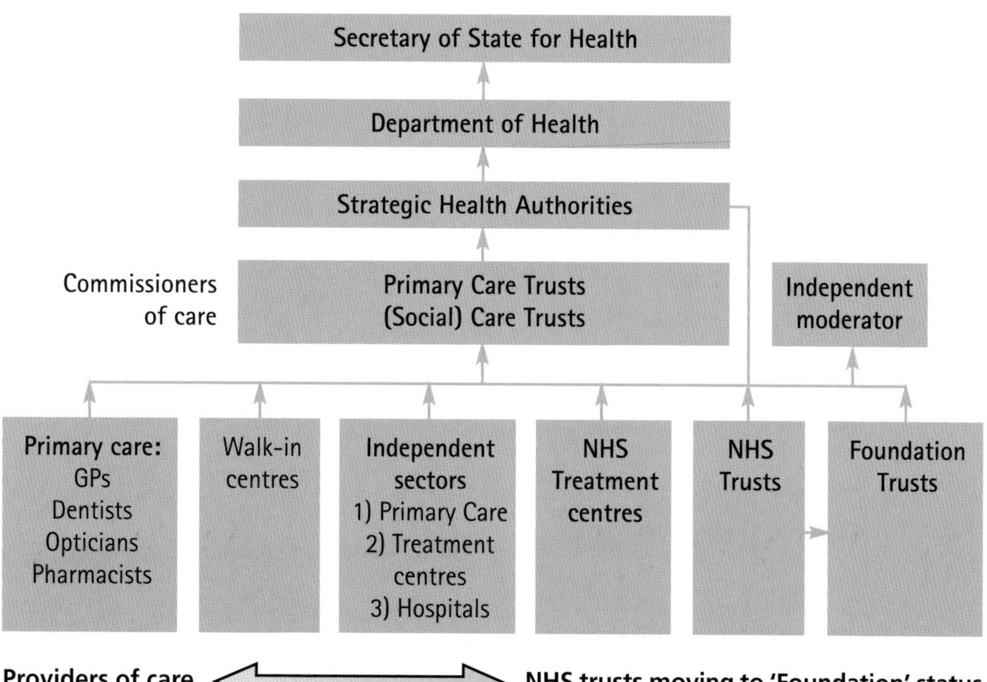

The Department of Health is directly run by the government and has a **Minister** in charge of all its work. It is responsible for health and social services. As part of the new structure, the work of the Department of Health has been '**reduced**', with its main role now being to set the prices at which services are sold in the new 'health care market'. This is known as setting the 'national tariff', so that all services are to be paid on the basis of 'payment by results'. This means that the payment for every treatment will be set by the Department of Health, and those providing services will not be able to compete by cutting prices for any of their services. Some treatments are likely to be profitable and others not so profitable, and service providers will obviously want to do more of the former rather than the latter.

NHS hospitals, ambulances, community care trusts, and so on, will be **regulated** by:

- the Healthcare Commission
- the Independent Moderator.

The Healthcare Commission supervises and inspects, and, in the case of private and voluntary health care providers, also provides licences for all secondary and **tertiary care**. It also 'rates' all NHS Trusts and produces a '**league table**', which shows how effective the provider has been. If the trusts do well, it means that they will move much more quickly towards 'Foundation' status.

Foundation Trusts (FTs) are trusts that have been found ready to support themselves in the health care market without having any support from the Department of Health. This means that they are allocated funds and are able to decide for themselves which services they will offer. They are entirely responsible for their own budgets. It is the Independent Moderator who makes the decision that they are ready to manage their own affairs and, once given this status, the Strategic Health Authority (SHA) no longer supervises them.

The Strategic Health Authority manages those trusts that have not yet reached 'Foundation' status. There are 28 Strategic Health Authorities and they supervise all aspects of the trusts' operations, especially whether they are meeting all of the government's national targets.

...WORD CHECK

Minister – a person responsible in government.

reduced – to lower.

regulated – putting controls over.

tertiary care – specialist health care.

league table – a table to show results, for example, how well a setting has performed.

A hospital responsible for health care of the local population.

The Strategic Health Authorities look after the population in their area. They receive funding from the Department of Health and, with it, they buy health care for the people who need it in their area. The Strategic Health Authority's objectives are:

- To reduce the incidence of avoidable diseases and injury of the population.
- To treat people with illness, disease or injury quickly and effectively on the basis of need.
- To enable people who are unable to perform essential activities of daily living to live as full and normal a life as possible.
- To maximize the social development of children within stable family settings.
- To be accountable to Ministers for the overall performance of the NHS, personal social services and the Department of Health.
- To manage the resources and staff of the Department of Health so as to improve performance.

(Source: Department of Health, Departmental Report 2004, London)

Since 2002, Primary Care Trusts (PCTs) have been responsible for commissioning primary, secondary and community health care services for their local populations. Some of the PCTs have merged and are organized into 'clusters', with joint management teams to improve the organization of health care. The main roles of PCTs are to:

- improve the health of the community
- secure high-quality primary, secondary and community care
- **integrate** local health and social care services.

PCTs take the lead in partnership work with local authorities and other agencies, for example, voluntary and private service providers. The 1999 Health Act enabled the PCTs to pool resources with local authorities so that they can undertake joint purchasing of social care services for groups requiring both health and social care services, such as those for older adults, and people with mental health needs.

The **independent sector** comprises both voluntary and private organizations. In October 2000, '*The NHS Plan*' outlined a new relationship between the NHS and the independent sector, which intended to make the independent sector a mainstream provider of some identified secondary services and a mainstream provider for **intermediate care**, such as services for older adults. This is seen to be the means of increasing patients' choice and, effectively, the independent sector has become a **component** of the NHS.

Some services are delivered by private and voluntary groups. Examples of such services are:

Voluntary services	Private services
Meals on Wheels	Hospitals
Red Cross	Shop mobility
Cruse (bereavement counselling)	Services offering complementary approaches

...WORD CHECK

integrate – mixed in; together and not isolated.

independent sector – those that are not statutory (by law), for example, voluntary and private.

intermediate care – between one operation/situation and another.

component – constituent parts; ingredients, parts of an object.

Group Activity

Look for a hospital in your local area and try to find out its status, for example, Foundation or PCT. With your tutor's permission, invite a person from the hospital (Training Department) to your centre to help you find out about its status and the services it offers. Also find out about the needs of the individuals who use the hospital and how those needs are met.

Make a record of the information given; it could be useful for your portfolio.

WHAT SERVICES ARE AVAILABLE TO CLIENTS?

A wide range of services are available to individuals from all life stages in all main sectors. A few examples are included in the table below:

Individual client	Health care services	Social care services	Children and young people services
Babies and children and young people (including those with disabilities)	Hospital in-patient Hospital out-patient care, for example, physiotherapy GP Birthing/maternity services Mental health care Speech therapy Dentistry Optician School medical services Health promotion Complementary approaches Community services, for example, dietician Hospice	Foster care Adoption Child protection Residential care Child and family support groups Child psychologists Community services Youth workers Youth offending services Counselling Clinics (sexual health, smoking, alcohol, and so on)	Childminders Nursery schools Playgroups Family centres Crèches Toy libraries Parent and toddler support groups After-school clubs Holiday clubs Specialist education Training schemes
Adults (including people with disabilities)	Hospital in-patient Hospital out-patient, for example, radiography GP Mental health care Dentistry Optician Health promotion Complementary approaches Day-care centres Community services, for example, District nurse Chiropody/podiatry Nursing homes Special services, for example, dialysis Rehabilitation Hospice	Residential homes Day-care centres Training/resource centres Psychologists Psychiatrists Luncheon club Home-care services Community services Counselling Social services, for example, social worker Support groups	
Older adults (including those with disabilities)	Hospital in-patient Hospital out-patient, for example, radiography, physiotherapy GP Mental health care Dentistry Optician Health promotion Complementary approaches Day-care centres Community services, for example, district nurse Chiropody/podiatry Nursing homes Special services, for example, dialysis Rehabilitation Hospice	Residential homes Day-care centres Training/resource centres Psychologists Psychiatrists Luncheon clubs Meals on Wheels (with voluntary sector) Home-care services Community services Counselling Social services, for example, social worker Support groups	

The NHS provides a whole range of services. The chart below shows you some of the settings within the NHS and examples of the services they offer.

Health setting	Examples of services provided
Hospital	Maternity, caring for people who are ill, surgery, x-ray, physiotherapy, pharmacy, speech therapy, occupational therapy, orthodontal clinic, ophthalmic clinic, out-patient clinics, geriatric care, clinical counselling/psychology, chiropody, nutrition clinic
Dentist	Treatment for teeth and gums, oral hygiene, advice
Health centre/ GP surgery	Health diagnosis, physiotherapy, chiropody, health advice, counselling, maternity, family planning, giving prescriptions, monitoring health, vaccinations, immunizations
Pharmacies	Making up prescriptions, advice, health monitoring
Community services (health)	Nursing care, advice about health, psychiatric nursing, medical care, monitoring health
Optician	Eye testing, diagnosis of conditions of the eye, advice, providing glasses and frames

CASE STUDY Sasha

Sasha has a severe kidney problem and has to take medication every day to keep her condition stable. She collects her prescription once a fortnight. Sasha also has to have regular health checks to make sure that her condition stays stable and visits the local hospital for this. She also has incontinence problems and is visited at home by a health care assistant.

1. Draw up a table to show all the health services Sasha would use because of her condition. For each, show the treatment she would receive.
2. Carry out some research to find out about:
   - walk-in centres
   - hospices.

   Who are the clients for each?

Local authorities

Local authorities are based in the area in which an individual lives. They are responsible for the needs of people who live in their area. These are needs that are not 'health' or 'medical'. For example, the local authority has a 'Personal Social Service Department', whose responsibility it is to provide services for people who have care needs on a **temporary** or **permanent** basis.

One of the services provided by the local authority is fostering services, for example, who provide a short-term home for children and young people. The adoption service arranges for a family to keep a child or young person for life, which is long-term care.

Some of the services offered by the local authority for children and young people are:

- child protection, fostering and adoption
- providing for children and young people with disabilities
- children's and young people's homes
- youth justice.

...WORD CHECK

temporary – not long lasting; not permanent.

permanent – for ever.

...WORD CHECK

at risk – in danger.

learning disabilities – a dysfunction of the brain that prevents a person from using the brain.

interaction – mixing with others.

The local authority also keep a register of people who are suitable to work as childminders and they keep a register of early years groups, such as playgroups and nurseries. Local authorities will also purchase places in playgroups and nurseries for children and young people who may be '**at risk**' or where the family may need support.

15 Why is it important for the local authority to keep a register of all the early years providers in their area?

Local authority services for adults

Examples of some of the services made available by the local authority for adults are:

- Contributing financially to places for clients within private residential homes and nursing homes for people who need 24-hour care and support, for people who may not have enough money to pay for their care themselves.
- Accommodation and workshop facilities for people with physical and **learning disabilities**.
- Day centres for clients who may wish to live in their own homes, but who may need to have some social **interaction** with other people.

The local authority keeps a register of residential and nursing homes in their area and will carry out inspections of these as required by law. Some examples of settings and services made available by the local authority for clients are shown in the table:

Learning skills for work and learning to socialize.

Local authority settings	Examples of services
Day-care centre for older people	Personal support, supervision, advice, chiropody, aids and adaptations, meals
Community care and support	Advice and guidance, counselling, psychiatric support, home-care services
Fostering and adoption	Children's and young people's homes (temporary and permanent)
Playgroups/nurseries	Purchasing places in playgroup/nurseries
Family centres	Day care for children and young people, support for adults
Resource training centres for clients with disabilities	Training for work, education, advice and guidance

CASE STUDY Debbie-Ann

Debbie-Ann is in her late fifties. She lives on her own but she is becoming very forgetful. She sometimes leaves the lights on all night and wanders around the road and garden in her nightdress talking to herself. She is not feeding herself properly and does not often wash herself. She has no one to talk to as her family live abroad and the house next door is empty.

1. Produce a table to show three services or ways that the local authority could provide support for Debbie-Ann.
2. For each service described, investigate how they would help Debbie-Ann.
3. Carry out research to identify a voluntary group that could help Debbie-Ann. Describe the support they could give.

CASE STUDY Andre

1. Andre is four years old. His family are having personal problems and are finding it difficult to care for him. Find out and explain the different ways that the local social service department could provide help and support for Andre and his family.
2. What is meant by 'learning difficulties'? Find out about one service for people who have learning difficulties in your area and describe how it provides support.
3. What advice would you give to a parent who has a young child with physical disabilities about how to find out about the early years services available?

How are private services organized?

Private services are not provided by law. They are sometimes called '**non-statutory**' services.

They are often set up by large companies to make a **profit**. Some offer medical care and others are involved in giving care and support, for example, counselling.

Examples of private services are:

- hospitals
- childminders
- home-care assistants.
- dentists (some)
- playgroups/nurseries

...WORD CHECK

non-statutory – not law.

profit – to make money on.

insurance policies – taking out cover to help in an emergency, for example, health and safety policy.

How will making a contract with the private sector be beneficial to a hospital?

People who use private organizations or practitioners who accept private patients have to pay for the services they receive. Some people have **insurance policies** to help them with the expenses for their treatment. Others will pay for their treatment from their savings.

People often choose to have their medical care carried out by a private organization, for example, a hip replacement operation, because they can choose the time and the place when it can be done. This might be an important consideration if you have a business to run or if child care is a problem.

Practitioners who treat people privately often work in a private hospital or from their own home. Alternatively, they could have their own premises that have been set up with all the specialist equipment they will need.

17 How would paying to have private treatment for an operation help someone with child care problems?

Some clients combine treatment from universal services/statutory services with that of private care.

CASE STUDY Eddi

Eddi had cancer of the lungs and received treatment in hospital for this. He had a small part of his lung removed and then received chemotherapy. When Eddi came out of hospital, he made an appointment to see a local alternative therapy care worker.

This practitioner gave Eddi some herbal tablets to help relieve his stress. He also recommended that Eddi should have some aromatherapy in his own home. Eddi continued to keep appointments at his local hospital for chemotherapy.

Eddi combined traditional medical treatment with alternative approaches to try to improve his health.

How do you think Eddi was helped by the methods he chose? Would you choose alternative approaches for treatment? Give reasons why you would or would not do this.

Examples of other private organizations are playgroups or nursery schools. These are privately organized but are monitored by Ofsted and records are kept by the local authority. A diagram of how the services are organized is shown below:

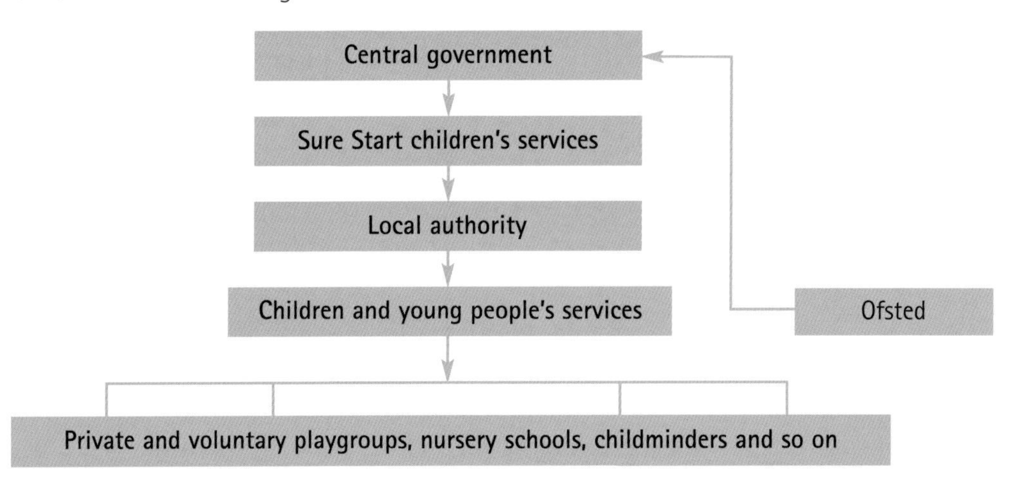

...WORD CHECK

contract – a legally binding agreement.

Voluntary organizations (sometimes known as the 'third sector')

Voluntary organizations are those that provide services or advice about health, social care and early years services because they see there is a 'gap' or a need for these services. Usually services that are made available by the voluntary sector are free of charge, but this is not always the case. Occasionally a small charge is made for the service.

Most of the workers give the care and advice are 'volunteers', who are not paid for the work they do. Any profit that is made by voluntary organizations is used to make the service better or to offer a wider range of services. They are, therefore, often called 'not-for-profit' organizations.

Meals on Wheels involves charities working with universal/statutory services.

Keep a look out in your local high street for 'charity shops'. You might find Help the Aged, Sue Ryder, Oxfam, Age Concern, British Heart Foundation and others. These shops will be selling clothes, china, books, pictures and other items that they have been given by the people who live in the area. Most of the helpers will be doing the work without any pay. The money that is collected from selling the goods is used so they can organize services for people who have a health or care need.

When does the third sector work with other sectors?

Sometimes voluntary organizations will also work together with the statutory service providers. An example is the provision of Meals on Wheels. In this case, social services make a **contract** with voluntary services so they can supply hot meals for clients in their own homes. This helps when the clients are unable to cook for themselves.

Often, when a contract is made between a statutory provider and the voluntary sector, the person who takes charge of the project for the voluntary sector is paid for their skills and expertise. This is because a large project may require at least one full- or part-time paid employee.

A summary of the work of the voluntary sector:

- a large number of people who work in the voluntary sector give their services free of charge
- a few people who organize major projects are paid for the work they do
- voluntary organizations often provide services free of charge
- voluntary services sometimes work with statutory care to run particular projects and receive some money in the form of a grant or a contract for the service they give
- sometimes voluntary services will charge clients a small fee for the service they have given.

There are times when the private sector and the voluntary or third sector work together to provide services. Below is a table that shows where this could occur:

Private and voluntary	Examples of services provided
Day centre for older people	Meals, chiropody, personal support, aids and adaptations, leisure activities, care planning, counselling
Residential homes	24-hour care and support, chiropody, alternative therapies, volunteer friends
Nursing homes	Medical care and support 24 hours a day, volunteer friends
Playgroups/nursery schools (private)	Care and education
BUPA hospitals **Nuffield hospitals**	Surgery, medical nursing, physiotherapy, x-ray, consultations about health conditions, audiology
Help the Aged day centre for older people	Meals, leisure activities, personal help and support, chiropody
Community services	Nursing care in clients' own homes, for example, MacMillan nurses
Hospice	Medical care, personal care and support, alternative therapies

HOW DO THE UNIVERSAL (STATUTORY), VOLUNTARY AND PRIVATE SECTORS WORK TOGETHER?

The '*NHS Plan*' and the 1999 Health and Social Care Act made it possible for a voluntary partnership to be formed between local health and social care organizations. In such an arrangement, PCTs (Primary Care Trusts) and local authorities both commission and provide services for the people within their local area.

Additionally, statutory, voluntary and private sectors often work together to meet the needs of clients. This approach is being encouraged by the government to help people get the treatment they need more quickly. If a client has been waiting a long time for an operation or treatment that they need, a trust hospital (statutory) will make a contract with the private hospital to carry out a certain number of hip operations or knee operations, for example. This means that the client will receive their operation and aftercare in the private hospital but they will not be paying, the payment will be made by the organization that has made the contract with the private hospital.

A **multi-disciplinary approach** means that professionals from different sectors, for example, health and social services, work together as a team rather than in isolation. Sometimes the voluntary sector will also be involved, depending on the type of care that is needed.

...WORD CHECK

multi-disciplinary approach – a team from different sectors or areas that work together, bringing different skills and thinking to the work they do.

Meeting as a multi-disciplinary team.

Group Activity

With your tutor's permission, invite a person who works with other services/sectors to your centre. Find out how this process is managed. What are the benefits? Are there any weaknesses?

Write up the information provided.

There are advantages to this type of approach. For example:

- all will know what the targets are for the individual for whom they are caring and will be working together to achieve these
- notes will be shared between all those involved
- there will be discussion and agreement as to who will be responsible for each task
- timings will be **coordinated** to prevent overlap during visits
- discussion will take place with the whole team in order to achieve monitoring and evaluation
- costs will be shared.

The features of a multi-disciplinary approach are:

- carrying out observation – to see what is needed
- having regular meetings of the team – to check on what each is doing, to prevent duplication of activities
- all to be involved in drawing up the care plan so that each knows what the other's role is
- all to meet together to review the care plan so that they can evaluate the contribution each has made, to have an holistic approach, so that together future planning is meaningful
- leaving notes to say what the previous professional has done to keep each member of the team informed – to prevent duplication
- keeping a log – to see what has been done, to avoid duplication, to provide a record
- working out shared cost of care to keep within the budget – to save money, to save human resources, to save on material resources
- shared responsibility so decision making is not dependent on one person.

Have you or any of your relatives or friends ever used services that have a multi-disciplinary approach?

CASE STUDY Dimitar

Dimitar lives at home with his wife but he has Alzheimer's disease. He is forgetful and often wanders outside. His wife has to keep the doors locked or he will wander into the road. Dimitar loves to chat with people. He can remember quite a lot from the past but not very much about the present. Sometimes he forgets where the toilet is and just urinates where he is. His wife is finding life very difficult and is quite worn out. His GP arranges for an assessment to be made.

1. Identify which services could help provide care for Dimitar and:
   - explain the help they could give
   - explain how this would help Dimitar and his wife to cope.
2. Explain how the services could work together to support Dimitar.

INFORMAL CARERS

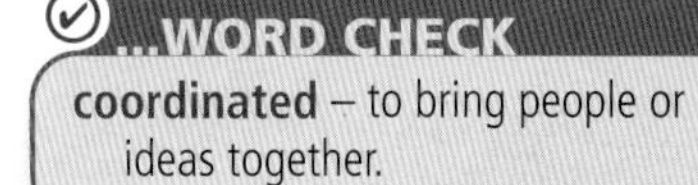

...WORD CHECK

coordinated – to bring people or ideas together.

Informal support is the care given by those who are not paid to do so. In most cases, such people may be unskilled but may be available at times when professional care workers are not. Informal care workers are most likely to be individuals who the client knows and trusts. For example, these could include:

- **Immediate family members** – husband, wife, sons, daughters. Family members are likely to be involved in the personal care of the client, for example, washing, changing, cooking and serving meals.
- **Extended family members** – grandparents, aunts, uncles, nieces, nephews. Members of this group could contribute by shopping, sitting with the client for periods of time, helping to write letters or assisting with the laundry. The way in which they help is likely to be less personal.
- **Neighbours** – those living near at hand. A neighbour can help by providing a snack, sitting and talking with a client, making sure that medication is taken if family members are not able to do so, or even by shopping for the person who is ill.
- **Friends** – people who know the client well and want to help. For example, they may take the client for a walk or drive, take them to an appointment or just sit and share the news about what is happening in the world.

Other groups of people who are classified as informal carers could include:

- **Volunteer friends** – untrained or retired people, or people who do not work and feel they can contribute to the client's care, for example, by driving them to or collecting books from the library.
- **Faith groups** – individuals who belong to a faith group, who probably know the client and wish to visit to keep the person company, to pray or to help in any other way that is useful.
- **Informal networks** – this is a group of people who may be experiencing the same problem as the person who is ill or has a particular need. For example, a group of people who have previously had an alcohol- or drug-related problem and who meet to talk through how they are feeling and the issues they have faced. By meeting and talking, they provide support for one another, which helps them to feel more confident about the future.

18 Talk to a person who has been an informal carer. Find out what type of jobs they have done. How did this help the individual for whom they were providing support?

Informal carers are invaluable as they can fill the gap left by professional care workers and can deal with all the daily routines, which, if not completed, could cause the client to worry.

ASSESSMENT PRACTICE: PREPARATION

You have been asked to investigate one sector (this should be the same sector as chosen for Assessment 1 and Assessment 2). Your investigation must include:

- information about services that are available locally to meet the client group need
- a map on which you have marked a wide range of services, showing clearly to which sector they belong
- information about demographic factors that could have influenced the development of the sector
- an explanation of how the services in this chosen sector are organized and how they have developed, including future plans for working together
- for one service, you should focus on:
  - how the service has developed
  - the structure and organization of the service
  - showing, by producing a diagram, how the service fits into the national structure and explain the diagram
  - showing how the service meets the needs of the population, particularly how it works with other services or various organizations to provide for several needs of the individuals who use it.

Note: Continue with the plan and the bibliography

The principles of care that underpin all care work with clients

What values do care workers promote through their work?

Getting started

You will understand that care practitioners use guidelines and codes of practice to empower clients by:

- promoting quality and diversity of people who use services
- promoting individual rights and beliefs
- maintaining confidentiality.

With young people care practitioners follow the '*Every Child Matters*' agenda and ensure that they:

- make the welfare of the child paramount
- keep children safe and maintain a healthy environment
- work in partnership with families and/or parents
- make sure that children are offered a range of experiences and activities that supports all aspects of their development
- value diversity
- promote equal opportunity
- maintain confidentiality
- ensure anti-discriminatory practice
- work with others
- are a reflective practitioner.

You will understand the balance that services have to achieve between getting involved in people's lives or not, including the risks to both individuals and society associated with both action and inaction.

CODES OF PRACTICE

derived – taken from; produced from.

Codes of practice set out the standards required from professional care workers. They are **derived** from law and, from them, policies are developed. Codes of practice control the standard of care provided as they can be monitored, by observation, to check whether they are being implemented. Codes of practice set out procedures that are to be followed by professional care workers when carrying out their day-to-day tasks. Some apply to specific settings, while others have influence on how individuals work across a number of settings. The table on the next page shows the 'Nursing and Midwifery' Code of Practice (previously UKCC) that is applicable to health care and its main function:

Code of practice	Main function
Nursing and Midwifery Council	Recently formed, the code of practice states that registered nurses and midwives should: • respect all clients as individuals • obtain consent before giving treatment • protect confidential information • cooperate with others in a team • maintain professional knowledge and competence • be trustworthy • act to identify and minimize risks to clients.

The table below gives two examples of other codes of practice that exist in health and social care:

Code of practice	Main function
Equal Opportunities	The Equal Opportunities Commission has published a code of practice that removes all instances of sexual discrimination. An equal opportunities policy can be developed by an organization or setting and should include: • the statement • the implementation plan • the monitoring policy • the evaluation of the policy • targets.
SEN Code of Practice	Primary and secondary schools follow the guidelines given within this policy. The code is also recommended for use in health, social services or any other service concerned with the education of children and SEN. Actual policies and procedures recommend: • early identification • mainstream provision if possible • LEAs to make multi-disciplinary approach to child assessment • annual review of the child's assessment • the child's view to be considered.

ACTIVITY Finding out

1. Working in pairs, find out about **one** of the following:
   - A code of practice for residential care.
   - A code of practice for those professionals dealing with clients who have mental illness health needs.
   - A code of practice that applies to social workers.
2. Present your findings to the rest of the group.
3. In groups, compare one code of practice with one other code of practice. What are their similarities and differences?
4. Invite a person from a setting to your centre (with your tutor's permission), to help you find out about their code of practice. How does this code of practice affect the care that they provide?

   Alternatively, you could find out the answers from work experience.

The 'principles' or 'values' of care have their **foundations** in human rights, information about which is given earlier in this unit on pages 23–24. The 'values', or 'principles', mean treating others as you would wish to be treated yourself, if you were in the same position as the client. The care values or principles are statements that underpin all practical caring. In order to meet the needs of individuals, the professional care worker will need to establish a good relationship with the client, which will involve:

...WORD CHECK

foundations – the basis of.

- promoting the equality and diversity of individuals who use services
- promoting individual rights and beliefs
- maintaining confidentiality.

Each of these care values or principles can be broken into components, or parts, as follows.

Trust
The individual must feel that they can discuss issues without the professional care worker ridiculing them.

Confidence
Knowing only information that is on a 'need to know' basis will be passed to others and all else will be kept confidential.

Positive attitude
The individual will be provided with non-judgemental support by the care professional, which does not label, stereotype or show prejudice.

Communication
Speaking in a way that does not patronize the individual and which presents the facts, allowing the individual to make decisions and choices.

Recognition of culture
Allowing the individual to express their views and to follow the traditions of their own religion or beliefs, for example, providing a place for prayer.

Recognition of social values
Recognizing that in some cultures care by a person of the same gender is preferred.

Competency in knowledge and skills
Carrying out tasks and skills with confidence.

Help the client to feel valued
Promoting a positive self-esteem by not putting a person down or ignoring them.

Help the client to feel fulfilled
By giving mental stimulation and encouraging participation.

▲ Applying care values in an early years setting.

Promoting equality and diversity of people who use services

This includes:

- not showing prejudice, stereotyping or labelling
- understanding and valuing the benefits of diversity
- having knowledge of the bases of discrimination, such as gender, race, age, sexuality, disability or social class
- understanding of own beliefs; assumptions not being prejudiced.

What does this mean in practice?

Professional care workers must treat individuals with respect, for example, calling a person by their preferred name and not calling them 'love' or 'dear'. Each of us has a name and the correct name should be used to address a person. If their nickname is their preferred name, and the client has consented to its use, this is acceptable.

Allowing an individual to give their views and opinions is also a way of encouraging respect. For example, a professional carer should give their full attention when communicating and employ '**active listening** skills'. An individual should not be cut off in mid-sentence, neither should a sentence be completed for them, unless there is a medical or psychological reason for doing so.

When carrying out tasks, the professional care worker should do so to the highest quality possible. Just because an individual is from a different culture from the care worker does not mean that they should receive sub-standard care. Professional care workers should have thought about any views or opinions they may have that could affect the quality of care that they may be giving. Sometimes our **prejudices** can influence the way we respond to others. For example, if we think that everyone should be dressed in a particular way, and then we are asked to attend to a client who is dressed quite differently, our prejudice could be shown through speaking rudely to the individual or not giving them the care to which they are entitled.

▲ Professional carers should employ active listening skills.

ACTIVITY Role plays

Work with another person and prepare a role play for one of the following scenarios.
You should demonstrate the wrong way to deal with each situation AND the correct way of dealing with the situation.

1. A care assistant at a day-care centre leaves the toilet door open while a client is using the toilet. She also shouts, 'Are you ready, love?'
2. The nursery nurse tells Graham that he cannot play in the kitchen because the girls want to play there and it's more suitable for them to do so.
3. Maureen keeps wandering around, moving other clients' belongings from one place to another. She thinks she is being helpful but a care assistant shouts at her and tells her she will lock her in the cleaning cupboard if she does not stop.

Ask the group to say which of your actions are wrong and why.

Ask the group to say how quality care is being provided, how diversity is being respected, and which of your actions are correct and why.

Promoting individual rights and beliefs

This includes:

- the right to be different, for example, sexual orientation, beliefs
- freedom from discrimination, for example, not to be singled out and treated differently
- confidentiality, for example, to have all personal information kept private
- choice, for example, to be able to make own decisions and to be consulted
- dignity, for example, to be treated with respect
- effective communication, for example, to have things explained and to be listened to
- safety and security, for example, to be protected from harm
- privacy, for example, having own space that is not invaded by others without consent
- to be able to worship or believe in whichever belief you value and to practise those beliefs
- to promote your own customs.

...WORD CHECK

active listening – to make sure all concentration is on the speaker; concentrating the mind on what is being said.

prejudices – being biased; making up one's mind about someone or something before really knowing what they are like.

We are all different. We like different books, different music, different films and different food. Some individuals may be different in their beliefs, customs or sexual practices; therefore, professional care workers need to make sure that they do not discriminate against those who do not **conform** to their own values. Having a same sex partner, for example, is acceptable, providing the two people concerned are of the **age of consent**.

...WORD CHECK

conform – abiding by the rules and regulations; keeping within the rules set.

age of consent – the age at which something is permitted by law, for example, having sex.

All individuals have the right to use their own GP (doctor), rather than being told that they must have the same GP as all the other residents in a residential home. Making choices about what we wear, what we have to eat, who we sit next to and at what time we go to bed, are all examples of choices that adults have the right to make.

Individuals who are receiving health, social care or early years services also have the right to be part of the decision-making process and to contribute to discussions when the subject for discussion affects them.

CASE STUDY Joy and Margaret

Joy and Margaret have been partners for over 15 years. They are now in their late 60s and Joy has been admitted to hospital because she has had a mild stroke.

Margaret visits Joy each day and when she greets Joy, she kisses her fully on the lips and gives her a cuddle.

On seeing this, one of the nurses rushes to the sister in charge of the ward to complain about Margaret's behaviour. Some of the other visitors are a little taken by surprise by this behaviour.

1. As a group, discuss why the behaviour of Joy and Margaret has caused concern.
2. How should this situation be dealt with in your opinion? Give reasons why.

ACTIVITY More role plays

Work with another person and prepare a role play for one of the following scenarios. Show the wrong way to deal with each situation AND the correct way of dealing with the situation.

1. Bob and Patrick tell the social worker that they want to share a bed when they move into a residential home. The social worker becomes very angry.
2. Treatment is being planned by staff at a meeting following an assessment of Helana's needs. Helana attends the meeting but is not asked what she would like.
3. Tom and Betty are watching a TV programme in the lounge of a residential home. Violet enters the room, looks at the programme, and goes and switches the programme over to something she wants to see. The care assistant takes Violet's side as he says, 'The programme being watched by Tom and Betty has nearly finished'.

Ask the group to say which of your actions are wrong and why. Then ask them how you have shown quality care and respect for diversity.

Maintaining confidentiality

Confidentiality means keeping information given to oneself. That is, not sharing it with anyone who does not 'need to know'. It means making sure personal and private information cannot be accessed by others. Any information given by the client should not be disclosed without the client's permission. Personal information can include:

- information being discussed orally, for example, care workers discussing proposed treatment with the client
- written information, for example, a care plan being stored safely
- electronic records, for example, a person's medical history being stored securely, with only authorized personnel having access.

Disclosure is passing on personal information given by a client in confidence and which was considered to be secret between the client and the care worker.

Care workers should never promise not to pass on personal information. They should explain to the client that they will not pass on personal information unless there is a very good reason to do so.

Disclosure of information can be necessary in special circumstances. For example:

- if a client intends to harm themselves
- if a client intends to harm others
- if a client is involved in a criminal activity.

19 A neighbour of a client who has been admitted to hospital asks the nurse 'What is wrong with Nellie?'
What should the response be? Why?

Maintaining confidentiality means:

- Keeping personal information secure and away from people who do not need to know.
- Preventing access to files containing personal information by keeping them in locked filing cabinets.
- Having passwords that must be used for accessing electronic records.
- Not gossiping about clients or speaking about them by name in front of others so that they can be identified.

...WORD CHECK

disclosure – passing on confidential information.

▲ Maintaining confidentiality, which is correctly applying the care values.

How can professional care workers apply the care values?

A practice nurse in a GP surgery

A practice nurse, who is changing a dressing, needs to find out how the client is feeling and whether they have taken their medication regularly, as well as changing the dressing on the client's leg. How can they do this and apply the care values? This could be achieved by:

- drawing the curtains around the client when changing the dressing, to help maintain dignity
- calling the client by their correct name, which promotes respect between the client and the practice nurse and promotes client rights
- explaining to the client that they need to find out what medication has been taken. Using effective communication, they should ask open questions to encourage the client to talk and ask closed questions to obtain specific answers. They should use the correct tone of voice, vocabulary that is not too difficult and allow the client to ask questions besides listening carefully

- keeping their voice low in order to maintain confidentiality
- making sure that any cultural requirements or beliefs are met, for example, having a female nurse if the client is a female and if it is traditional within her culture to have a same sex nurse in attendance
- not talking about the client to others in a way that means they can be identified, in order to maintain confidentiality.

Other care workers will endeavour to apply the care values in a similar way. The table below gives examples of how each of the professional care workers listed could achieve this:

Professional care worker	How the care values would be applied
Health care assistant	• Explaining to the client what they are going to do when taking temperature or a pulse (effective communication) • Asking the client when they would like a bath (rights) • Talking quietly to a client about their treatment (equality and confidentiality)
Occupational therapist	• Explaining how aids could be used and adaptations of the home made (effective communication) • Talking to the client about needs and their availability (rights and equal opportunities) • Recognizing that the client has a different sexual orientation from their own and accepting the arrangements in the client's home (accepting diversity)
GP or consultant	• Diagnosing illness and active listening (equal opportunity and effective communication) • Providing information about the range of services available (choice and rights)
Social worker	• Actively listening to the personal problems experienced by the client (confidentiality and communication) • Making an assessment of needs (rights and equal opportunities) • Talking with the client about the range of services available (choices/effective communication)
Nursery nurse	• Organizing different cultural events to be celebrated (promoting personal beliefs) • Asking a child what they would like to do out of the activities being offered (choice) • Talking to the child using language they can understand (effective communication) • Finding out from parents about their requirements, for example, who to contact in an emergency (rights/choice)

CASE STUDY Ray and Asif

Ray and Asif are same sex partners. They have been together for 15 years, but Ray is now in need of an assessment of needs as he has mobility problems and some loss of short-term memory. Asif has a nasty ulcer on his leg that will not heal. A social worker has arranged to meet both Ray and Asif in order to discuss this.

1. Explain how the social worker can apply the care values when making an assessment of Ray's needs and when talking to both Ray and Asif about the situation.
2. The social worker agrees with Ray and Asif that they will require a health care assistant to help with monitoring health, giving each a bath, and changing dressings on Asif's leg. Explain how the health care assistant will apply the care values while helping Ray and Asif to cope.
3. It is agreed that an occupational therapist will visit Ray and Asif at home to talk to them about aids and adaptations. Explain how the occupational therapist will apply the care values when talking with both of them.
4. Both Ray and Asif need to visit the physiotherapist for treatment. Explain how the physiotherapist would apply **all** of the care values/principles while making an assessment and carrying out treatment.
5. Evaluate how clients may feel if the care values are not applied.
6. Two years later, Ray and Asif decide that they should move into residential care. Analyse how the professional care workers at the residential home could apply the care values for Ray and Asif.

EVERY CHILD MATTERS AGENDA

When caring for children and young people, practitioners try to follow the agenda set out in '*Every Child Matters*'. For further information, see earlier in this unit on page 12.

Early years care values

The welfare of the child is paramount	The welfare of the child is most important. They should be listened to and their views taken into account.
Keeping children safe and maintaining a safe environment	Safe working practices must exist.
Working in partnership with parents	Sharing, openly, information about children and families' development and progress. Respect must be shown for family traditions.
Children's learning and development	Children should be offered a range of experiences and activities that support all aspects of development: physical, intellectual, emotional and social.
Valuing diversity	Information relating to traditions should be presented in a positive manner.
Equal opportunity	Each child should be offered equality of access to opportunities to learn and develop, and so work towards their potential.
Anti-discrimination	Expressions of prejudice by children or adults should be challenged.
Confidentiality	Information about children and adults should never be shared with others without consent. Secure storage of records is legally required.
Working with other professionals	Liaison with other care professionals should only take place with prior permission.
The reflective practitioner	Early years workers need to reflect on their practices and plan for developing and extending practice.

Care workers must behave in a **non-judgemental** way, working to the principles of good practice by valuing clients for their individuality and diversity, enabling them to direct their own lives. All individuals, whether clients of health, social care or early years, must be accepted for who they are. They must not be judged by standards that govern the professional care worker's life. Personal values have to be put aside so that individuals are given the best possible treatment and care.

...WORD CHECK

non-judgemental – considering something without already having made a decision or judgement.

ACTIVITY Applying the care values to achieve quality care

Usha is working as a nursery nurse in a local playgroup. Fawzia is working as a care assistant in a day-care centre.

1. Compare how Usha and Fawzia will apply the care values in the workplace. You should consider similarities and differences.
2. Fawzia is going to take an older person to the toilet. How will she:
   - maintain dignity?
   - use effective communication?
   - provide choice?
3. Usha is responsible for providing a healthy and safe environment for the children who attend the playgroup. What will this involve?
4. How can applying the 'care values' and 'principles' of care contribute to helping clients to improve the quality of their lives?
5. Explain how a professional care worker could apply the principle of 'being a reflective practitioner' in their work at the playgroup.

MAINTAINING A BALANCE

...WORD CHECK

tensions – unpleasantness between two or more people; a balance between one thing or another.

Balancing a client's rights against the responsibilities of a professional care worker can cause **tensions** and disagreements. Professional care workers have a responsibility towards those who are accepting the service. Individuals who are receiving care also have rights. Balancing these two perspectives could at times be very difficult. For example, if a client tells a professional care worker of some very upsetting occurrence in their lives, and how they feel hurt and upset by what has happened, the professional carer must stand back and not become personally involved. This does not mean that the professional carer should not be sympathetic, but their duty is to deliver care, not to become involved in personal disputes.

There could be times when the professional care worker could become involved because the upset or dispute is reflected as part of their job role. However, care must be taken to ensure that the professional care worker recognizes when there should be 'action' and when 'inaction' is more appropriate.

CASE STUDY Action or inaction?

Maurice attends the local playgroup. His parents have heard that two children with learning disabilities will be attending the group in the near future. They are very unhappy about this and tell other parents about what is going to happen. They also tell all the staff at the playgroup that they are going to talk to these children's parents, to tell them letting the children with learning difficulties attend is unacceptable.

1. Discuss what the staff should do in this case. Action or inaction? Why?

Isla is found, by a care assistant, sitting in her room crying. When the care assistant talks with Isla, she discovers that another resident keeps coming into Isla's room and borrowing her clothes.

2. Discuss what the staff should do in this case. Action or inaction? Why?

ASSESSMENT PRACTICE: PREPARATION

Choose **one** of the short scenarios given below. The scenario chosen should match with the sector chosen for the earlier Assessment practices.

Scenario 1 Britany works as a nurse in the local Foundation Hospital.

Scenario 2 Banazir is a social worker in the local community.

Scenario 3 Selina is a nursery nurse in a playgroup in the local area.

1. Explain which guidelines and which code of practice would guide the chosen practitioner in their day-to-day work.
2. How would the code of practice affect the work that each does on a daily basis?
3. Which care values will influence the day-to-day work of your chosen practitioner?
4. Explain how the care values will be applied by the practitioner in their day-to-day work.
5. How will the application of the care values help to empower clients?
6. What are the likely effects on clients if the care values are not applied?
7. Discuss how the service/sector chosen can maintain a balance of 'action' and 'inaction' in the lives of clients.

Main work roles and skills

What does care work involve and what skills and qualities do care practitioners need to perform their work roles?

Getting started

- You need to know about the roles of practitioners who deliver care in services:
  - primary practitioners, for example, nurses, GPs, social workers, care assistants and nursery nurses, who work directly with people providing care
  - secondary practitioners who support work indirectly, for example, medical receptionists and porters.
- You need to:
  - understand the qualities, qualifications and skills needed for main work roles of care workers and how these may be achieved academically and vocationally
  - understand how changes in services and service provision can affect the job roles of care workers and change the skills required for those jobs
  - understand why care workers need good interpersonal skills
  - know how care workers use communication skills to develop care relationships, provide and receive information, and report on the work that they do with clients
  - know how effective communication can help support relationships with colleagues, clients and their families, and how poor skills can reduce the effectiveness of care work or damage care relationships
  - understand the differing communication needs of client groups using care services in a multicultural society.

CARE PRACTITIONERS

Primary practitioners

Jobs in health, social care and early years sectors can be divided into direct and indirect roles. **Direct** care roles are jobs where the practitioner is in personal contact with the individual and caring for them is the main purpose of the role.

WORD CHECK

direct – straight to the person/openly; to be responsible for a person's care.

Examples of direct jobs in health care:

Nurse | Physiotherapist | Social worker | Dietician | Midwife | Doctor/Consultant | Health care assistant

Examples of direct jobs in social care:

Social worker | Care assistant | Adoption/fostering officer | Home tutor

Examples of direct care jobs in early years:

Nursery nurse | Care assistant | Play leader | Support assistant

Some professionals work in the community, caring directly for individuals who need support. Such professionals come from all three sectors: health, social care and early years. Examples are:

Professional	Job role
District nurse	Attends to health monitoring, changing dressings, health needs
Health visitor	Promotes good health through diet and exercise, and gives advice
Care assistants	Works in the client's own home, in day-care centres or residential settings. Assists with dressing/undressing, shopping, cleaning
Home tutors	Assists learners who are unable to attend education centres, for example, because of disability, pregnancy or illness
Childminders	Cares for children in the childminder's own home while parents are at work
Chiropodist	Visits individuals in their own home to help provide foot care
Health care assistant	Assists with health monitoring in the individual's own home and with bathing/showering
Occupational therapist	Will help the individual to decide what aids or adaptations are needed in the home
GP (doctor)	Will visit individuals who are over 70 in their own home to give medical help

Registered nurse

A registered nurse could work in:

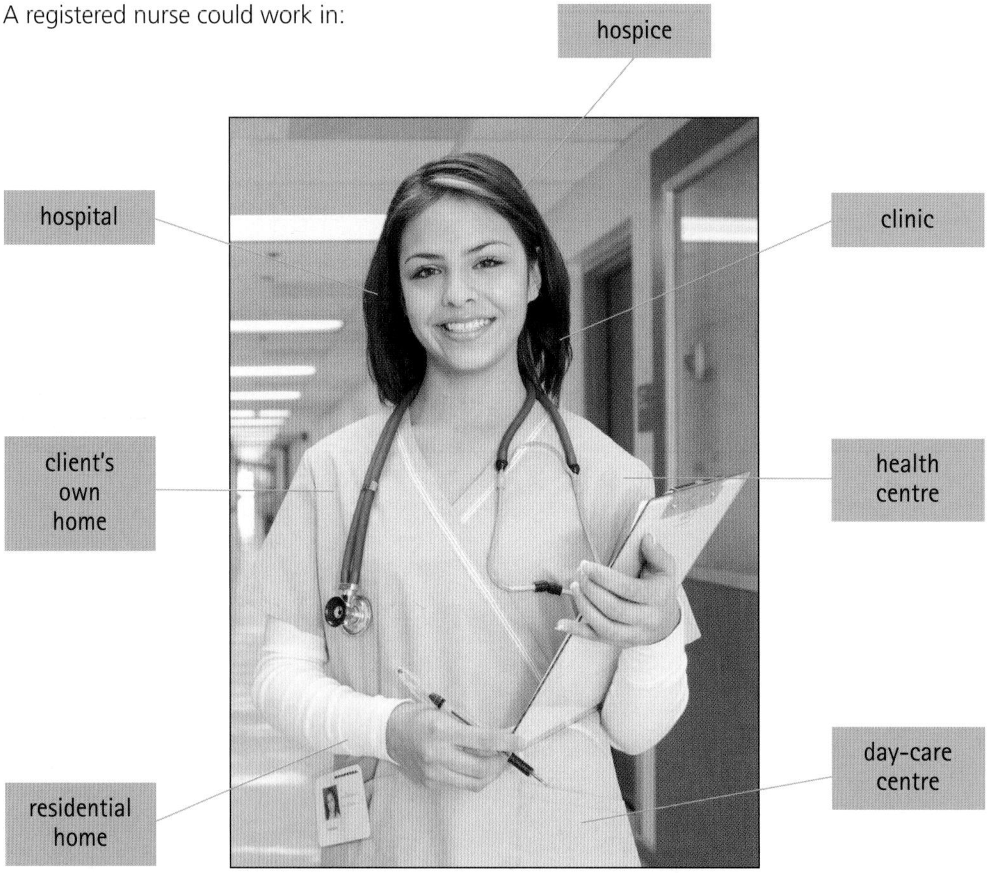

hospice
hospital
clinic
client's own home
health centre
residential home
day-care centre

A registered nurse would have a variety of different tasks to carry out, but underlying all is their attention to health care. If the registered nurse was based in a hospital, examples of the main tasks could be:

- assisting with client's medical treatment
- monitoring the individual's health, for example, temperature, pulse, blood pressure
- changing dressings
- supervising the distribution of drugs
- writing reports
- talking to clients and relatives
- looking after the general care of clients
- liaising with other agencies, for example, physiotherapist, social worker
- accompanying the doctor on their rounds of the ward.

A typical day for a registered nurse in a hospital could follow the one outlined below, but it must be remembered that no two days are ever the same as individual needs will change!

...WORD CHECK

briefing – a meeting held to pass on important information.

*I start work at the hospital at 8:00am and work through until 4:00pm. I get an hour for lunch and two coffee breaks. When I come on duty I have a meeting with the sister and the other nurses on the ward, and we find out what has happened to the clients during the night. This is called our '***briefing***'.*

I greet all the patients in the ward and ask them how they are. I usually tell them what the weather is like outside. The patients will have had their breakfast, so my first job is to make sure all the breakfast things are removed and then to help them get washed. Some will be able to go to the bathroom by themselves but others will need help with washing.

Some patients will need bedpans and I have to help them to sit comfortably on these and empty them when the client has finished. I work with other nurses to do this as we are not allowed to lift patients on our own. We always have to do a risk assessment before doing this.

I then have to make sure that the beds are made properly and that each patient is comfortable.

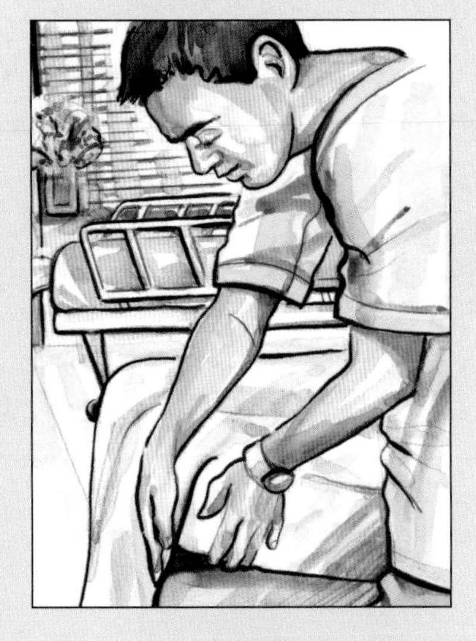

Making sure beds are made properly.

The patients are left to sleep, read or watch TV while I check their records and make sure these are in order for the doctor's round. The doctors do the rounds of the wards between 9:30 and 11:00am. I go round with them and answer their questions about the medication the patient has received and also tell them about any changes in the patient's condition. The doctor will talk to each person and ask them how they feel. The doctor will then decide whether there is to be any change in medication or treatment for that person.

Doing the rounds with the doctor.

At around 11:00am the tea and coffee arrives and I help to make sure that everyone gets the drink they want.

Some patients will need a dressing changed or will need to be prepared for physiotherapy or surgery.

Lunch arrives around 12:30pm. I make sure the patients who have to remain in bed are in a comfortable position so they can eat their lunch.

Throughout the day I talk to all the people in the ward and try to brighten up their day. Some are worried about their condition or about the treatment they are to have and I try to support them by reassuring them and explaining exactly what is going to happen. I find people are not so afraid if they know the facts.

Continued on next page

After lunch we monitor the patients' health by taking temperatures and pulses. Sometimes a health care assistant is available to do this. Whether I do the monitoring or the health care assistant does, the measurements are recorded on charts. Some patients will need medication and I accompany the sister who is giving out medication to check that the correct medication, in the right amount, is being given to the right person.

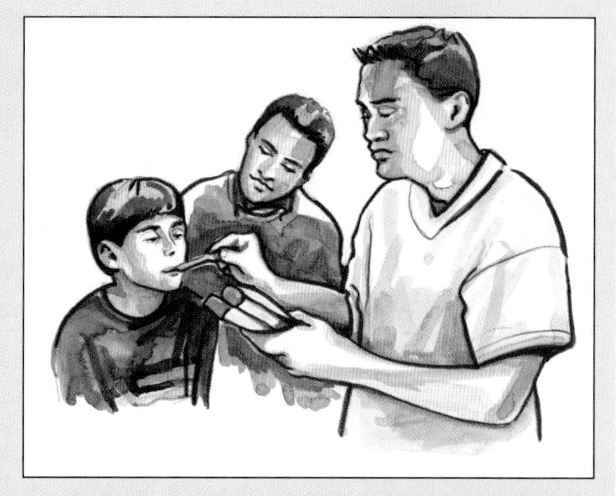

Monitoring the patient's health is an important part of the job.

Visiting time starts at 2:00pm. At this time I make sure that all the records are up to date. I also chat with patients who do not have any visitors. Sometimes I have to change more dressings or give some help to patients who are feeling very unwell.

Before I go off duty, I have a meeting with the staff who are coming on duty so that we can exchange information about the patients' health and the treatment and medication they have received.

Group Activity

Try to arrange for a registered nurse to visit your centre (with your tutor's permission). Ask them to outline what they do in a typical day.

Remember to make lots of notes for your portfolio if needed.

Snapshots of different direct job roles

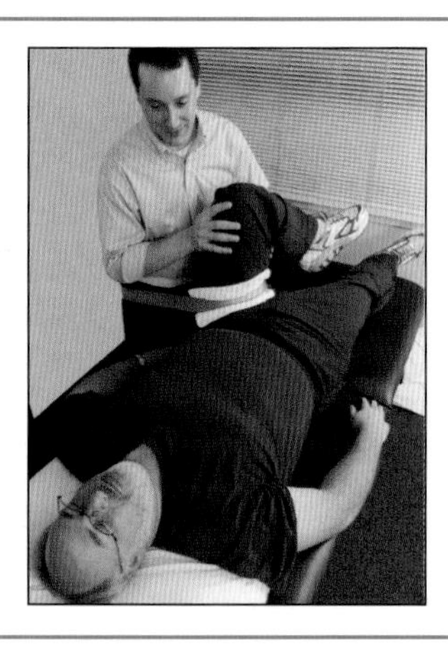

Physiotherapist

I work at the local hospital where I design programmes of exercise for patients who have broken bones or muscle injuries, to help strengthen the injured part. Sometimes I use heat and massage to help with the treatment. I have to keep very careful records of the exercises each patient does and of the effects these seem to be having on the injured part. I have to make sure that the patient understands how to do the exercises correctly, so communication skills and getting on with clients is a very important aspect of my work. I have a degree in Physiotherapy and also a qualification in Remedial Gymnastics.

Helping people through exercises and massage.

Childminder

I care for children in my own home. Sometimes a child will come for half a day, some will stay for the whole day and some will come after school until a parent comes to collect them.

I try to make the time they spend with me interesting. If they are staying all day, we start with activities like playing with a variety of toys, for example, cars, dolls, building bricks.

Halfway through the morning, the children have a drink and sit quietly. I then read them a story. After lunch, if it's dry, I take them for a walk with our dog. We collect things like leaves, flowers or conkers.

Then they can watch TV, read or draw until they are collected by a parent.

Optician

My shop is in the high street. I test the eyesight of individuals and while I am doing this, I am checking for eye diseases and conditions such as squints and double vision. I have to know how to use the equipment that helps me to do the diagnosis. If I think there are really major problems, I refer the person to a specialist. I have to make sure that the client has the correct strength of lens, as if the prescription is not accurate, damage could be caused to the eye. I have to be very accurate in my work and pay attention to detail. My training was quite long but I do have a degree in Optometry and other ophthalmic qualifications. While I own my own shop, other opticians work in hospitals or in clinics or laboratories.

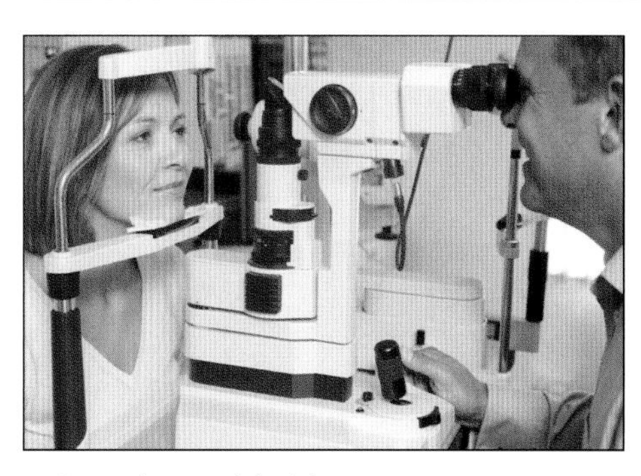

▲ Improving people's sight.

Volunteer in a charity shop

I help in a charity shop, which sells anything that people decide to give our collectors. The charity raises money for the local children's hospice, so I do not get paid for the work I do. Sometimes I serve customers and help them to find something they may be looking for. On other occasions I work upstairs helping to sort the items that we have received and to freshen them up, such as ironing clothes or wiping off dust. I do enjoy my work.

Complementary approaches therapist

I own my business, which is working with people who want to try alternative approaches to medicine. I specialize in aromatherapy, massage and acupuncture.

Many people are nervous about acupuncture but many find it very therapeutic. I know exactly where the needles should be placed and the treatment does relieve pain.

Group Activity

Carry out research to explore the tasks carried out by a social worker. Produce a handout for others to use.

Stephen: care assistant at a local day-care centre

Stephen has a job as a care assistant at a local day-care centre. This is a typical day experienced by Stephen. It should be remembered that a care assistant working in a different setting could have an entirely different day.

My day starts at 8:00am with a staff briefing, where the manager talks to us about which individuals to expect for the day and about any special conditions or needs they may have. Our supervisor will also talk to us about the programme for the day and make sure that we know who is responsible for each activity.

At 10:00am the first people start to arrive in the social service buses. I help to receive the individuals and help them with their coats, making sure they are sitting comfortably and with their friends. I then fetch them a coffee or a tea. By 10:45am all the clients have arrived and they are busily talking to one another.

Continued on next page ▶

▲ A care assistant must be prepared for anything.

I join each group and read them what is on the menu for lunch. I ask each one what they would like but I make sure they know what choices they have first. When all the lunch orders have been taken, one of the care assistants will start a quiz for the whole group. We take turns to do this.

At lunchtime, I help the clients to the meal table and make sure they all have the meals they ordered. One resident needs feeding. I ask her what she would like to eat first and tell her what I have on the spoon. The feeding takes some time, as the client cannot swallow very quickly. I try to make sure the feeding maintains the client's dignity, by not spilling food down her chin or on her clothes.

When the residents are settled in the community room again after lunch, they can do their own thing. Most read the papers or have 40 winks!

Later, I help the people for whom I am responsible. Some want me to help them write a letter. One gentleman likes doing crosswords, so I help with this. Another person may just want to talk to me or may ask about a problem that is worrying them. We have tea at 2:45pm and then play bingo. At 3:30pm the transport comes to take them home. I then have to do my record keeping.

Group Activity

Try to arrange for a care assistant from a different setting to visit your centre (with your tutor's permission). Ask them to outline what they do in a typical day.

Remember to make lots of notes for your portfolio if needed.

Nursery nurse

There are quite a large number of jobs available working with children and young people. One of the most well-known jobs is that of a nursery nurse. Below is an example of a typical day in the life of a nursery nurse. However, it must be remembered that job roles as a nursery nurse will vary considerably according to the type of setting.

I arrive at work around 8:00am and work through until 4:00pm. Most of the children stay with us for the whole day, but some leave at lunchtime. Our nursery is only open for these times, whereas some are open from 7:00am until 9:00pm.

Most of the children's parents are at work and we look after the children while they are there. We have to be quite sure that we know what each individual child is allowed to do or eat. We also have to be sure that we have a contact number for the parents in case of an emergency. The children's names and family records are kept on computer, but only two of us have access to the information.

There is a short staff meeting to check that we all know what is expected from us. The equipment is put out by the member of staff employed to do this but we are asked to check each section.

▲ Checking the equipment in the playroom.

We greet each child in our group individually and make sure we have asked the parent about any special things that have happened or that they want us to do. As the children arrive, a register is kept so that we know exactly which children are in the building. The parents know that they must actually hand the child to a member of staff and not just leave them to play.

At 9:30am we all join together and greet one another. We have to make sure that the cultural needs of each child are observed when we are greeting one another, so we have different poems and short sayings read out each day during the greeting. This session usually lasts for ten minutes.

Continued on next page ▸

Activity time is next. Some children will paint, some will stick and glue, some will colour. Each helper or nursery nurse supervises an activity. We make sure there are lots of different materials from a range of cultures for the children to use.

At 11:00am there is a drinks break. The children sit in a circle and have a drink and a piece of fruit.

At 11:15am we have story time or singing. This is led by one of the staff but the children join in and take part in the actions or mime.

Before lunch we have 'large' equipment or 'outdoor activities', which means the slide and trampoline are brought out and all the large tractors and cars. The children can go outside if they wish. Sometimes we organize a walk to the park to find something for the 'interest table'.

Quiet music is played after lunch to help the children relax. Each day a tune from a different culture is played.

The children can choose which activity table they sit at in the afternoon. Some activities are different from those provided in the morning. Sometimes we have some finger painting, cooking, or paper mâché work for the older ones.

Around 3:30pm we have a sing along for five minutes before the free play at the end of the day. Staff try to talk with each parent of the children in their group as they arrive to give them information about how their child has got on.

I enjoy working with the children. It is very satisfying to watch them develop, and become more independent and confident.

▲ Story time!

▲ Different activities are available for the children.

What are indirect care workers?

Indirect job roles are jobs where the person is providing support to those who are personally or directly caring for clients. Examples of such jobs are:

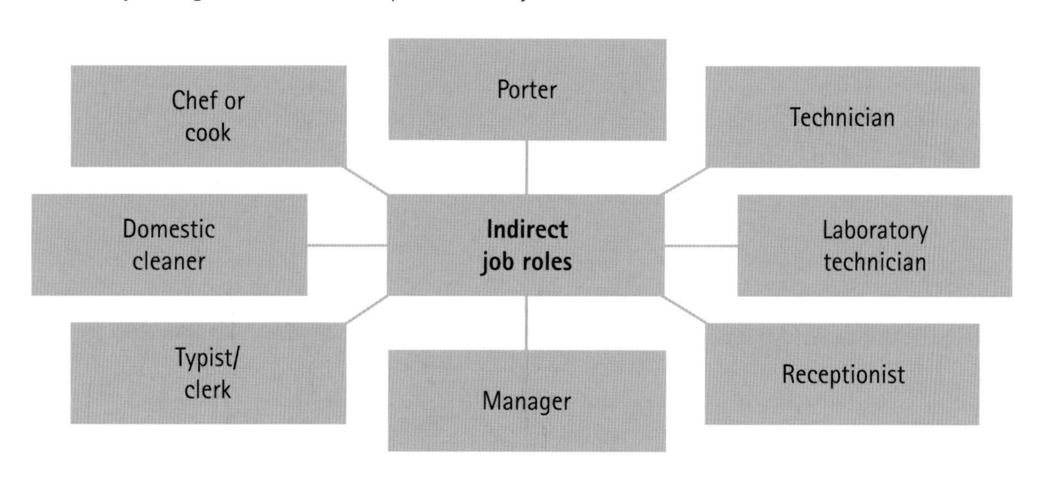

...WORD CHECK

indirect – not directly responsible/not obvious.

Both direct and indirect job roles are important, as the client will only receive the best care when both are working together to **promote** the interest of the client. Individuals working as indirect care workers are very important, as without them the practitioners would not be able to do their jobs successfully. The receptionist, for example, may be the first person to greet a client and this is the first impression a client will get of the care setting and the people who work there. The receptionist will need to have good communication skills because greeting people, making them feel welcome and directing them to the care worker they need are important aspects of their role.

Snapshots of indirect care job roles

Kieron (hospital porter)

I enjoy my work as each day is different. I sign in at 7:00am and finish at 3:45pm. I have a contact radio and when I am needed I get a call. Sometimes I have to collect a parcel, equipment or set up equipment ready for the specialist to use. At other times I will be asked to take a patient down in the lift to the x-ray department. I try to talk to the patient if they are well enough, as this cheers them up and stops them worrying about what is going to happen next. I meet some interesting people in my work.

Making things as pleasant as possible.

...WORD CHECK

promote – to put forward; to support something.

genetic – inherited, passed down from one member of the family to another.

individuality – specific to that person and no other.

trait – a characteristic; a feature.

reflect – to think back over something; to consider an action that has been taken.

characteristic – a feature; a trait.

Medical receptionist
- answers telephone
- makes appointments for clients
- gives directions to clients
- answers questions

Cleaner
- brushes/mops floors
- dusts surfaces
- talks to clients
- cleans basins/baths/toilets

QUALITIES, QUALIFICATIONS AND SKILLS

What are qualities?

Qualities are what we are like as a person. They are partly the result of our **genetic** make up, which is inherited from our parents. Qualities are also the result of factors that have influenced our development, for example, family, education, income, social class and where we live.

No one thing has contributed to our **individuality**. We are the way we are because of inherited factors and the experiences that we have had. For example, a person brought up as an only child may be less likely to share things with others than a person who has several brothers and sisters. A person whose mother always panics in a crisis may have inherited the same **trait** from her.

Qualities contribute to the person that we are and often **reflect** the things that are important to us; the things that we value. They are things we do naturally because they are part of our make up or a **characteristic** that makes us so unique.

When providing practical care for clients, qualities that come naturally to us will help to improve the care that is provided.

What qualities could we have and how would they help when providing care?

Patience
Being prepared to spend time listening to an individual who finds it difficult to speak or think quickly.

Empathy
Being able to see things from the same perspective as the individual.

Understanding
Being able to see an individual's point of view even if it is different from our own.

Calmness
Not going into a panic when a difficult situation or problem arises.

Honesty
Speaking the truth and being open about situations.

Sense of humour
Being able to laugh and find a funny aspect of the situation.

Respect
Being able to make the person feel valued.

Willingness
Being helpful, showing nothing is too much trouble and wanting to do as much as possible.

Cheerfulness
Looking at things from a happy perspective.

CASE STUDY Maya

Maya is a care assistant who is trying to settle a dispute between two older adults in a day-care centre who are quarrelling over words used in a game of Scrabble. Maya takes time to listen and to talk to both adults to find out exactly what is the problem and to suggest a solution. She does not rush away to find someone else to deal with the problem. While listening, she smiles and looks happy. She makes it clear to the adults that she is expecting them to listen to what each has to say but while speaking she tells a joke, which makes both adults smile. Once the difficulties are sorted, Maya asks both adults if they would like a cup of tea and goes off to fetch one for them.

1. Find all the qualities shown by Maya in the case study. For each, give an example from the case study.
2. In pairs, write a case study of your own which shows a professional care worker demonstrating qualities. Do not explicitly give the quality.
3. On a separate sheet of paper, write the answer, for example, willingness – being prepared to help over and above the call of duty.
4. Exchange the case study with another pair and try to guess the qualities they have included, giving the example.
5. Exchange answers and give oral feedback.

Skills

...WORD CHECK

acquire – to obtain; to gain.

academic – theoretical; knowledge; ability to understand knowledge at a high level.

Skills can be learnt by individuals while they are carrying out their jobs. Individuals **acquire** some skills quite quickly, as they seem to have a natural ability to be able to do them. Other skills have to be practised many times before a person feels comfortable in doing them. Some skills are used in practical situations, for example, they are demonstrated in carrying out specific tasks in day-to-day work. Bed making, taking a pulse or giving an individual a bed bath are examples of practical skills carried out by nursing staff.

Other skills are more **academic**, in other words they are carried out through the brain thinking about a particular problem or issue. Such skills include accounting, reading, dealing with mathematical problems and finding solutions. These skills would not necessarily have to be carried out by doing practical tasks while working, they could be achieved by sitting at a desk.

Whether skills are practical or more academic, knowledge will be required in order to be able to demonstrate the skill. A nurse would be unable to take a pulse unless they had been taught the correct way to do it.

ACTIVITY Skills

Work with another person to divide the skills listed below into two main groups, for example, mainly practical skills and mainly academic skills:

- cooking
- cleaning a ward
- measuring out drugs
- reading instructions
- keeping records
- planning care for an individual
- talking to a client
- making a time plan
- solving a problem.

Share your list with another group and compare the similarities and differences.

Other skills that are most likely to be used are:

- working as a member of a team
- interpersonal skills (customer/client care)
- planning and organizing
- time management
- problem solving.

In what situations would these skills be used?

A nursery nurse needs many skills to do her job well.

A nursery nurse is concerned with the care, education and well-being of children, and will take responsibility for the children in their care. The duties of a nursery nurse will depend on the age of the children for whom they care. For example, if they are caring for toddlers and pre-school children, they will focus on developing language skills and exploring through the world of play. Some nursery nurses will be required to organize and supervise outdoor play if they are caring for children who are between two and four-and-a-half years. If they are caring for babies, then quite a lot of practical and physical caring will be involved, for example, feeding, cleansing and changing nappies.

Nursery nurses may also be involved in keeping records for the children for whom they care, and for observing and assessing children. Meeting and talking with parents, main carers and other professionals is also likely to be part of their work. They will also be involved in organizing, planning and managing activities for the children.

Nursery nurses can be employed in:

- day nurseries, playgroups and crèches
- schools, where they provide support for teachers
- hospitals, where they will be involved in caring for infants, children and young people who are ill
- as nannies in private homes.

What tasks would be part of a nursery nurse's job role if they were working in a nursery that provided care and education for children between two and four-and-a-half years? What skills would be needed?

Some ideas are given in the table below:

Tasks carried out by a nursery nurse	Skills used by a nursery nurse
Greeting children and parents	Oral communication skills, listening skills
Putting up play equipment	Practical skills, problem-solving skills
Planning activities with others	Interpersonal skills, communication skills, organizational skills
Story telling	Communication skills, interpersonal skills
Preparing practical activities, for example, dough, paint	Scientific skills, creative skills, practical skills, mathematical skills
Talking with children and answering questions	Oral communication skills, listening skills, problem-solving skills
Keeping records	Written communication
Comforting children	Interpersonal skills, oral communication skills
Giving basic first aid	Scientific skills, interpersonal skills, practical skills, oral communication

From the list of tasks it is possible to see that a large number of skills would be needed. Some of these skills would be learnt while actually doing the job or would have been learnt while training. Others would probably be present in the nursery nurse already, as we often choose jobs that we 'are good at' and for which we have already shown some **aptitude**.

From the table it can be seen that the main skills needed by a nursery nurse are:

- communication skills, for example, the ability to speak clearly and listen carefully
- interpersonal skills, for example, when relating to children, parents or other clients
- practical skills, for example, in providing help with activities
- scientific skills, for example, an awareness of health and safety, first aid.

The nursery nurse will also need additional skills such as:

- being able to work well in a team
- organizing, presentation and management skills
- problem-solving skills, for example, how to cope in difficult situations and find solutions.

How do the skills required by a nursery nurse compare with the skills of a Registered General Nurse (adults) who is working in a recovery ward of a hospital?

Such nurses care for clients (patients) who are over the age of 16. They do a lot of practical nursing such as checking temperatures, blood pressure and respiration rates. They often assist doctors with physical examinations as well as giving drugs, injections, cleaning and dressing wounds. Taking the **clinical history** and helping to draw up a care plan in consultation with

...WORD CHECK

aptitude – having a natural tendency to be able to do something.

clinical history – what has happened in the past from a medical perspective.

doctors and others is part of the role of a Registered General Nurse and, frequently, they are required to counsel clients and relatives, providing emotional support to help them cope with their current situation. Sometimes a nurse in a hospital will be responsible for supervising health care assistants.

What would be the day-to-day tasks and skills needed by a Registered General Nurse?

Day-to-day tasks of a Registered General Nurse	Skills required to carry out the tasks
Greeting clients and talking with them	Communication skills, interpersonal skills
Taking temperature, pulse and monitoring blood pressure	Scientific skills, practical skills
Recording the health measurements taken	Communication skills
Hygiene routines	Practical skills, communication skills
Cleaning a wound, changing a dressing	Practical skills, scientific skills
Admitting new clients to the ward	Communication skills, interpersonal skills
Helping with the physical examination of a client	Practical skills, scientific skills
Working with others, for example, nurses, doctors, physiotherapists	Interpersonal skills, communication skills
Planning care for clients	Organizational skills, communication skills

Some of the skills used by an RGN are very similar to those used by a nursery nurse. Both will use communication, interpersonal, practical and scientific skills. It is likely that the RGN will use more scientific skills than the nursery nurse because of the tasks carried out.

ACTIVITY

1. Copy and complete the table below to show which skills would be needed by a physiotherapist when completing each task.

Task	Skills needed
Greeting client	
Making notes about the client's needs	
Showing the client how to do the suggested exercise	
Observing the exercise being carried out by the client	
Keeping records	

2. Explain, using examples, which skills could be used by a care assistant when carrying out tasks in a client's own home. Choose one task that the care assistant will carry out.
3. Explain, by using examples, which qualities would help a nurse who had to give distressing news to a client.
4. How would a care worker show empathy?

Qualifications

A qualification is proof that the person to whom it is awarded has achieved a certain standard of knowledge or a recognized standard of skills. Most qualifications involve both skills and knowledge, but occasionally they are weighted towards either one or the other. The table below gives information about some qualifications that can be achieved by individuals who wish to obtain work in the health, social care or early years sectors:

Qualification	Type
National Vocational Qualification (NVQ)	Based in the workplace and involve learning skills relevant to the particular sector, for example, health or child care. Slightly more skill based but knowledge of the subject also included. May be at Level 2 or Level 3.
OCR Nationals	Based in a school, college or with a training provider, having a slight emphasis on theory but this knowledge must be applied through work experience or simulation to practical situations in the workplace, for example, bed making, taking temperatures, activities with children and young people. They may be achieved at Level 2 or Level 3.
AS and A2	Based in schools, college or with training providers. Theory based with some practical knowledge and application of knowledge to practical situations.
EDEXCEL Diplomas and Certificates	Some of these are focused particularly on specialist pathways, for example, child care. While similar to the OCR Nationals, are more general preparation for working in health, social care or early years settings.
Council for Awards in Childcare, Health and Education (CACHE)	Specific child care courses to prepare individuals for working with children and young people, for example, childminding, pre-school leader, nursery nurse.
Diploma in Society, Health and Development	A new qualification that incorporates the principal learning related to health, social care, early years and justice sectors, as well as functional skills (English, Maths and ICT) and an Extended Project, besides requiring some additional learning, for example, OCR Nationals or GCSE in Health and Social Care.

These are only examples of qualifications that are available but are some of the most common. Smaller qualifications can be in subjects such as first aid or food hygiene, for example. Each qualification obtained by an individual, no matter how large or small the qualification is, will contribute to an individual's ability to carry out a role in that particular area effectively. When all qualifications are put together they show the employer that the person who has achieved them has been successful in following a particular course of study to an agreed national standard.

ACTIVITY Becoming qualified

Sanjay wishes to become a nurse.

Marcus would like to be a nursery nurse.

Telfer would like to be a social worker.

1. Investigate the qualifications, skills and qualities required for **one** of these job roles.
2. Identify and discuss at least **two** different ways of achieving the qualifications, skills and qualities for the job role.
3. Discuss the advantages and disadvantages of each way of obtaining the qualifications, skills and qualities.

Changes in service provision can affect job roles

Service provision is changing rapidly as the development of highly technical treatment and medicine means that many clients require an 'integrated service'. This, in turn, means that professionals will require a range of different skills and so will need to be 'multi-skilled'. Specialists will work together in groups based on the disease or condition that is being treated and clinical teams will be system based, which will cut across traditional professional boundaries.

Community networks should allow:

- early diagnosis of conditions/diseases
- quality and safety systems to be in place
- accessibility to services
- integration of care
- teaching and research
- continuity in long-term management.

As a result, jobs will change in order to meet these needs and requirements.

Why are good interpersonal skills important?

Communication is an important part of all our lives as we use it every day for a variety of reasons. Oral conversations are such common, everyday events that we often think they do not require any special skills.

Work with another person to think about the number of conversations you have already had today. Were they formal or informal conversations? Make a list and see which could be put under the headings 'formal' and 'informal'.

Informal conversations, for example, when you have spoken with friends or family members, could be to find out specific information or to exchange ideas. Other conversations will be more formal, for example, when you have had a conversation with a professional care worker, such as a dentist, teacher or employer. In all these conversations, specific skills will have been used, such as body language, gestures and active listening.

Giving and obtaining information and showing an interest.

A major part of a care worker's day-to-day task is to make sure their communication is effective. People who use health, social care and early years services are often dependent on professional care workers for obtaining and giving information, and they may also want to express their feelings and emotions. Individuals will want to know that they can rely on the care worker to value them as a person and that the information shared will be kept confidential.

Effective communication is at the heart of any relationship. This means that professional care workers need to be aware of the skills required to communicate effectively with clients. When communicating with clients and other care workers or relatives, the care workers should remember that those with whom they are communicating will need to understand what is being said. The ability to understand others and to help understanding is a skill often taken for granted. If, for example, an older person in a residential home or a day-care centre does not understand what the professional care worker has said, their reply

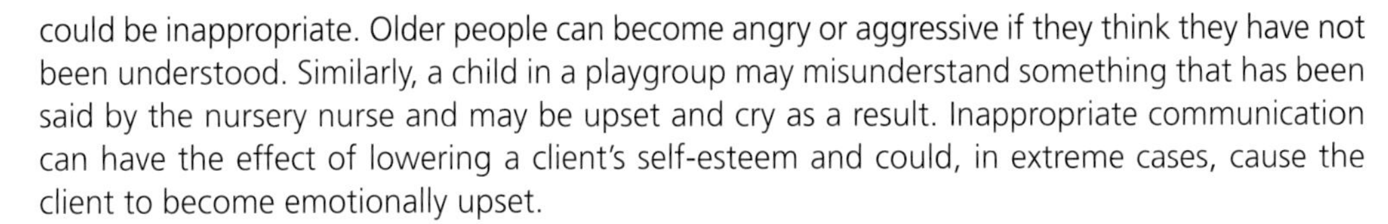

could be inappropriate. Older people can become angry or aggressive if they think they have not been understood. Similarly, a child in a playgroup may misunderstand something that has been said by the nursery nurse and may be upset and cry as a result. Inappropriate communication can have the effect of lowering a client's self-esteem and could, in extreme cases, cause the client to become emotionally upset.

When working in a care setting or if you are an informal carer it will be important to know how to communicate effectively with clients and others who are involved in their care.

Using communication skills to interact with clients

When communicating we do so in order to:

- obtain information, for example, about the client's history
- give information to others, for example, which services are available
- exchange ideas and opinions with people with whom we form relationships.

Communication is the interaction between two or more people. That is, two people, or more, talking or having a conversation with one another. Effective communication is dependent on the use of appropriate skills.

When talking to people, individuals often use non-verbal signals as well as speech, such as gestures or smiles. This is known as 'body language' and is a way of giving messages to those with whom we are speaking, for example, smiling will convey friendliness. Other methods of communication used in care settings can be:

- in written form, such as letters, menus or care plans
- emails are used to send messages to people electronically using computers, for example, information from a GP about a client can be sent directly to a hospital or to another professional.

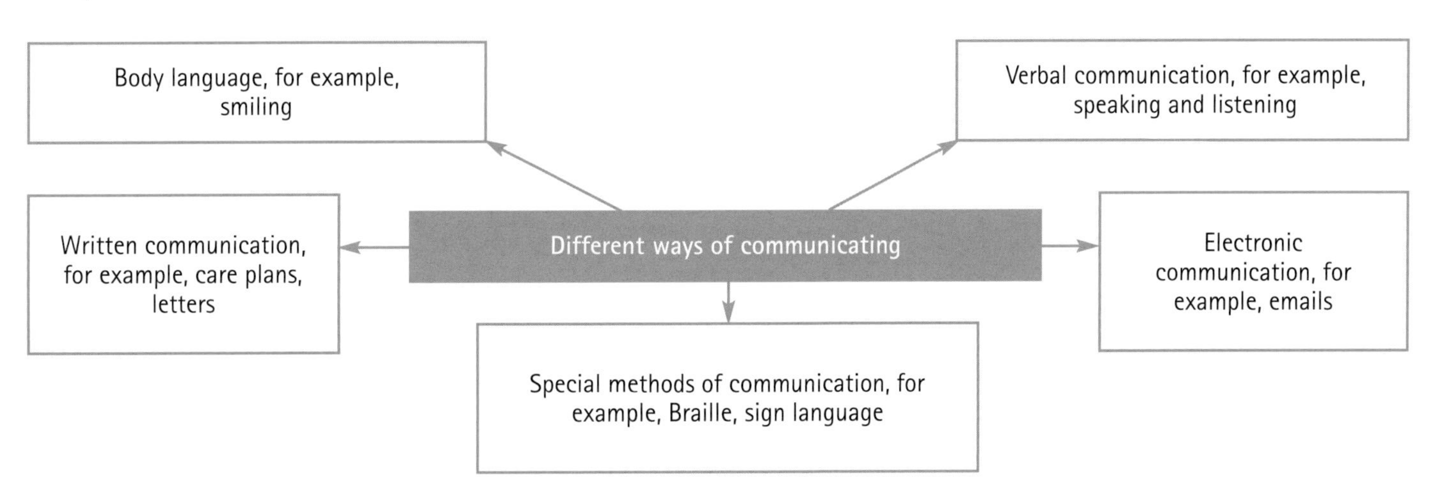

Having a meaningful conversation with someone requires the development of skills and social coordination. It means:

- being interested in the person and the topic
- having the skills to maintain the conversation
- being able to start conversations and end them.

Skills that are involved when communicating could include any of the following:

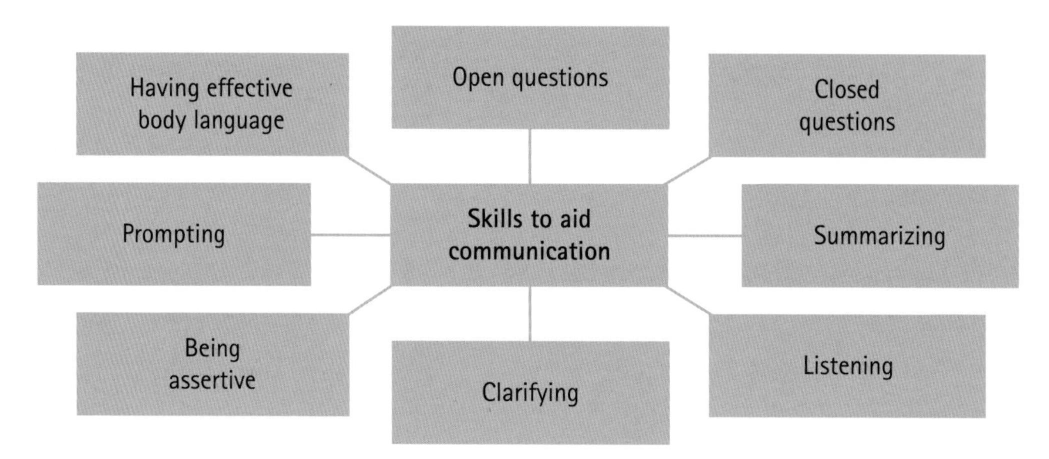

Professional care workers should know how to use skills when communicating and when to use them. The work that is done in care settings depends very much on using effective communication. Effective communication requires professional care workers to:

- **analyse** their thoughts and to think about what they are going to say
- use skills to help to **interpret** the language they hear
- understand and **draw conclusions**
- present the ideas for continuing the conversation.

When communicating with one another messages are sent that **disclose** information. When communicating orally, messages are encoded by a sender and decoded by a receiver. The diagram below shows this process:

Sending and receiving messages

Source: Argyle, 1983

How would this apply to messages given and received in a care setting? Here is an example:

A care worker (**sender**) puts words together (**encodes**) to say 'How are you feeling today?' (**message**).

The client (**receiver**) listens, the brain interprets the signal (**decodes**) and then the message is received.

...WORD CHECK

analyse – to examine in detail.
interpret – change words into something that can be recognized by a person, for example, a language or simplified words being used.
draw conclusions – to make judgements.
disclose – passing on confidential information.
sender – the person speaking/sending a message.
encodes – how the message is put together.
message – what the sender communicates or sends to the receiver.
receiver – the person who receives a message.
decodes – how the receiver interprets a message.
complex – involving many parts; complicated; intricate.

Communication in health, social care and early years settings is likely to be of a **complex** nature and may have several purposes. Care workers will need to be aware that each individual will have their own way of interpreting messages. Effective communication means more than just passing on information. It means involving or engaging the other person. The process of communicating involves various stages within a cycle:

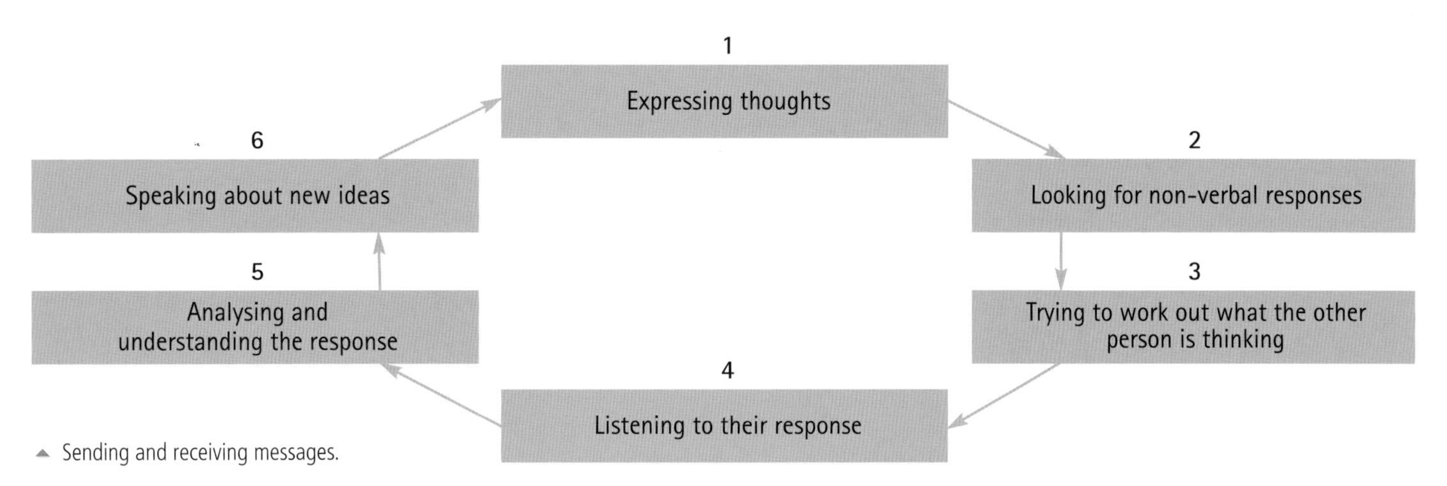

▲ Sending and receiving messages.

Communicating has to be a two-way process where each person is trying to make sense of what the other person is saying. Often it is easier to understand people who are similar to ourselves, for example, a person who has the same accent, or a person who is in a similar situation to ourselves. Our decoding equipment in the brain tunes in, breaks down the message, analyses this message, understands it and interprets its meaning, and then creates a response or answer. This is all helped by the body language or signals, such as smiles or gestures, that have been given by the person who is sending the message. When a care worker is speaking with a client, they are forming a mental picture about what they are being told.

Professor Neil Thompson's interest in language and communication began in his early years, where he realized that language shaped identity, and from his social work, where he spent a great many years helping people with their problems. Thompson recognizes that the caring professions, such as medical, counselling, social work and alternative therapies, all need communication and language as building blocks to good practice. He states that 'communication is not simply a matter of transmitting information but also involves transmitting a relationship'. Thompson recognizes that communication is part of every individual's social and working life and the power relationships that accompany these aspects of our lives. Because communication has such a strong link with power, it is important that those in the care world have at least a basic understanding, so that the positives can be used effectively and the negative aspects or barriers can be avoided as much as possible. A high level of competency is needed in order to communicate effectively.

Thompson considers that when interacting with others we should not:

- make judgements about others
- try to take control of others through manipulative use of language
- be overpowering but should try to respond to people spontaneously
- be fixed in our ideas but should be open to other people's ideas
- consider ourselves to be superior but should try to develop congruence and empathy.

Thompson considers communication in terms of being:

- enhancing
- inhibiting
- supportive
- defensive.

For example, if an individual simply states the facts rather than making evaluative statements about a person, they are more likely to be supportive. If, however, a person is inflexible and really defensive in their approach, they are more likely to inhibit communication. Thompson believes that 'high-quality work without high-quality communication is not really the order of the day'. Commitment to a high standard of communication is necessary if care practice is being effective.

Other forms of communication used in care settings

Written communication

The written word is common and is an established form of communication. The rules that govern writing are very different from those rules that are followed for spoken language. In all health, social care and early years settings accuracy of the written word is extremely important. If inaccuracies occur when keeping formal records, a client could have the wrong treatment or be given incorrect information with disastrous results. This could lead to a complaint being made or to court proceedings being taken. False, inaccurate or misleading written records could result in:

- inappropriate actions
- failure to act
- complaints and litigation.

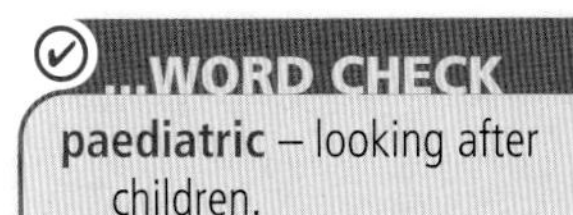

paediatric – looking after children.

When writing information down it needs to be clear, legible and accurate. In many care settings written communication is used to record personal history. A children's unit (**paediatric**) in a hospital could use a written record as shown below for this purpose:

Name of child	
Name of parent	
Address	
Telephone number	
Emergency contact number 1	
Contact address 1	
Emergency contact number 2	
Contact address 2	
Medication	
Dietary needs	
History	

Communicating in writing helps care settings to keep in contact with parents and other professionals. It can be a means of:

- giving information
- obtaining information
- exchanging ideas.

In many settings, the communication policy will lay down that all written communication must be shown to the manager before it is passed on. Copies of written communication should be kept in case they are required for future reference.

Types of written information kept by a care setting could include:

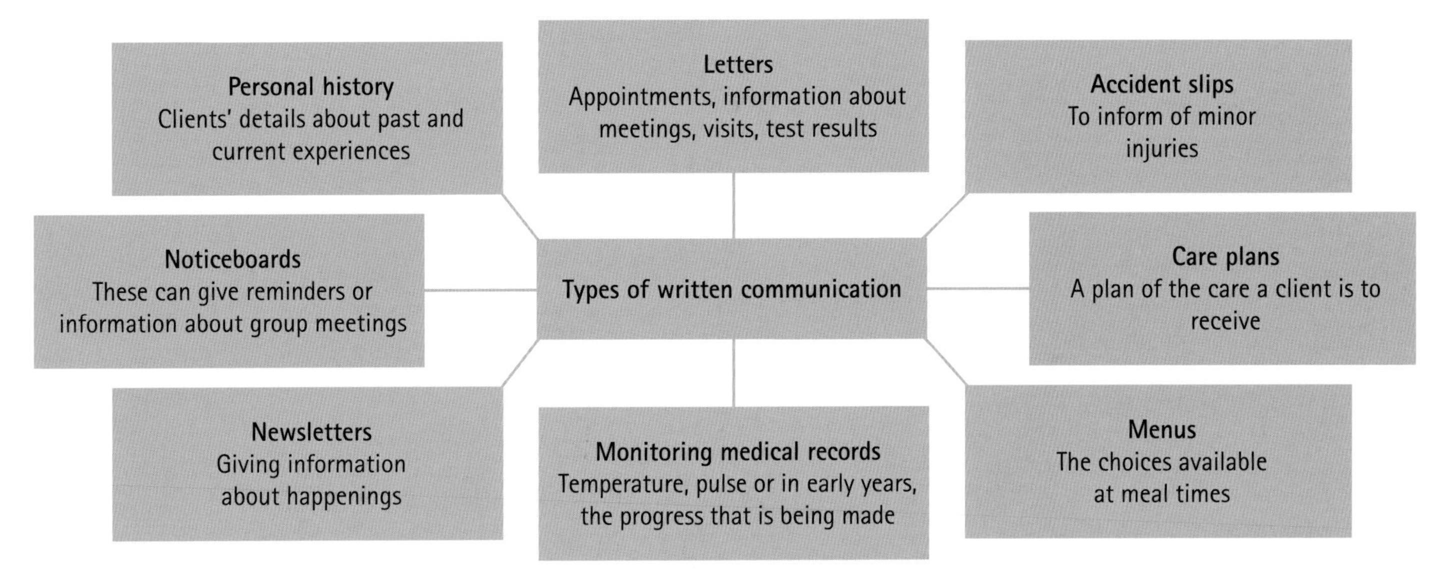

Clear, concise writing cannot be produced in a hurry. Expressing oneself clearly and effectively in writing is a skilful activity that will need to be mastered by all who work in health, social care and early years settings.

Computerized communication

In recent years, electronic mail (email) has proved to be quite a significant form of communication. Emails can be both formal and informal depending on their purpose. An advantage of email is that it provides a very quick way of interacting with another person or organization as answers can be received in a matter of minutes, rather than having to wait for several days. A disadvantage is that on some occasions emails are lost and, as a consequence, the sender has to repeat the process. Care also has to be taken to ensure that confidentiality is maintained and 'secure' systems are necessary before confidential personal information can be exchanged.

The Internet, too, is more often being used as a source of information for a variety of purposes.

Special methods of communicating

All health, social care and early years settings need to be prepared to provide for clients who have special needs where communication is concerned. Special needs could include:

- difficulty in hearing or deafness
- poor eyesight or blindness
- language difficulty, for example, not speaking English as a first or preferred language.

Braille

The communication system known as Braille was first introduced by a blind person called Richard Braille in 1829. The system is one of raised dots that can be felt with a finger. For people who have limited vision or who are blind, the system provides the opportunity for independent reading and writing as it is based on 'touch'. It is possible, with the correct computer software, to change the printed word into Braille and to print it out using special printers.

Braille can be extremely useful to clients who have poor sight as they are able to access leaflets and handouts that give information about their treatment, as well as being able to read books and magazines to satisfy their intellectual needs.

Some clients need special methods of communication.

Makaton

Makaton is a large collection of symbols that can help people who have a hearing impairment or learning difficulty to communicate with others. It is a system that uses signs, speech and symbols. Those using Makaton may use all three methods to help them communicate with others. Makaton uses an established set of hand movements to convey meaning. It is usually taught to children when they are young and as soon as it is realized that they have a need.

How can Braille and Makaton help clients with sensory impairments to communicate?

British Sign Language

It is thought that nearly 70,000 people use sign language in the British Isles. British Sign Language (BSL) is used by a large number of these people. Children find sign language fascinating and, as a result, learn the signs quite easily. The BSL has a phrase 'make your fingers count', which appeals to children. Sign language can be taught at any age and is used by those with a hearing impairment. It is a language that has developed over hundreds of years and enables interaction between people who otherwise might experience difficulty.

Using communication to support relationships

Working with people involves interaction. That is, the coming together of two or more people, who may have common aims but sometimes have conflicting points of view. Any form of interaction can sometimes change people, increase their awareness or improve their quality of life. It is important, therefore, to use the skills that best suit the individual and their needs.

The needs of human beings are complex and care workers often work with clients who may be afraid or don't understand what is going to happen to them. The client could feel threatened by the situation that they find themselves in.

When giving information, accuracy is important. The person receiving it will probably want to use the information that has been given. If that information proves to be incorrect, the client is likely not to place any trust in future information given by that particular care worker. Information is given by professional care workers so that clients can make informed choices and decisions.

Positive communication factors that can influence relationships are:

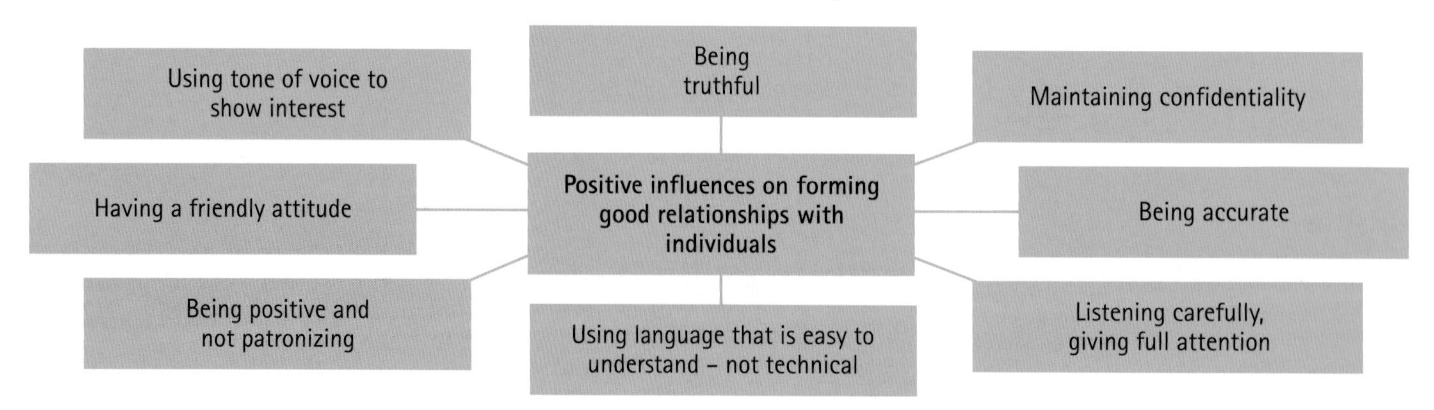

When these factors are the focus of any communication whether oral, written or in the content of an email, the result is more likely to meet the needs of the individual, particularly their emotional, social and intellectual needs.

Communication in a multicultural society

For clients for whom English is not a preferred or first language, **interpreters** can help with communication. In the past, some interpreters have been people who are members of the client's own family but this has now been discontinued as far as is possible. It was considered that using family members was not a very good idea, as they were then privy to information that the client may want to keep confidential. For example, a mother whose daughter was interpreting for her may not want her daughter to know that she has an incurable disease.

In many health, social care and early years services, leaflets concerning health topics or health facilities are not only produced in English but also in several other languages, so that many in our multicultural society can access the information.

...WORD CHECK

interpreters – change words into something that can be recognized by a person, for example, a language or simplified words being used.

ACTIVITY Parkside Residential Home

Parkside caters for residents who are over 60 years of age. Many of the residents have special needs when communicating.

1. Kathy has very poor vision. Suggest how her communication needs could be met by the staff at Parkside.
2. Marcus has a severe hearing impairment. How could the staff provide for Marcus' communication needs?
3. Ji-Sung has difficulty with English as it is not his first or preferred language. He needs to have information about the different health and social care services in the area. Explain **two** ways the staff could help Ji-Sung.

ASSESSMENT PRACTICE: PREPARATION

For the sector that you have chosen for the earlier Assessment Practices, select **one direct** job role. For the role selected, carry out research to find out:

- What is involved in the job role – the individual's role within the service.
- The qualifications, skills and qualities required, giving a wide range of examples to show how these would be used in the job role.
- About the day-to-day tasks carried out as part of the role chosen, making sure you know how the health and social care needs of the individual clients have been met as part of the tasks performed.

Try to interview an individual who has this job role. Write up the interview.

When you have completed your research, write up the investigation to give a comprehensive and detailed explanation of the role, making sure you include all the points above.

Note: Remember to continue the plan and the bibliography

Now that you have completed your investigation, you will need to write an evaluation drawing conclusions. This must include:

- The effectiveness of the investigation, considering your plan.
- Did you meet your aims and objectives? How did you meet these? Were they effective?
- What improvements could you make for future investigations?
- What are your overall conclusions?
- Have you produced a bibliography showing all the sources of your investigation?

2 Understanding Personal Development and Relationships

Contents

About this unit

The focus of this unit is to develop an awareness of the norms of development and to apply and compare these to the development of individuals in the different life stages. You will need to understand how factors can influence growth and development and contribute to the development of self-concept. At the end of this unit you will need to be sure that you have learnt all the facts as the External Assessment (test) will decide the mark you receive for this unit.

You will need to learn about:

- the stages of human development
- the different factors that can affect human growth and development
- the development of self-concept and different types of relationships
- major life changes and sources of support.

Introducing this unit

Individuals develop at different rates. The rate at which an individual develops is measured against 'the norms' of development. An individual's development is compared to these norms or averages to make a judgement about whether their development matches the 'norm' or is ahead of or behind the 'norm'. In this unit understanding how individuals who are in different life stages compare with the 'norm' in their physical, intellectual, emotional and social development will be one of the main focus points.

To Do...

Work with another person to find out when you each learnt:
- to crawl
- to stand up
- to walk.

Find out how this compares with the norm.

Human development is affected by many factors that may have a positive or negative influence on our lives. Understanding the factors that influence human behaviour means that the '**nature versus nurture**' debate must be considered. For example, which has the stronger influence – nature or nurture? Inherited factors such as an inherited disability, known as the 'nature' factor, or the experiences an individual has, for example, education, known as the 'nurture' factor. In other words, are the skills that we possess inherited or are they learnt from social experience? An individual will be influenced by these factors and will behave in a particular way because of such influences.

To Do...

Draw a picture of 'you' in the middle of the page (a rough outline will be sufficient).
Around the picture write words to show what has influenced your development, for example, family.
Now share the results with another person.
Which factors are similar? Which are different? What has made you different from the other person?

...WORD CHECK

nature versus nurture – the qualities we are born with that make us what we are, versus how we are influenced when we are young and by our environment.

Why do we need to study the behaviour of people? The answer is that if we intend to work in health and social care settings, we will be very close to people who need to feel respected and worthy of respect. Individuals will also need to understand their own feelings and attitudes to make sure that they do not treat others with disrespect or prejudice. When people feel 'at risk' they often become aggressive or defensive, behaving in a way that is threatening to the professional care worker. This is because they do not feel in control of their lives. Not all people will want to be happy, but they will want to have a positive emotional feeling about themselves and to feel satisfied with their lives.

The behaviour of individuals is not constant, but forever changing as a result of environmental, social, economic or cultural issues. Promoting a positive environment for individuals, both ourselves and others, will encourage good physical health, promote mental health and make individuals more able to interact with others.

Human behaviour is very complex, and to understand why people behave in a particular way it is necessary to study the influences that have affected the development of an individual such as inherited, social, economic, environmental and psychological influences. It is these influences that will help us to form our 'self-concept'. That is the image that we have of ourselves.

TO DO

Work with another person. One of you should, in three minutes, tell the other 'how you see yourself', for example, independent, confident, happy, shy. Say 'why' you think you have these characteristics. Then change roles and, for three minutes, your partner should tell you about themselves. The whole group should then sit in a circle and one person should stand behind their chair. They should say, 'I would like to introduce X. He/she is..........' referring to their partner. This person will then sit down and their partner should stand behind their chair and say, 'I would like to introduce X ... '.
As a whole group, discuss what makes us see ourselves as we do.

Throughout life we will experience change. Some changes will be for the better, while others may be unexpected and may be upsetting. Life events can have a major impact on an individual's personal development. Some life events are predictable, for instance everybody starts school at the same age. Everybody goes through physical changes such as puberty around the same age and all women go through the **menopause** at some time in their life. Other life events, such as serious road accidents, are completely unpredictable. A certain number of people will be killed and seriously injured on the roads each year, but there is no way of telling who it will happen to, or when.

...WORD CHECK

menopause – the age when females stop menstruation or having their periods.

Becoming disabled as a result of an accident is unpredictable, but disability as a result of a genetic disorder is becoming increasingly predictable as medical techniques advance. Most life events come somewhere in the middle. We may expect to meet a partner, settle down and have children, but we don't know exactly when, and some people discover that they cannot have children. Everybody who enters a relationship hopes that it will work out, but some relationships fail, and end in separation or divorce. Some changes in work may be expected and planned for, but some may come as a complete surprise, for example if a company unexpectedly closes and all the employees lose their jobs.

All life events cause stress, which may cause feelings such as anxiety and depression. This is a sign that the individual has to adapt to the life event in some way so that they can live with it comfortably. It is this adaptation that promotes personal development. During times of serious change or upsetting periods, it may be necessary to ask for support or be offered support to help us through. The source of support could be through family, friends, professional care workers or from voluntary organizations.

TO DO

Work with another person to find a newspaper article about a major life event or change, for example, an accident, a fire, a birth.
Read the article and then write down the effects such an event may have on the lives of the individuals. Who could offer them support? How could the support help?
Share the newspaper article with the whole group, stating what changes the event is likely to have involved for those concerned, who could provide support and how the support would help.

The stages and pattern of human growth and development

How do individuals grow and develop during each life stage?

Getting started

You should know that growth refers to an increase in physical size (mass and height) and development is concerned with the emergence and increase in sophistication of skills, abilities and emotions.

You should be able to describe expected patterns of physical growth and change, and the physical, intellectual, emotional and social changes that typically take place during **each** of the five main life stages. These are:

- infancy (0–3)
- childhood (4–10)
- adolescence (11–18)
- adulthood (19–65)
- later adulthood (65+).

HOW DO INDIVIDUALS GROW AND DEVELOP DURING EACH LIFE STAGE?

During periods of our life we are said to be in a particular 'life stage'. These are periods of time, which are given a name that is recognized as a normal stage of development for human beings. Because we all develop at approximately the same rate and do the same things at around the same time, scientists have called these '**norms**' of development. This means that if we compare our development with that of others of the same age and they are very approximately the same, it is considered that we have developed according to the 'norm' or expected rate of development.

Within each of the life stages, specific development **characteristics** occur. Some of these are physical, some intellectual, some emotional and others are social characteristics. These are often referred to as P.I.E.S. During each life stage there is usually development of all these characteristics, which contribute to making us who we are.

...WORD CHECK

norms – that which is considered normal for the majority of the population.

characteristics – a feature; a trait.

In all life stages there are two main aspects of growth and development. These are:

- growth, which is the increase of **size** and **mass**
- development, which includes **skills**, **intellectual ability** and **emotional responses** that a person gains at each stage of development.

...WORD CHECK

size – how big a person or an object is.

mass – how much someone weighs.

skills – having the ability to perform tasks.

intellectual ability – brain power.

emotional responses – answers that show feelings.

emotional – how individuals feel.

mature – to be well developed/ wiser.

self-image – the picture we have of ourselves.

self-esteem – how a person feels about themselves.

social – integration/mixing with others.

socialization – getting use to interaction with others.

Physical development is about growth or changes in our bodies. These changes happen to people in each of the different life stages. It is also about how people gain increased control over their bodies and become able to look after themselves and others.

Intellectual development is about being able to recognize and remember things, and to think about them. Thinking about our views and opinions and sharing them with others is something that most adolescents, adults and older adults like to do. Problem solving is a challenge and stimulates the mind. This is part of each life stage.

Emotional development is about feelings and how we behave when we have them. Love, hate, fear, anger, disgust, curiosity, surprise and guilt are all emotions. There are two aspects to emotional development. As people **mature**, they experience a wider range of emotions, get better at understanding the feelings of other people, and develop beliefs about themselves, their **self-image** and **self-esteem**. Emotional development is also about how a person learns to control their behaviour when they are experiencing emotions.

Social development is about relationships, how a person learns to understand others and develops the skills to get on with them. It is also about a person learning how others expect them to behave in certain situations. This is called **socialization**.

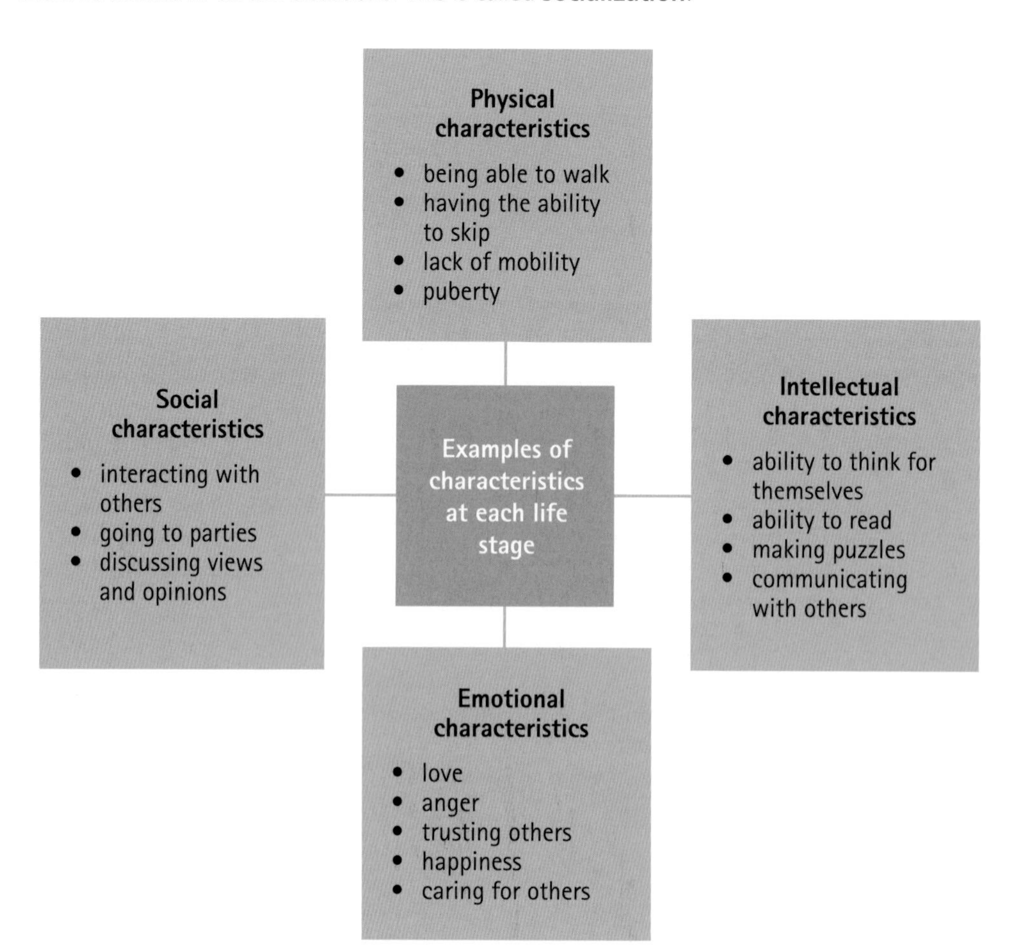

INFANCY

At the beginning of infancy the individual is completely helpless and dependent on their parents or main carers. By the end of the infancy life stage, the infant is beginning to be able to do things for themselves. They also learn to communicate with and relate to others.

Physical growth and development in infancy

Infancy is a period of very fast physical growth, where infants double their birth weight in their first six months. They double it again by the time they are three years old. Health visitors record infants' weights on centile charts to monitor their development. **Centile charts** show the normal range of weight or height for boys and girls at different ages. There are different centile charts for boys and girls, because boys are usually heavier at birth, and grow taller. It is important that you understand how to use these charts.

Length-for-age and weight-for-age percentiles (girls)

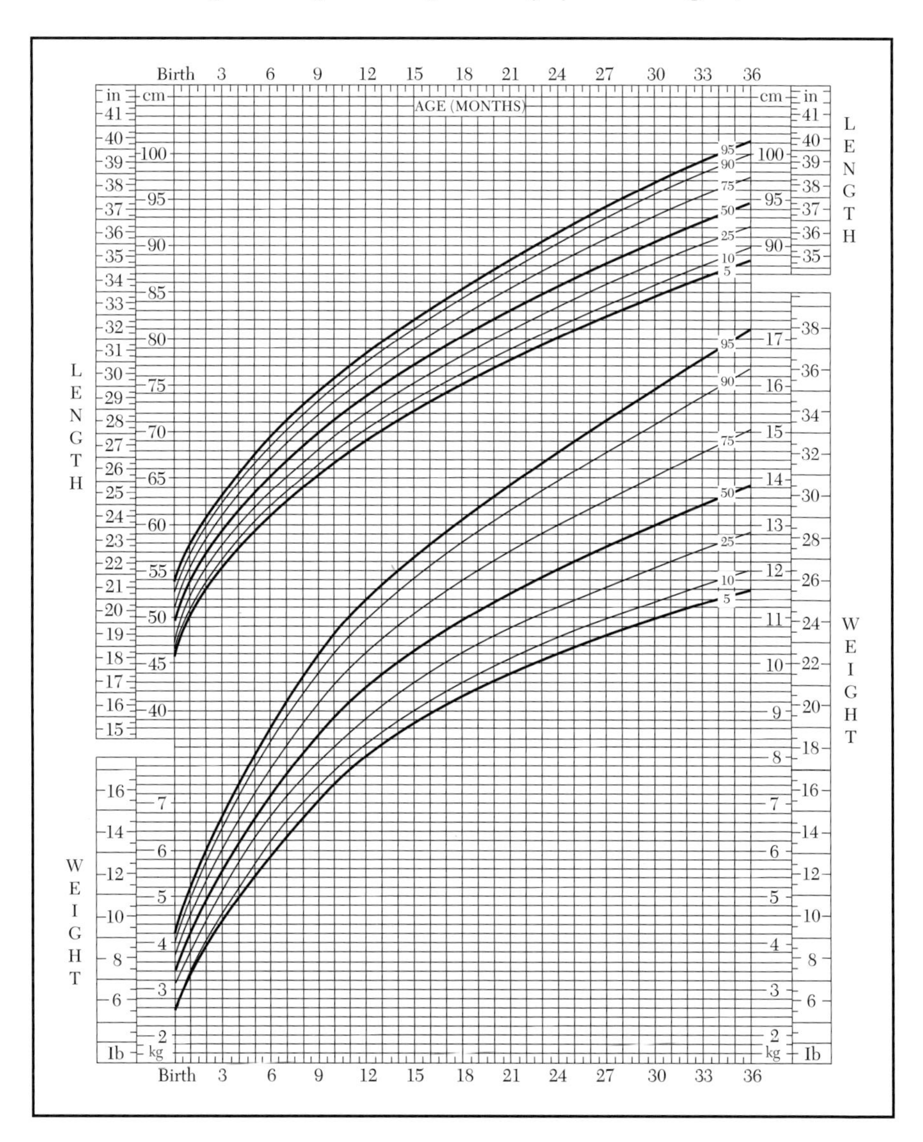

> **...WORD CHECK**
>
> **centile charts** – records that show norms of development.

ACTIVITY

Reading centile charts

...ACTIVITY

1. Find out how to read a centile chart.
2. Explain what the 50th centile is.

▲ Grasping reflex.

...WORD CHECK

primitive reflexes – basic reactions.

unique – special/particular to one person or thing.

milestones – stages in development.

What can infants do?

At birth infants are helpless, with little or almost no control over their bodies. They have **primitive reflexes** including:

- Sucking reflex — The infant will suck on a finger placed in their mouth.
- Rooting reflex — If the infant's face is stroked gently, they will turn their head, searching for a nipple.
- Grasping reflex — The infant will curl their fingers around anything placed in their hand.
- Stepping reflex — If the infant is held standing on a firm surface, they will make stepping movements.
- Startle (Moro) reflex — A loud noise or being moved quickly will cause the infant to open their hands and throw their arms back. The startle reflexes are automatic. This means that the infant has no control over them. Physical development will include the infant getting stronger and developing skills. These reflexes will be replaced with conscious control over their bodies.

1 What does the term 'automatic reflexes' mean?

Every person is **unique**, that is they develop at their own pace and reach milestones of development more quickly or more slowly than others. This could be for a variety of reasons, such as:

- the genes inherited from their mother, father or grandparents
- the influences that have occurred in their development, for example, where they live, their social experiences
- if they have been affected by illness.

An important term used when considering growth and development is **milestones**. This is used to describe major achievements in our growth and development, such as when we learn to crawl, stand or walk. Look at the table below, which shows some of the milestones in development for the infant:

Age	Milestones of physical development for an infant
3 months	Infants can sit with their head held steady for a few seconds, if supported.
6 months	Infants have more strength and muscle control. They can lift their heads, sit with support, and turn their head to look around. They can pull themselves up when their hands are grasped.
9 months	Infants can sit unsupported for ten minutes. They are starting to move independently by rolling or squirming. They can pull themselves to stand, and can stand holding onto something for a few moments.
12 months	Infants can get from a lying to a sitting position without help. They crawl rapidly. They can walk by holding onto furniture and stand alone for a few moments.
15 months	Infants can get to their feet alone. They can walk and crawl upstairs.
18 months	Infants can run, walk upstairs and crawl downstairs.
2 years	Infants can walk downstairs.
3 years	Infants can climb on play equipment, ride a tricycle and throw and catch a ball.

One example of increasing control is toilet training. Infants usually have bowel control by about 18 months. At first, carers have to watch out because infants can only show they need to go to the toilet by looking uncomfortable. Six months later they will tell their carer about their need in plenty of time. At about this time, they will also be dry during the day. By three years old, most infants will be dry all night.

Other changes take place in the infant's body. For example, first teeth, known as deciduous teeth, start to appear at about six months and a child has a complete set of teeth at about three years.

When thinking about the physical development of infants and children, the terms **gross** and **fine motor skills** will be used. Gross motor skills involve the use of muscles to control the body. Infants will learn to control muscles before they are able to balance and carry out more complex movements, such as walking. Control occurs first at the head end and then gradually moves down the body to the shoulders, arms and legs.

Fine motor skills involve hand–eye coordination and the coordination of the fingers. Examples are learning to pick up objects and to drop them. The table below gives some examples of gross and fine motor skills:

...WORD CHECK

gross motor skills – having the ability to use and coordinate the larger muscle groups.

fine motor skills – having the ability to use and coordinate fine movement, for example, use fingers correctly.

Examples of gross motor skills	Examples of fine motor skills
Can lift head at 3 months when lying on front	Plays with fingers at 3 months
Can sit unsupported for short periods at 6 months	Able to grasp an object at 6 months
Pulls into standing position at 8 months, holding onto furniture	Deliberately drops things on the floor at 9 months
Crawls very quickly at 1 year	Starts to show a preference for using one hand at 1 year
Can walk up and down stairs at 2 years	Can hold small crayons properly
Can run and walk at 3 years	

Group Activity

Work with another person to produce handouts showing gross and fine motor skills for infants at 3 months, 6 months, 9 months, 1 year, 18 months, 2 years and 3 years.

Produce two questions for each stage that could be used in a quiz. Separately, produce the answers.

Play the quiz with another pair, making sure you record the scores.

ACTIVITY The health centre

Ray is three years old. His mum, Sonia, meets Desmond, aged one, and his mum, and Jackie and her mum at the health centre. Jackie is six months old.

1. Investigate the physical characteristics that Jackie would have at the age of six months. Prepare a handout that the health centre could provide for Jackie's mother to show her the physical characteristics of a one year old, explaining how to meet the physical needs of Jackie.
2. Explain what the physical characteristics of Desmond are likely to be at the age of one year.
3. Give the physical characteristics of Ray, stating how his mother could meet his needs.
4. If Ray attended nursery school, how could his physical needs be met?

Intellectual development in infancy

...WORD CHECK

egocentric – self-important.

Group Activity

Work with another person and try to work out at least three different ways that an infant will learn to communicate.

How does an infant show frustration?

How does an infant show that they are happy?

At first, infants are **egocentric**. This means they can only see the world from their own point of view. They can't talk or understand language, so they can only learn through sight, sound, taste, smell and touch. This is why a six to twelve month old puts everything in their mouth.

A six-month-old child who drops a toy out of their cot will not look for it. If they cannot see it, they do not know that it still exists. By about nine months they learn that objects that they cannot see are still there.

As infants learn to talk, talking and listening become more important ways of learning. They begin to ask questions and put their thoughts into words. Infants, when they have leart to talk, are always asking 'why' questions.

Learning to talk is an important intellectual development in infancy. Communication is part of infant development but learning to speak depends on the opportunities an infant has to practise and use language. Infants learn to smile and use their eyes to make contact with people. Frustration is common in infants and before they learn to talk they often find it hard to get their message across.

The chart below gives some examples of the milestones of intellectual development for an infant:

Age	Milestone in intellectual development
3 months	Infants make noises when they are spoken to.
9 months	Infants practise making sounds, repeating syllables like 'mum-mum' and 'dad-dad'. They begin to learn that the sounds their carers make mean something. They understand a couple of words, like 'no' and 'bye-bye'.
12 months	Infants know their own name and understand several words. They understand simple commands with gestures, like 'Give it to mummy'.
15 months	Infants understand and obey simple commands, like 'Bring it here'. They can say a few words and understand many more.
18 months	Infants will try to join in with nursery rhymes. Soon after this they can put a few words together to make simple sentences.
2 years	Infants can use around 50 words and understand many more.
2½ years	Infants use around 200 words. They can say a few nursery rhymes. They ask questions all the time, like 'What's that?'
3 years	Infants have learnt a lot more words and can carry on simple conversations with adults.

ACTIVITY At the playgroup

Bethany, aged two, and William, aged three, attend Bowleze Cove playgroup.

1. Draw up a table to show the milestones in intellectual development that Bethany and William should have reached.
2. Explain how the playgroup could meet the intellectual needs of both Bethany and William.
3. Explain why it is important to meet the intellectual needs of infants.

Emotional development in infancy

Emotional development relates to the way a person feels about themselves and others. During their first year, an infant will develop a strong emotional **bond** with their parent or main carer. Have you ever heard a young infant crying because they were hungry or uncomfortable? If you have, you will know how simple their emotions are. Because they have little control over their bodies, they do not have a wide range of responses to their emotions. As they get older, they develop a wider range of emotions.

These are connected with other forms of development. For example:

- they have to bond with somebody and experience **attachment** before they can feel jealous
- they must be able to tell between strangers and people they know before they can feel shy
- if bonding does not occur, the child can become disruptive and may feel unloved and unwanted.

An infant can experience a wider range of emotions by the time they are two years old. You may have seen a six-month-old infant beginning to be shy of strangers. It is common to see a two-year-old child showing how jealous they are of a new brother or sister.

At two years old, an infant still can't control how they respond to their emotions. You have probably heard mothers talking about the 'terrible twos'. A two year old will often have tantrums when frustrated. An infant lying screaming on the floor in the supermarket because they are refused sweets is not doing it to embarrass their mother. They have no idea how the mother feels. They only know they aren't getting something they want, and they can't control their feelings about it. Tantrums are less frequent when infants are three and can better control their emotions.

The way infants are treated by carers affects their developing self-concept. If they are encouraged and treated kindly, they will feel better about themselves than if they are criticized and shouted at.

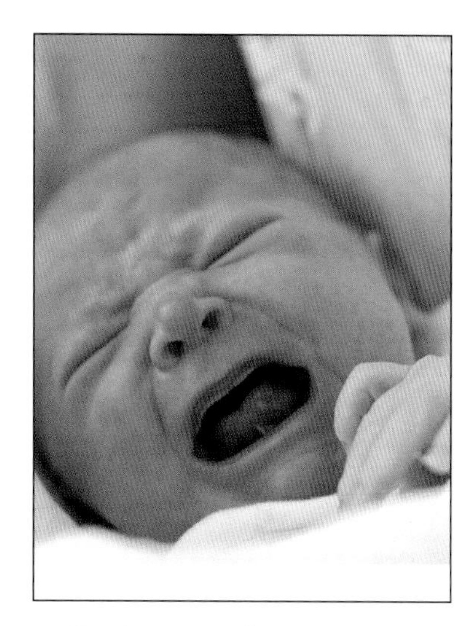

▲ Showing our emotions.

...WORD CHECK

bond – grow(ing) close to someone.

attachment – forming a close relationship with someone.

Milestones in emotional development

Age	Examples of emotional development
Newborn	• enjoys having a cuddle from parent or main carer • gazes into parent's eyes • moves whole body to express enjoyment • smiles at parent
3 months	• recognizes familiar people and smiles • shows enjoyment at bath time • enjoys being talked to
6 months	• afraid of strangers • cries and laughs when others do this, so recognizing the emotions of others • laughs when enjoying activities
9 months	• expresses fear of strangers by crying • dislikes going to bed and will express their feelings • likes comfort objects, for example, teddy bear or comfort blanket • likes being noisy
1 year	• very affectionate towards family • enjoys playing games • shy towards strangers
2 years	• able to express their feelings • gets angry if they cannot express themselves • likes to try out new activities • can be confident and independent, or clingy and dependent on parent or main carer
3 years	• begins to be interested in others and can be friendly • happy to share toys with others • enjoys pleasing adults • can show concern for others

CASE STUDY Kelly's family

Kelly is married to Tony and they have two young children, Alicia, aged 3, and Mark, who is 18 months old. Alicia attends nursery for three mornings each week.

1. Produce handouts to show the milestones in development for a 3 year old and 1 year old for emotional and intellectual development.
2. Explain how Kelly and Tony could provide intellectual stimulation for both children when they are at home.
3. Explain how Kelly and Tony could meet the emotional needs of the children when they are at home.
4. How could the nursery school meet Alicia's emotional needs?

Social development in infancy

...WORD CHECK

bonding – grow(ing) close to someone.

Newborn infants have no sense of personal identity but they do like company. They know nothing about the world, and don't understand that there are other people in it. They are very interested in faces and soon get to recognize their main carer. They get to know their carer's face, voice, smell and touch. This is called **bonding**. The way an infant is cared for affects their social development. The better they feel about themselves, the easier they will find it to make friends.

By the time an infant is six weeks old, they will smile at their carer. This is an infant's first social action. The infant soon learns to enjoy being played with by people. By the time they are six months old they can tell people they know from strangers. They become shy with people they don't know.

▲ Bonding between mother and infant is important.

They still don't understand that other people have thoughts and feelings. Because of this, they will not be interested in playing with other children for a long time yet.

- Up to the age of two, infants will play alone (solitary play).
- By two years, infants will play near other children but do not know how to play with them (parallel play).
- By two-and-a-half years the infants are interested in other children playing. They may join in for a few minutes, but still have no idea how to share playthings.
- By the age of three, infants play with other infants and understand how to share (cooperative play). They can cope with being away from their carer for a few hours.

Infants begin to develop their self-esteem, which helps them to cope with any situation and to develop independence. Parents and main carers should try to be positive at this time by giving praise, providing older infants with choice, allowing them to express their opinions and to gain independence.

ACTIVITY Information for new parents

1. Cut out a picture of an infant and paste it onto the centre of a page of A4 plain paper. Draw a line out toward the four corners and write on each physical, intellectual, emotional and social characteristics.
   For each area of P.I.E.S. give **five** physical, **five** intellectual, **five** emotional and **five** social characteristics.
2. Produce **four** handouts to explain the terms physical, intellectual, emotional and social development, giving **three** examples for each of the P.I.E.S.
3. Draw a timeline and mark in the life stages and the age span for each.
4. Arrange to interview a parent who has a child between nought and three years of age. Find out how they helped to develop their child's self-esteem.
5. Arrange for a health visitor or other specialist to visit your centre (with your tutor's permission), to find out how to use a centile chart, and how it helps to check on health and well-being for the infant.
6. Correctly read two different centile charts.

The development of infants is a continuous process and 'milestones' are not achieved on one particular day or time.

ASSESSMENT PRACTICE

Megan is one year old.

1. Which life stage is she in? Give the age span for this life stage. [2]
2. Describe **two** intellectual characteristics for a one year old. [2]
3. Describe **two** emotional characteristics for a one year old. [2]
4. Describe **two** social characteristics for a one year old. [2]
5. Describe **two** physical characteristics for a one year old. [2]
6. Some milestones in development are:
   - can smile
   - can walk
   - can stand
   - can skip
   - can roll over from back to front

   Identify the order that these milestones of development would usually occur. [5]
7. Emma is three years old. Describe **three** ways that positive emotional relationships could be promoted in Emma's life. [6]
8. Explain how a playgroup could promote Emma's intellectual development. [5]
9. Explain how attending playgroup could promote Emma's social development. [5]
10. What is meant by the term 'self-esteem'? How could Emma's parents promote Emma's self-esteem? [10]

CHILDHOOD

Childhood is considered to be from the age of four years until ten years. In this life stage, children develop much more control over their bodies, and their emotions become more complex. Children do have more control over how they respond to them and they develop more communication skills, learning to relate to and interact with others.

Physical growth and development in childhood

...WORD CHECK

growth spurt – to grow quickly; to develop at a fast rate.

proportions – component parts.

features – an aspect or characteristic.

concepts – ideas, thoughts, theories.

Physical growth in childhood is more gradual than in infancy, although there is a **growth spurt** between five and seven years. Throughout this period, the **proportions** of the child's body change. A child's head is larger than an infant's, but is smaller in proportion to the rest of the body. Fine motor skills are developing and the sense of balance is improved. It is very important that children make time for physical activity in order to help the body to function normally and to improve motor skills.

Examples of milestones of physical growth and development in childhood

Physical growth and development in children

- A child can run, skip and hop between the ages of 4 and 6 years
- A child will become stronger and taller during this life stage
- A child enjoys playing ball games
- Muscle tissue will increase and 'baby' fat will be lost
- A child will develop distinct features
- The second or permanent teeth grow
- A child's head is larger but is smaller in proportion to the rest of the body
- Facial features will change very little after this period of growth

Intellectual development in childhood

During childhood, children learn to talk and develop a much wider vocabulary. By the end of this stage, that is around ten years of age, they understand **concepts**. These are ways in which we use our minds to organize thoughts and information. Concepts include colour, number, size and symbols. A child understands that a number of different red objects are all the same colour, and that ten beans is the same number as ten buttons. The child now has a simple understanding of right and wrong.

2 What are concepts?

When a child starts school at around five, they begin to learn how to organize their thoughts. They are helped to do this through the various activities provided by the teacher. The child also begins to learn new vocabulary as they listen to other children within their class and the new words introduced by their teacher. These new abilities are then applied to activities that occur outside of school.

CASE STUDY Thelma

Thelma is six years old. She attends the local primary school where she has lots of friends and enjoys doing different activities. She learns how to read, how to form letters and write, and how to count. Thelma also enjoys making things, particularly cakes, and also painting and building objects.

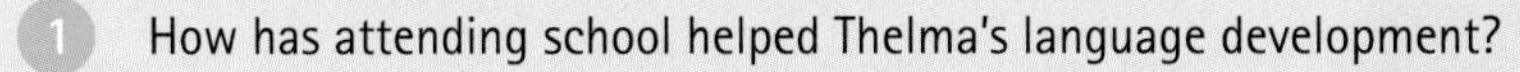

1. How has attending school helped Thelma's language development?
2. Explain how making cakes and painting are helping with Thelma's development.

At this stage, the child is no longer egocentric. This means that they can now see things from someone else's point of view. They are beginning to be able to work things out, but need to see and touch things to understand and solve problems.

What do theorists think about the intellectual development of children?

Piaget is a theorist who wrote about child development. He was a Swiss scientist who thought that children were born with some basic abilities and that a person's intellectual potential gradually developed as a result of their experiences. Piaget thought that children would try to draw conclusions from their experiences.

Piaget studied the development of children very carefully. He thought that there were several stages in the intellectual development of the child. These were:

- The sensory motor stage, which occurs between nought and two years. This is where babies find out about the things around them and what they do.
- The pre-operational stage, which occurs between the ages of two and seven years. This is where thought processes are developing. At this stage, children need to see and feel things in order to learn.
- The concrete operational stage, which occurs between eight to eleven years of age. At this stage of development, children can think more logically and follow rules.

Margaret Donaldson (1926) is a 'constructivist theorist' who considered children's development. She encouraged practitioners to focus on what children are able to do rather than concentrating on the things that they cannot do. She believed that in order to educate young children effectively it is necessary to try to present things from a child's point of view.

Group Activity

Work with another person and find out about the theory of Margaret Donaldson, Erik Erikson or Carl Rogers.
Produce a handout to help parents understand one of these theories for the childhood life stage.

Emotional development in childhood

Children can experience a wider range of emotions than infants. This is because more complicated emotions depend on other learning and development. At the beginning of childhood, a child will base their judgement on the rights or wrongs taught to them by other people. But as they progress through the life stages, things become more complex. They learn that they should express their emotions differently in different situations. A child might lash out if they were angry with another child, but would not do so if they were angry with a teacher. The behaviour of the child in lashing out at another child is wrong. The child will need help to understand why this type of behaviour is unacceptable.

▲ Feeling happy and secure.

Children still depend on their carers and close family members. How they are treated by their carers is still very important for their self-concept, but now there are other influences as well. As children get older they meet more people outside their family. Their self-concept will be affected by their relationships with others, for example, school friends and teachers. If they are popular at school and have lots of friends, it will have a positive effect on their self-concept. If they are not popular, or if they are bullied, then it will have a negative effect. For example, a child who has a positive self-concept will feel secure and will probably be full of energy and enthusiasm about the things he or she is asked to do. On the other hand, a child who is bullied is likely to have a negative self-image. They could become withdrawn or they, too, could become aggressive and bully other children.

Examples of milestones of emotional development in childhood

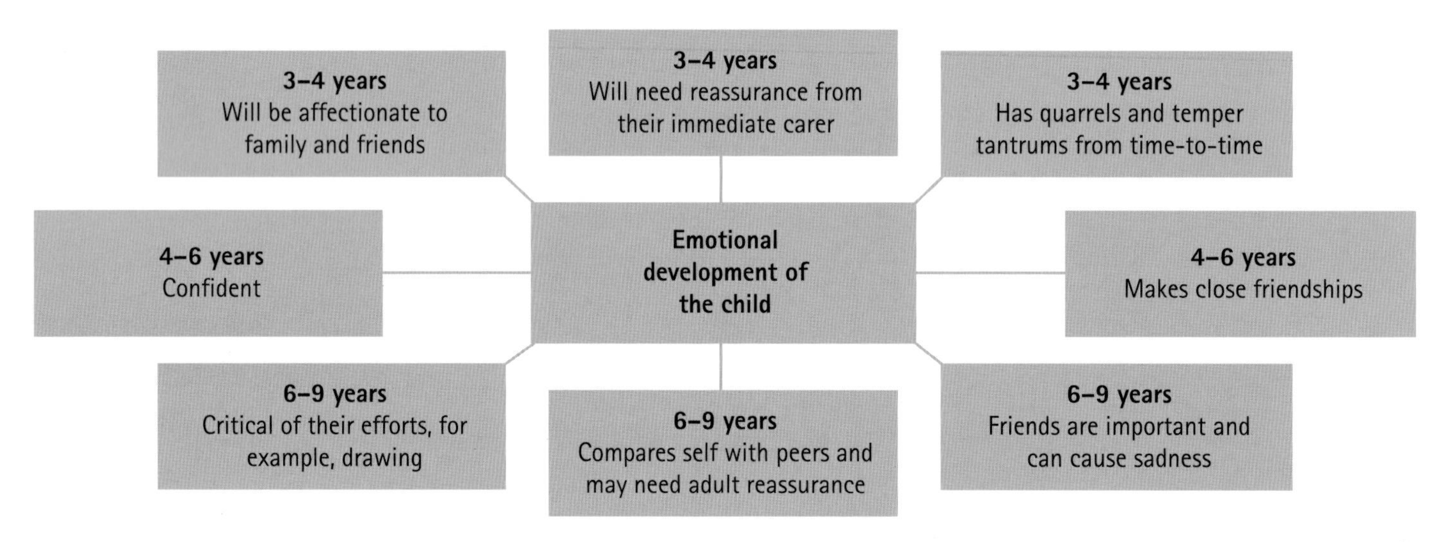

Having emotional stability is important in the development of the child as it is likely to influence their actions and attitudes throughout their life.

Social development in childhood

> **...WORD CHECK**
>
> **siblings** – brothers and sisters.
>
> **role models** – someone to copy/set an example.

Social development for children between the ages of four and ten years alters dramatically. They may have younger **siblings** to cope with, who require more of their parents' or carers' time, so they have to learn to share. Also, the number of people they meet will expand to include not only their extended family but also teachers, new friends and their parents' wider circle of friends.

Attending school will mean that the child will extend their vocabulary by talking and listening with others, and through learning new skills. Good **role models** are essential at this time, as the child will start to compare themselves with others at a very simple level and will either admire or dislike people. Parents, teachers and others they meet will influence their actions and beliefs.

Examples of milestones of social development in childhood

By the age of four, children need other children to play with. They are much better at understanding the feelings of others.

By five years old, children are attending school, meeting lots of new children and choosing their own friends.

Children understand how to take turns. They can be separated from their main carer without distress.

At five years, children cooperate with others in their peer group in games, and understand rules and fairness.

At five years of age, because children understand more about how others are feeling, it becomes more important to have the approval of the other children.

By the age of seven, children are aware of sexual differences and prefer to play with children of the same sex.

By the age of seven, children are usually quite independent.

By the age of eight, some children maybe self-conscious and may need encouragement to join in activities.

At ten, children enjoy talking with others and are able to build relationships with a broad range of people.

CASE STUDY Amber

Amber is nine years old. She has grown quite tall over the last two years. She likes looking at herself in the mirror. She thinks she looks like her mum. She enjoys going to school as she likes learning new things. She has started to learn Spanish and she is quite good at the subject. She also likes playing with her friends in the playground. She goes with her friends to junior youth club on a Friday evening. They enjoy the activities such as basketball and table tennis. In the summer the group are going away to a camp. Amber is looking forward to this.

1. How will attending junior youth club help Amber's intellectual and social development?
2. Describe Amber's emotional development in this life stage.
3. Explain how Amber's emotional and physical development is being aided through attending junior youth club.
4. Why is 'emotional stability' important for a child?
5. You want to find out about the physical, intellectual, emotional and social development of a child who is ten years of age. As a group, discuss the questions you could ask the child's parents to find out about the child's growth and development. Produce a short questionnaire that could be used when interviewing the parents about the child's physical, intellectual, emotional and social development.
   Use the questionnaire to interview a parent(s) about the growth and development of their child. You could (with your teacher's permission) invite one parent to your centre to find out the answers to the questions or you could base the information on yourself.
6. Assemble all the information you have collected about the child and produce a 'Child Study'. Draw some conclusions about the growth and development of the child against the milestones for physical, intellectual, emotional and social development.

ASSESSMENT PRACTICE

1. Malik is five years old. Describe **two** physical, **two** intellectual, **two** emotional and **two** social changes that Malik is likely to experience over the next five years. [8]
2. Explain the meaning of the terms 'growth' and 'development'. Give **one** example of each. [6]
3. Describe **three** ways an effective social relationship with a parent could have a positive influence on development. [3]
4. Identify whether the activities below are examples of physical, intellectual, emotional or social characteristics of development. [6]

Activity	Physical, intellectual, emotional or social characteristic
1 Playing on a swing	
2 Learning to spell correctly	
3 Chatting with friends	
4 Being comforted after falling over	
5 Washing hands	
6 Counting marbles	

5. Explain how being bullied could affect a child's development. [5]
6. Explain how parents or main carers could encourage the positive emotional development of a child when they are at home. [6]

ADOLESCENCE

...WORD CHECK

maturation – when development is complete.

puberty – the period during which a person becomes sexually mature.

Adolescence begins at the age of 11 years and ends at around 18 years. It is the life stage in which a person achieves sexual maturity or **maturation**, which is often called **puberty**. In the adolescent life stage intellectual skills are developed, for example, being able to think in an abstract way. The adolescent starts to become independent and develop a sense of their personal identity. They also want to make their own decisions and are often torn between the advice they may receive from parents and what they actually want to do. As a result it is often said that an adolescent is very 'moody'.

▲ Adolescence can be a very difficult time.

Physical growth and development in adolescence

Both boys and girls have a growth spurt caused by the production of **hormones** by the pituitary and other glands. Hormones are chemical secretions that pass directly into the blood from the endocrine glands. These hormones affect the thyroid gland at the neck and the pituitary gland located at the base of the brain. The boys' growth spurt is usually greater than the girls', and this is why adult men are usually taller and heavier than women.

The most important physical development in adolescence is puberty, when adolescents become sexually mature. Girls usually start puberty at between 11 and 13 years while boys start about two years later.

...WORD CHECK

hormones – chemical messengers that affect how the body functions.

abstract thinking – to have ideas not concrete facts.

Changes that take place in adolescence:

Physical development in girls	Physical development in boys
• Develop breasts • Grow pubic and underarm hair • Hips widen • Start to menstruate (have periods) • Growth spurt	• Penis and testes grow larger • Larynx (the voice box) grows, and the voice breaks and becomes deeper • Grow pubic, facial, chest and underarm hair • Muscles develop, and chest and shoulders broaden • May have wet dreams, which shows they can ejaculate sperm

Human physical development usually follows a predictable or 'normal' pattern. Some individuals may find the changes occurring slightly earlier, while others may find they happen slightly later, but this period is usually one of enormous physical change.

Intellectual development in adolescence

Adolescence is a time when there is also a growth spurt in the mind as well as in the body. It is a time when adolescents learn to think in different ways. They can understand more difficult concepts than children. They learn to synthesize information. That is, to blend information together from several different sources. They can also use their imagination to solve problems in their heads, without having to see them. This is known as **abstract thinking**. Sometimes this new ability to think for themselves leads to arguments between the adolescent and their parents, and with others.

Adolescents want to exercise their intellectual ability to make their own decisions. Within a peer group, someone who has developed the ability to think independently can exercise power over other members of the group. On other occasions it can be used to produce a sense of humour that will influence others.

Adolescence is a period of time when examinations are important, which will mean learning new skills and knowledge that has to be applied to real situations. It is a very busy and intense period of time, which can at times cause stress.

Adolescents and their parents often have terrible quarrels.

Emotional development in adolescence

Group Activity

Work with another person and think about what makes each of you feel secure. What could improve your feeling of security? Have a whole-class discussion to note the similarities and differences in what makes individuals feel secure.

The hormone changes that cause puberty also affect adolescents' emotions. They often experience mood swings. An adolescent may be excited one moment, and depressed the next. They may be very moody and get angry very easily. It is sometimes very difficult for adolescents and their families to cope with these mood swings.

At the same time, adolescents are looking for a sense of personal identity, or to discover 'who' they are. One way of doing this is to react against their parents' ideas and values. These may be ideas about politics, religion, or smoking and drinking. This time can be particularly difficult for adolescents.

Insecurity can be a part of an adolescent's emotional development, so parents and friends need to be very patient and understanding. Adolescence is a time when an individual's **personality** is developed. This means that characteristics, habits and experiences come together to form that person's personality.

Social development in adolescence

...WORD CHECK

peers – people who are the same age.

peer group – the group of people who are the same age as ourselves.

experimental – to conduct tests/to try out.

attachment – forming a close relationship with someone.

delinquent – someone who does not obey the rules or laws.

During adolescence, relationships with parents and **peers** change. Peer groups become increasingly important, while parents' views and opinions decrease in value to the adolescent. Adolescents need to grow independent from their parents. It becomes very important to the adolescent to fit in with their **peer group**. Peer-group approval becomes of utmost importance. It may be important to wear the right kind of clothes or listen to the right kind of music to fit in with friends. Peer groups serve a positive function in that they allow adolescents to interact with members of the opposite sex in a non-intimate way. For those who are left out of such cliques or who do not have a strong friendship group, the outlook is not bright! In early adolescent years, teenagers tend to form groups and do things together. It is in the safety of the group situation that **experimental** behaviour takes place.

With increasing sexual maturity, adolescents begin to look for a partner of the opposite sex and may start to experiment with sexual relationships.

First love.

The need for **attachment** is very important in adolescence, particularly where new attachments are formed with opposite sex partners. John Bowlby researched the relationship between the infant and the main carer and found that where the attachment was secure there was evidence of a healthy personality and development. Similarly, with adolescents, those who were able to form secure attachments in childhood are usually able to form new close relationships in adolescence with the ability to 'give and take'. They tend to be able to negotiate more easily.

Those who were insecurely attached in infancy tend, during adolescence, to be dependent, clingy and jealous. Or they may put up invisible barriers to stop people from getting to know them well. These adolescents are more likely to have a strained relationship with their parents and are likely to attach themselves to a **delinquent** peer group.

CASE STUDY Nehal

Nehal is 17 years old and has a small group of friends who are mainly from his own culture. When he is with his friends Nehal likes to listen to their ideas. He is very quick thinking and likes to have a joke.

Nehal is not getting on very well with his parents. He goes out a lot and does not get home until one o'clock in the morning. Nehal and his friends of the same culture do not drink alcohol. The group often try to bully people while they are coming home and chase them around side streets.

Nehal's parents are not pleased that he is out most evenings and not home until late. They have heard rumours of what happens on the way home, which is made worse when Nehal comes home with bruises on his face. He tells his parents that he fell on a rough piece of pavement, but family friends who live on the route that Nehal takes have seen what happens and tell Nehal's parents about it. Nehal's parents want him to do well at college and to go to university to become a surgeon.

1. Why do you think Nehal likes being in a group?
2. How could Nehal's parents help to improve their relationship with him?
3. Describe the physical, intellectual, emotional and social development of an adolescent.
4. Why do you think Nehal and his friends 'bully' other people while on their way home?
5. What could be the possible result of such behaviour?
6. How do feelings of insecurity affect the emotional development of adolescents?

ASSESSMENT PRACTICE

1. Describe **four** characteristics of intellectual development during adolescence. [4]
2. Describe **three** social changes that occur during adolescence. [3]
3. Describe **five** physical changes that occur in both an adolescent male and adolescent female. [10]
4. Describe the changes that are taking place between an adolescent and their parents. Explain why the changes are happening. [5]
5. Explain why being in a group is important to an adolescent. [5]
6. Why is security important to adolescents? [5]
7. Explain what is meant by the statement, 'Adolescence is the time when an individual's personality comes together'. [10]

ADULTHOOD

Adulthood is the period where an individual has achieved physical **maturity**. Compulsory education is finished and the young adult either tries to find work or may go on to higher education studies. Settling into a career becomes a very important aspect in the life of an adult and during this period of life, **promotion** will be sought. Additionally, most people find a partner, leave home and start their own families.

...WORD CHECK

maturity – to reach the age where wisdom is probably evident/older adult stage/grown up.

promotion – to advance or progress (at work).

Physical growth and development in adulthood

...WORD CHECK
sedentary – a sitting down job/not active.

There is little growth during adulthood. Adults tend to gain weight as they age, but this is probably due more to a **sedentary** lifestyle than the ageing process, although the current emphasis and encouragement to 'keep fit and healthy' has led to more adults taking up walking, cycling and other sports in order to reduce weight gain. Physical development is completed early in adulthood and physical decline also starts quite early, although at first it is too gradual to notice.

An important physical development for women towards the end of this life stage is the menopause. Usually between the ages of 45 and 55, women's periods stop, and they are no longer able to have children. This is caused by hormonal changes in the body. Sometimes a woman may feel a sense of loss when the menopause occurs, while others will be glad that they no longer have to worry about becoming pregnant and so have a sense of freedom.

Intellectual development in adulthood

▲ Learning new skills at work.

Intellectual development continues throughout adulthood. Getting a job involves learning new skills. If a person wants to progress in a career, these skills have to be developed and extended. Most people will have more than one job throughout their lives. This is because old jobs go and new ones are created, which frequently means that adults are required to retrain in order to learn new skills. Lifelong learning is necessary to enable people to learn new skills and keep old ones up to date.

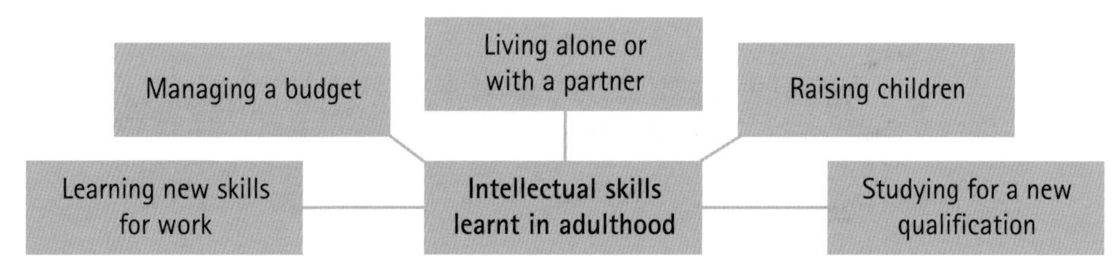

Even outside of work, adulthood is a period of intellectual development. You need a lot of skills to leave home and live independently.

As adults age, they react more slowly and find it more difficult to remember information under pressure. However, to balance this, they have learnt from experience and are better at problem solving and making decisions. This more than compensates for any sluggishness in intellectual ability over the life stage.

Emotional development in adulthood

The statement 'behaving in a mature manner' usually means that individuals are controlling the way they respond to the emotions they are feeling, such as being angry or very fond of another individual.

When an individual leaves home, they have to be independent and self-reliant in order to cope. They have to be able to not only consider how they themselves feel but also how other people are reacting to specific situations. Living with a long-term partner takes a high level of emotional maturity if the relationship is not to break down when problems arise. People have to understand their own emotions and those of their partner. They also have to be able to control the way they respond to their emotions. If they cannot, the result is often the breakdown of the relationship, and sometimes violence, if one partner cannot control emotions such as jealousy and anger.

The arrival of children means accepting new responsibilities. Babies are very demanding, and cause a lot of stress to the people who care for them. Adults have to be emotionally mature to cope. Emotional maturity involves:

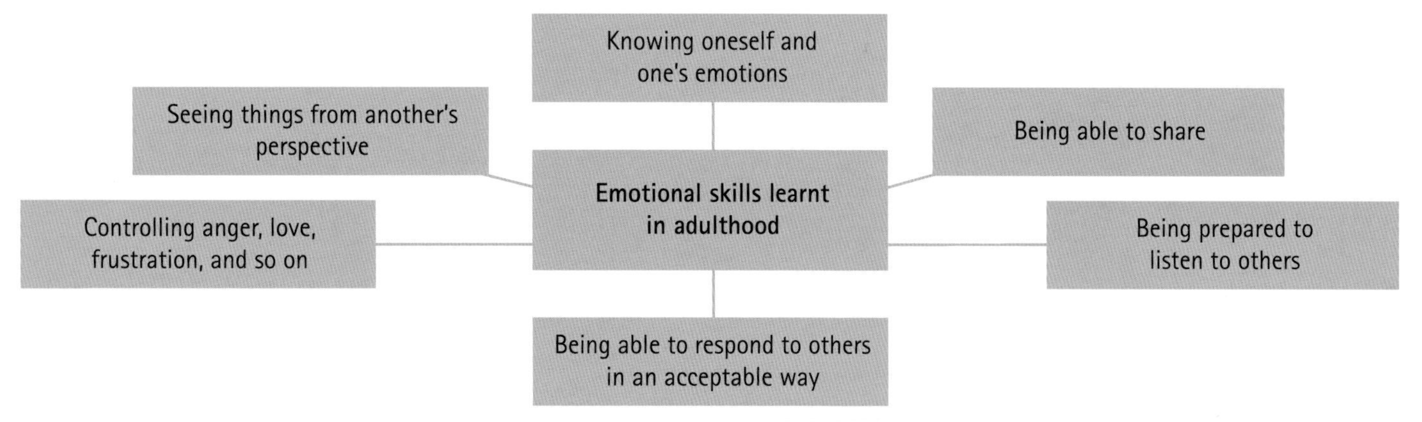

CASE STUDY Joanne

Joanne enjoys spending time with her friends Pauline and Sophia, and their families. Their children are around the same age and attend similar clubs, so the three of them have a lot in common. They meet at weekends in one another's homes for either barbeques or supper, and often go camping together for half term or the summer holidays. Their husbands also appear to get on well and have quite a lot to talk about; except that George, Joanne's husband, never joins in the conversations very much, he just listens.

One evening, after spending a lovely afternoon together, George seems very quiet when he reaches home. Joanne, having put the children to bed, asks him if anything is wrong.

George stands up and walks up and down the living room talking about how he is 'fed up with having to listen to how good Paul is at this and how Adrian's children are so good at that'. He becomes very angry and tells Joanne it is 'all her fault, as she is the one that arranges the family get togethers'. He then slams the door and walks out.

1. What are the emotional issues raised in this case study?
2. How is Joanne likely to feel about this emotional problem?
3. Explain possible solutions to the problems.
4. Explain the likely effects of this emotional upset on the other families.

Social development in adulthood

When young adults leave home, they have to develop new and different types of relationships. They may have a partner or get married and this means making decisions, accepting responsibility and sharing. Relationships with parents change as the young adult starts to relate to them more as equals. Parents realize that their offspring are now taking responsibility for themselves, and maybe others as well, and may speak to and treat the young adult with more respect.

Starting work involves developing working relationships with people. These are a different type of relationship. The same choice is not available with working relationships as with other social relationships, as it is compulsory for individuals to work with those with whom they are employed.

Sometimes the relationships are distinguished by calling them **formal** (**working relationship**) and **informal** (family and friendship) relationships. Working relationships are formal because there are rules that have to be followed, particularly at work, or if on a committee, as some people can tell others what to do since they are the employer or the supervisor.

...WORD CHECK

formal – a relationship that has rules that must be followed/a framework.

working relationship – getting on with a person while at work.

informal – not professional.

3 How does socializing in a job contribute towards an individual's personal development?

4 How are working relationships different from social relationships?

Settling down with a long-term partner makes many changes to people's social lives. Marriage or having a partner means acquiring a set of new relatives or people, for example, in-laws. Even if people are just living together, this often involves building new relationships with their partner's family. People often find that the way they socialize changes when they settle down with a regular partner, and that they tend to mix more with other couples.

5 How might the arrival of their first child change the relationship between two people who are partners?

As adults near the later adult life stage, they may find that their parents are declining physically, and begin to depend on them more and more. This could bring increased responsibility as the older adult may require physical help, such as shopping, or may have dementia, which could mean that they forget things easily and are not safe to live on their own.

LATER ADULTHOOD

Retirement from work is a major feature of this life stage. An older adult has to get used to the idea that they are no longer a wage earner and, usually, they are not responsible for others. This new role can cause some people to feel distressed if they have not made the proper preparation for retirement. They may feel useless as they are no longer making decisions for others and may have to rely on others for financial and physical support.

Physical growth and development in later adulthood

Individuals in later adulthood often have a reduction in height as their posture becomes less upright and their spine becomes compressed. A person can lose up to 3 inches in height! The physical decline that started in early adulthood becomes more obvious, especially after the age of 75 years.

Many of these problems can be overcome or managed so that the older adult can enjoy a better quality of life. Keeping fit can help to maintain our health and well-being, and may help to prevent or delay some aspects of physical decline. Activities, such as swimming, walking and jogging, can help to maintain our health and mobility if engaged in regularly.

Glasses and hearing aids can compensate for deteriorating sight and hearing. New technology means that older adults have a range of products from which to choose. If joints become damaged, particularly hips and knees, they can now be replaced. Such operations are now common and are not the major events they used to be. Older adults are asked to wait as long as possible before having treatment though, as the new knee or hip joint does wear out.

◂ Exercise can help to maintain health and well-being if done on a regular basis.

Sight worsens as the eyes' lenses stiffen and are less able to focus on close objects, so reading is difficult.

Hearing declines with the gradual deterioration of the mechanism of the ear.

Mobility may be affected as joints stiffen and become worn or inflamed. Balance is often poorer, and falls are more likely.

Older adults are more vulnerable to the cold, making older people susceptible to **hypothermia**.

Sense of taste and smell is poorer. Teeth may decay and cause problems with eating, and also contribute to a lack of confidence.

Bones are more fragile, as thinning makes them lighter and more brittle, particularly in women.

Body organs continue to become less efficient, including the heart, lungs, kidneys and liver.

Skin wrinkles because of loss of elasticity in the tissues.

Hair thins and goes grey. Men often have hair loss, which could progress to baldness.

Intellectual development in later adulthood

Because of the gradual deterioration of the nervous system, older people have difficulty in remembering things quickly, particularly when they are under pressure. Their reaction times are also slower. However, they may have more experience than a younger person, and could make better decisions as a result.

Older people can become confused and may be unable to manage their own affairs. Confusion is not a normal part of ageing. Confusion is different from dementia, as with dementia actual brain cells cease to function. This cannot be restored. Confusion is temporary and usually passes when the person is less flustered.

The occurrence of confusion and dementia is growing, and this is becoming one of the major health issues of the twenty-first century.

...WORD CHECK

hypothermia – a condition that develops when the body temperature falls.

CASE STUDY Edith

Edith is living in Portesham View residential home. She is 75 years old and has the early signs of Alzheimer's disease. Edith wanders around the residential home at night and during the day, going into other people's bedrooms and taking bright objects. These are often found in her own room. She also wanders into the small kitchen and takes snacks that have only been partially prepared and puts them on the table for lunch.

One of the care workers who works part time shouts at Edith when she finds she has been up to her 'old tricks' again and threatens her by saying, 'I will tie you to a chair if you do this again. You are a stupid old woman.' When this happens, Edith goes to the locked front door and tries to get out.

1. Carry out research to find out how Alzheimer's disease affects older adults.
2. How could Edith be helped to ensure that she has some meaningful social interaction?
3. How could older adults be affected intellectually by the ageing process, other than having Alzheimer's disease?
4. What actions should the care assistant take to empower Edith?

Social and emotional development in later adulthood

Poor physical and mental health can have a harmful effect on social and emotional aspects of ageing. In the previous section, some of the physical effects were discussed, but these do not occur in isolation, as one is likely to influence the function of another aspect of development.

Mobility problems, whether the result of muscular-skeletal problems or circulatory dysfunction, can result in increased segregation as a client may be unable to go out for everyday activities, for example, shopping or social events. The impact is likely to be that the client may not have the opportunity to talk to other people, to share views and opinions or ideas. This could mean that they rarely see others and become very inward looking. Their emotional health may deteriorate as a result, and they may become withdrawn and lonely. Additionally, because they are not meeting other people, they will not be using their skills of communication and may talk to themselves.

Such behaviour could lead to the client not valuing themselves and having poor self-esteem. Loss of self-esteem could mean that the client starts to think that nothing is important. Intellectual stimulation is not available, socially they are not meeting others and, consequently, they become demotivated. Some older clients could just sit in a chair watching television all day, but even then they may not be actually registering what the programmes are about.

This type of behaviour is to be avoided. Michael Argyle, a psychologist, puts forward, as part of his theory, that an individual's self-concept and development of personal identity is formed by looking at the reaction of others towards themselves, and that people judge themselves according to this. Argyle also indicates that people commonly regard their social role as part of who they are. Older people, therefore, if they are withdrawn and socially isolated, will not have any social role with which to define themselves and consequently will feel that they have nothing to contribute.

Cummings and Henry (1961), who are also theorists, defined the state of older people cutting themselves off from society as '**disengagement**'. They considered that this was 'an inevitable process in which many relationships between a person and other members of society are severed and those remaining are altered in quality'. This involves the reduction of life activities and ego in old age.

...WORD CHECK

disengagement – to withdraw.

A person whose life is prone to isolation because of mobility problems is likely, therefore, to be encouraged to visit day-care centres, luncheon clubs and to join in other recreational activities that are beneficial for older people, to avoid them spending too much time looking inward or backwards to events that have happened in previous life stages. The aim is to provide a purposeful role and interest, and to help them become socially integrated.

Some of the illnesses and conditions that can be experienced by older adults, which influence social and emotional development, are:

Illness	Effect on the individual
Stroke	Paralysis, lack of mobility, loss of speech, loss of vision
Incontinence	Lack of bladder and bowel control
Diabetes	Impaired glucose regulation
Dementia/Alzheimer's disease	Inability to remember in the short term

It is important for older people who are ill to feel valued and that an emotionally safe environment has been created. The practice of treating each person as an individual is recognized by 'The General Care Council' as being very important. This means respecting the views, wishes and dignity of those who are ill. In order to achieve such aims, a supportive relationship is needed between the client and the care worker. Managing clients who are experiencing illness calls for a wide variety of skills. These include:

...WORD CHECK

occupational – associated with the job.

bereavements – deaths of a friend or relative.

Effective communication
Speaking at an appropriate pace, using vocabulary that can be understood and actively listening

Allowing choice
Giving the client options from which they can choose what is best for them

Assertive behaviour
Being confident and accepting other people's needs as well as your own

Giving support
This could be practical care or psychological, so that the client can talk about issues that are causing them concern

Being respectful
Calling a client by their preferred name, listening carefully and responding in a sensitive manner

Minimizing risks
Preventing difficult situations arising and avoiding triggers for aggression

Creating trust
Staying calm and meeting the other person's self-esteem needs

Promoting self-confidence
Giving genuine praise when a client has achieved a goal

Maintaining confidentiality
Not passing on information given to other clients, relatives or friends

Some older people miss the regular contact with workmates. Others enjoy having more time to devote to hobbies and interests. How people are affected may depend on their income. Many older people with pensions from jobs are well off. Others, who do not have an **occupational** pension, may find it hard to make ends meet. Many older adults may use their retirement to travel around the world or to start new activities.

As people get older, they suffer more **bereavements**, of friends, close relatives, and perhaps their partner. They have to adapt to a smaller social circle.

Meeting up with friends can help older adults stay socially and intellectually active.

CASE STUDY Mr Simkins and his family

Mr Simkins is 70 years old and lives with his wife in their own home. He has a good pension from his job, and considers himself quite well off. Their two children are married and live nearby. They have five grandchildren, who they see regularly.

Mr Simkins drives, but he is thinking of giving up his car. He took up painting when he retired and he enjoys doing this now, but has given up hill walking.

He is a member of a number of local organizations. He sometimes says he doesn't know how he found time to go to work.

1. Explain why painting is a better hobby for Mr Simkins than hill walking.
2. Why do you think Mr Simkins is considering giving up his car ?
3. Describe the social developments for the Simkins in the life stage they are in.
4. How does an individual's relationship with their child change during the older adult life stage?

ASSESSMENT PRACTICE

1. Describe **two** physical developments and **two** intellectual developments that occur in the adult life stage. [4]
2. Explain how an older adult's development is likely to be affected in this life stage. [5]
3. Explain what is meant by the term 'disengagement' when thinking about older adults' behaviour. [5]
4. Explain how physical ill health can affect the emotional and social development of older adults. [10]
5. Mrs Price is 72 and lives alone. Her children and her grandchildren live 50 miles away and her husband has recently died. Describe four ways that Mrs Price could keep good physical, intellectual, emotional and social well-being, explaining how each would help her to cope. [12]

The different factors that can affect human growth

What factors affect human growth and development, and how can they influence an individual's health, well-being and life opportunities?

Getting started

In this section you must be able to understand and give examples of factors that cause individual differences in patterns of growth and development.

- Physical factors including genetic inheritance, diet, amount and type of physical activity, sexual health, experience of illness or disease.
- Social and emotional factors including gender, family relationships, friendships, educational experiences, employment/unemployment, ethnicity and religion, life experiences such as birth, marriage, death and divorce.
- Economic factors including income and material possessions.
- Environmental factors including housing conditions, pollution, access to health and welfare services.
- You should understand how these factors can interrelate and how they can affect a person's:
  - self-esteem
  - physical and mental health
  - employment prospects
  - level of education.
- You will also need to identify what effect abuse and neglect can have on personal development.

FACTORS THAT CAN AFFECT HUMAN GROWTH

Human development can be affected by many factors, which may have a positive or detrimental influence. Understanding the factors that influence human behaviour means that the 'nature versus nurture' debate must be considered. For example, which has the stronger influence? Inherited factors, such as an inherited disability, known as the 'nature' factor, or the experiences an individual has, for example, education, known as the 'nurture' factor? In other words, are the skills that we possess innate or are they socially learnt?

Group Activity

Work with another person and think about which factors have influenced your own development, for example, family. Try to make a list of five different factors between you that have influenced your development.
Now write out the following headings: physical, social and emotional, economic, environmental.
Place the factors you have in your list under these headings. Try to have at least one factor under each.
Discuss your findings as a whole group.

The different factors that can affect human growth

Human development can be influenced by a number of factors. It is these factors that help to shape our personality.

Factors affecting health and development:

Physical factors
- genetics and diet
- physical activity
- illness and disease

Social and emotional factors
- gender and life experiences
- family relationships
- educational experiences

Economic factors
- income
- material possessions

Environmental factors
- housing conditions
- pollution
- access to health and welfare services

Effects of factors on development:

The effect on the self-esteem of the individual	The effect on physical and mental health of the individual
The effect on employment prospects for the individual	The effect on the individual of the level of education received

PHYSICAL FACTORS

Genetic inheritance

▲ Our genes make us who we are.

Genetic inheritance is having a mixture of **genes** from our parents, which acts as a plan of what we will be like when we grow. Genes are bits of information inside every cell in your body. They are the instructions that the body uses to build itself. The human body is very complicated and it needs a lot of instructions to build itself properly.

Each individual has a set of about 80,000 genes, but only about a tenth of these instructions differ from person to person. Nine tenths of the instructions are about the things that all human beings have in common, such as the structure of the body and how the organs work. The other tenth are the ones that make you an individual. These genes help decide things like your size, build, facial **features**, hair and skin colour. They also decide whether you are male or female.

We get half of our genes from our mother, and half from our father, but they mix differently each time a child is conceived. That is why children often look like their parents, and brothers and sisters often look similar, but never exactly the same. The only exception to this is identical twins. This is where a single fertilized egg splits and produces two embryos, which grow into two babies with identical genes.

How do our genes influence development?

The rate at which we mature is genetically determined. Maturation is the rate of physical growth and starts at **conception**. All normal foetuses develop at approximately the same rate (the norm), and after birth we all learn to crawl, walk and run within approximately the same time scales. All people pass through the same stages of maturation in the same order. However, we

...WORD CHECK

genes – part of a chromosome that controls a particular characteristic, for example, eye colour.

features – an aspect or characteristic.

conception– when egg and sperm join together to make a baby.

don't all mature at exactly the same rate. For example, some children stand at six months, but others not until ten months. Children are not all the same and this is because each person's combination of genes is different.

Why are all children not the same?

Some genes cause illnesses that affect the way that people develop. These illnesses are called **hereditary** or genetic disorders. They can cause physical and learning disabilities, and sometimes result in the early deaths of people who have them. Some examples of hereditary diseases are:

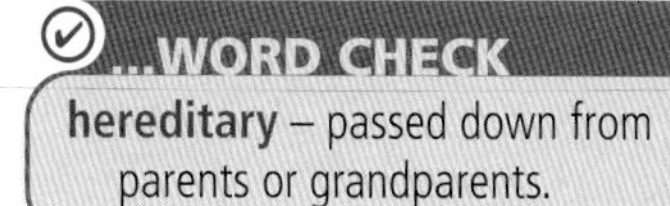

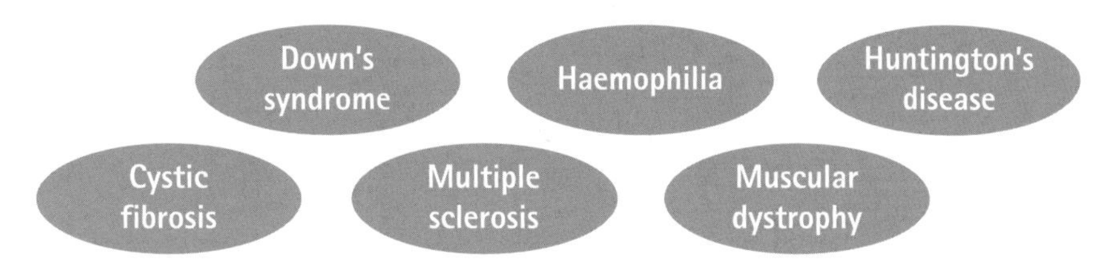

Nature versus nurture

Genes are the basic instructions for how our bodies develop and grow, but they are only one influence. All the other factors that we will discuss in this section can affect the way that our bodies develop. People sometimes talk about nature and nurture. By nature, they mean the genetic influences on our development. Nurture is about all the other influences, such as family, education and where we live.

The question is: Is how we behave inherited or is it learnt?

BF Skinner and others have studied behaviour and have concluded that our learning is shaped by our direct personal experiences. Skinner thinks that this is likely to mean that we will want to repeat any good experiences we have and that we will want to avoid any that we have not enjoyed. Skinner called the things we would want to repeat 'positive reinforcements'. Examples of different types of positive reinforcements are food, praise and money. This theory is known as the 'behaviourist theory'. It means that we learn from 'trial and error'. We will learn from our experiences, the things in our environment that influence us.

A lot of people consider that our development is influenced by both nature (what is in us) and nurture (the influences around us). It is most likely the combination of nature and nurture that can influence a person's individual health, well-being and life opportunities.

What is meant by the nature versus nurture debate?

Diet as a factor that influences development

Diet is an important influence on growth and development. The food we eat meets our physical needs. We need food for two reasons:

1. So that the body can grow and repair itself when it is damaged.
2. To provide energy. Energy is needed to do the work of building and repair, to maintain temperature and to enable us to carry out physical activities.

Pictures of people who haven't got enough food or water to help them stay alive have probably been seen by all of us on TV and in the media. We see pictures of children who are caught up in war or famine. Their bodies are misshapen through lack of food or from not having a balanced diet. Many children in other countries die because they are suffering from malnutrition.

Our physical needs change as we go through different life stages. What we need for a balanced diet depends upon:

- our age
- our size
- our sex
- the amount of exercise we have
- factors such as pregnancy and breastfeeding.

If we do not have a balanced diet, this can have serious effects on our growth and development. To remain healthy, we need to make sure that our diet contains the correct nutrients. These are as follows.

...WORD CHECK

amino acids – chemicals that are the building blocks of protein.

Proteins

Proteins are the building blocks of our body. For children they are very important for building the brain, muscle, skin, blood and other tissues. Proteins also provide the materials needed to repair the cells in our body. Proteins are made up of complex chemicals called **amino acids**. To function properly our body needs 21 different amino acids.

The body can make 12 of these itself through complex chemical processes. The other nine are obtained from the food that we eat.

▲ Fish contain protein, essential for body building.

There are two types of protein: animal protein and vegetable protein. Animal proteins are obtained from products such as meat, fish, eggs, milk and cheese. These products contain all of the remaining nine amino acids that our body requires. Vegetable proteins come from plant products such as peas, beans, lentils and nuts. They are a very good source of protein, especially for vegetarians. The remaining nine amino acids that the body needs can also be found in vegetable proteins.

Fats

Fats are very good at providing energy and are found in both animal and vegetable products. There are three main types of fat, saturated, mono-saturated and polyunsaturated.

9 Investigate which foods contain saturated, mono-saturated and polyunsaturated fats.

Carbohydrates

Carbohydrates also provide the body with energy. Most carbohydrates come from sugars, starches and fibre. Foods such as biscuits, chocolate, cakes, honey and jams are high in carbohydrates. A second source of carbohydrates is foods such as pasta, rice and potatoes. These also provide a high energy source. In both fat and carbohydrate products this energy comes in units known as kilojoules or calories. These are the same calories that people count in their diets.

Vitamins

Vitamins are found in most food that is eaten. Their main function is to regulate the chemical processes that take place in our body. Small amounts of vitamins are taken from the food we eat. Deficiencies of vitamins can cause health problems. In Britain, the seventeenth- and eighteenth-century sailors constantly suffered from a disease called 'scurvy', through a lack of vitamin C in their diet. Lack of vitamin C led to conditions such as skin problems, bleeding gums and caused teeth to fall out. The deficiency was eventually combatted when it was noticed that Spanish sailors did not have this problem because they ate oranges as part of their diet on board ships.

Find out about vitamins A, B, C, D and E. What do they do and which foods are they found in?

Minerals

These are simple elements, such as iron, calcium and potassium. They are found in most of the foods that we eat, some foods being higher in certain minerals than others. Minerals are also needed by the body in small quantities so that it can function correctly. There are 22 minerals that are essential to remaining healthy. Minerals such as calcium help to build strong bones and teeth and iron helps in the formation of red blood cells. Minerals are divided into two main groups, minerals that are needed in relatively large amounts, major minerals or elements, and minerals that are needed in much smaller amounts, trace minerals or elements.

A deficiency of minerals in the diet can lead to disease, for example, a lack of iron in the diet may lead to anaemia (low red blood cell count).

Water

Water is probably the most important part of our diet. We can go without food for weeks and still survive. However, if our supply of drinkable water is cut off, we will die in a matter of days. It helps us digest our food and dispose of our waste products. We must not underestimate the value of water.

Fibre

Fibre in our diet adds bulk to the food that we eat. This helps the digestive system to move the food through the bowel. Without these muscular movements we would easily become constipated. Fibre is found in a variety of different foods such as:

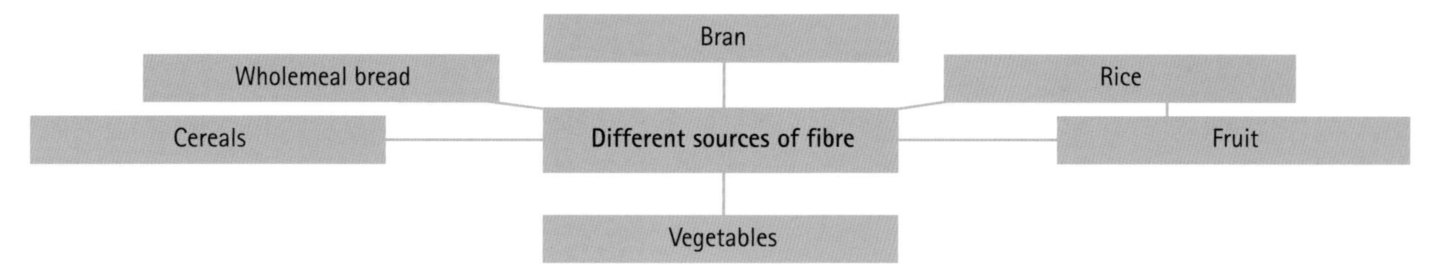

Without fibre we can suffer from poor digestion of our food, which can also lead to constipation.

What is a healthy balanced diet?

A healthy diet contains all of the nutrients needed by the body. Nutritionists and the government have worked out a rough guide to show what a healthy diet should include. The Department of Health has produced '*The Balance of Good Health*', which includes the government's five-a-day initiative for portions of fruit and vegetables.

Remember it is diets, not foods, which are unhealthy and it's the food you eat over months and years that will influence your health. Make changes for life, and don't be influenced by 'fad' diets. When deciding to make some changes to your diet, think carefully about what changes you will seriously be able to stick with. It may make more sense to make small changes over time, rather than radically altering your entire diet, if this means the changes are more likely to be permanent.

◂ Five portions of fruit and vegetables should be eaten each day.

ACTIVITY Ellie, Rupert and family

Ellie is six years old, Rupert is 13 years old and their mother and father are both in their late 30s. They have all been putting on a lot of weight and Ellie's mum has decided that they must change their lifestyle and food choices. They have been used to eating quite a lot of fried fatty foods, cake, bread and junk food.

1. Carry out research to find out what each member of the family's food intake should be.
2. Plan **one** day's menus for both Ellie and Rupert showing how they are well balanced.
3. Plan **one** day's menu for Ellie's father, who works on a building site. Show why it is well balanced.
4. Produce **ten** questions for a quiz about healthy foods, what they do and where they can be found. Work out the answers to the questions on a separate piece of paper. Take part in the quiz with the rest of the group.

▴ A family meal.

How can the foods we eat influence our development?

Eating can be a social activity as well as contributing to our physical health and well-being. It may be that people have breakfast together as a family. Or, because people are leaving for school and work, they may all meet together for an evening meal. Sometimes if we want to watch something on television, we may balance a tray on our laps while we are eating our food.

Whichever way we choose to have our meals, it is important that we make sure we have a balanced diet.

11 What is a balanced diet?

- If we do not get enough nutrients, it will affect our body's ability to grow and repair itself. We will be less resistant to infections and it will take us longer to recover from injury and illness.
- If we take in more energy than we use, we gain weight. If we take in less energy than we use, we lose weight. Being very overweight (obese) or very underweight is bad for our health and also affects our appearance.
- If we take in too much energy in the form of fats, it can increase our risk of heart disease.
- If we take in too much energy in the form of sugar, it can increase our risk of tooth decay.

Too much or too little of particular nutrients can cause us problems as we develop and mature, and also in later adulthood.

You have all probably heard the saying 'we are what we eat'. If we eat a well-balanced diet, keeping to regular patterns of eating, we are more likely to be healthy. If we eat excessively or have an unbalanced diet, we are more likely to develop conditions and illnesses that will affect our development.

It is unlikely that one diet-related factor would cause major health problems. It is when poor diet is combined with other factors, such as lack of exercise, stress or poor living conditions, that ill health is likely to result.

Miranda is one year old. Plan Miranda's diet for one day.

Murray is an older adult. How will his diet vary from that of an adolescent?

Gaye is pregnant. Plan her diet for her for one day.

Physical activity

Taking part in physical activity regularly throughout our lives is very beneficial. The type of exercise that is right for us will depend on the stage of our physical development. Different types of exercise will suit people in different life stages. The benefits of physical activity are:

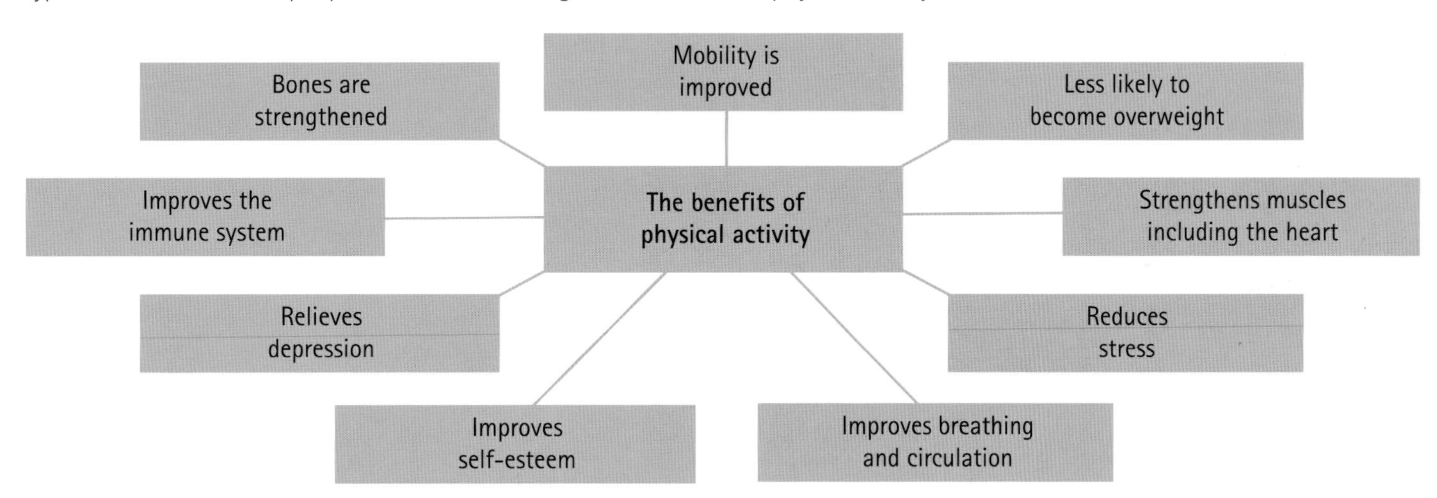

Exercise should be taken for 30 minutes five times each week in order to build up and maintain fitness. Exercise changes the body composition as it increases the amount of muscle the body has and reduces fat levels. From the moment they are born, babies begin to exercise their muscles. Children will exercise as part of their sports activities and as a major part of growing up. Exercise helps to protect against disease. There are two main types of exercise that can increase fitness. These are:

Aerobic

Involves moving muscles through their full range over a set period of time:

- walking
- jogging
- swimming

Anaerobic

Involves high intensity activity over short periods of time aimed at developing muscle:

- gymnastics
- weightlifting
- football

Regular exercise will improve **endurance** and muscular strength.

Babies exercise quite naturally, even before they can move around. We have all probably seen young babies kicking and stretching in their cots or at bath time. As babies develop and learn to crawl and walk, they try to explore their surroundings all the time.

endurance – staying power.

Children should get enough physical activity through walking to school, sports, games and play. There are worries that children may not be getting enough physical activity. As a result, more children are becoming unfit and obese. This could be because:

- More parents have cars and drive their children to school instead of letting them walk or cycle. They may do this because of worries about the danger of traffic or the risk of abduction. It may also be because more parents work and do not have the time to walk to school with their children.
- Children may be more interested in activities such as television and computer games. As a result they might be doing fewer physical activities.

Sitting all day can't be good for me.

Adolescents may also be getting less exercise because more of them are able to drive, and so they walk less. They may also have less active interests, such as computer games.

Fewer people work in jobs that require physical effort. Many more people now work in office jobs. Some jobs are physically easier because most of the work is done by machinery. This means that most types of work do not provide the amount of physical activity that is needed to keep healthy. Many work from home one day of each week, which again will probably involve sedentary work.

Adults can make sure that they get some physical activity through housework, gardening and walking to the shops. If they do not do a lot of these things, they may have to take care that they get sufficient exercise, perhaps by playing sports, running or going to the gym.

For older people, physical activity could be painful because of rheumatism or arthritis. They do still need exercise though, for the same reasons as people in any other life stage. They may need specially organized exercise programmes that are within their physical capability.

How can our experience of illness and disease affect growth and development?

All illnesses have physical effects on the people who have them. Sometimes we can have diarrhoea, vomit, have spots or ache all over. These symptoms are going to affect our development, but for only a short time. On other occasions, an illness will take us longer to recover from. An example would be glandular fever. Experience of illness and disease is sometimes linked with our diet. For example, we may get food poisoning or we may not have had enough iron in our diet, and as a consequence we could feel tired and lethargic. We are, in our lifetime, however, bound to have some experience of illness and disease.

Because infants are growing so quickly, most illnesses affect their physical development for a short while. Examples of these types of illness are chickenpox and mumps. The infant usually makes up for any loss in growth and development when they recover. Some common childhood illnesses can have long-term effects. Some illnesses have serious developmental effects, sometimes leading to death.

Infants are, to some extent, protected from infection in the first few months of their lives. This is because they have **immunity** in the form of antibodies. These have been passed from their mother to them while they were in the womb before birth. Their immunity to illness can be further boosted through breast feeding, as antibodies are passed on during this process. After a short while, the baby will start to produce their own antibodies in response to infections.

immunity – resistance to a disease.

degenerative – where a body organ or system slowly begins to break down.

Vaccinations can help to prevent individuals from getting some diseases. Examples are vaccinations against meningitis, whooping cough and tuberculosis.

Physical illness and disease can affect our emotional, intellectual and social development. For example, if a child misses a lot of school, they miss learning opportunities, as well as the opportunity to mix and socialize with other children.

CASE STUDY Sid

Sid is 53 years old. He is single because his partner left him as she could not put up with his heavy drinking habit. Sid worked, but his diet was very poor as he had lots of chips, beefburgers and takeaways. He seldom had any fruit and vegetables. He always had plenty to drink, however. He never cleaned his teeth.

Over several months, Sid developed severe toothache. His gums started to bleed badly and lumps developed at the sides of his mouth. Eventually he visited the dentist as he could stand the pain no longer.

The dentist immediately sent Sid to the hospital for x-rays. When the results came through it was decided that Sid would have to have immediate surgery to take all of his teeth out and to remove the parts of the gums that were diseased.

Sid was ill for a long while and could only eat food that was liquidized.

This severe condition was the result of:

- not eating a healthy diet
- drinking a lot of alcohol
- not cleaning the teeth properly
- not visiting the dentist regularly.

Sometimes illness and conditions are the result of our own neglect!

In later adulthood many people have **degenerative** illnesses such as arthritis and rheumatism. These have the physical effect of making it difficult for them to care for themselves. Other illnesses, such as Alzheimer's disease, have intellectual effects, such as confusion and memory loss. Having to rely on others for everyday care tasks may have emotional effects. People who are unable to care for themselves may become depressed. This is likely to happen if their carers are not careful to offer them choices. If illness makes people less mobile, they may find it difficult to leave their homes. This will have social effects and they may become isolated.

It should be remembered that:

- happy and contented people are less likely to be ill
- a balanced diet can contribute to good health
- having sufficient physical activity can contribute to the absence of illness and disease.

CASE STUDY Sheila

Sheila is an identical twin. She is very close to her sister, Mary. They both have fair hair and blue eyes. When they were children they had the usual childhood illnesses but Sheila also developed a mild form of meningitis and was away from school for several weeks.

At school they both did quite well in their examinations but Sheila found the language classes quite difficult. When she was ill she missed quite a few lessons and found it hard to catch up.

Both Sheila and Mary like playing the piano and enjoy jogging. When they were younger they used to go running with their father at the weekends. He was a member of the running club. Their father also taught them how to use a computer when they were six years old.

Sheila now has a job as a computer programmer. Mary also works with computers but in an office at the other end of the town. They meet for lunch twice a week and bring a friend with them. They usually have a snack including a jacket potato and salad.

On Thursday they play badminton in a group of four and on Saturdays they go swimming. They are members of the swimming club.

1. Sheila's growth and development has been influenced by several factors. List six factors that have influenced her development and give an example of each.
2. Explain how Sheila's family could have influenced her development.
3. Using the case study for Sheila, discuss the nature versus nurture debate. Give examples to illustrate the points you are making.
4. Think of your own development or find out about the development of a friend. Describe four factors that have influenced either your or their personal development. Give examples for each.

ASSESSMENT PRACTICE

1. List **three** physical factors that could influence an individual's development, describing how each could affect attitude and behaviour. [6]
2. Describe how illness and disease could affect the development of an older adult. [5]
3. Genes can be a physical factor that influence development. Explain the term 'genetics'. [3]
4. Explain, by giving examples, how it can affect development. [7]
5. How could an individual's attitude be affected by poor diet and lack of exercise? [10]
6. How could participating in regular exercise help to promote health and well-being of an individual? [5]
7. Use theory to help explain how physical factors could affect the development of an individual. [8]
8. Discuss the nature versus nurture debate relating the points discussed to the factors that can influence an individual. [10]

SOCIAL AND EMOTIONAL FACTORS THAT CAN AFFECT DEVELOPMENT

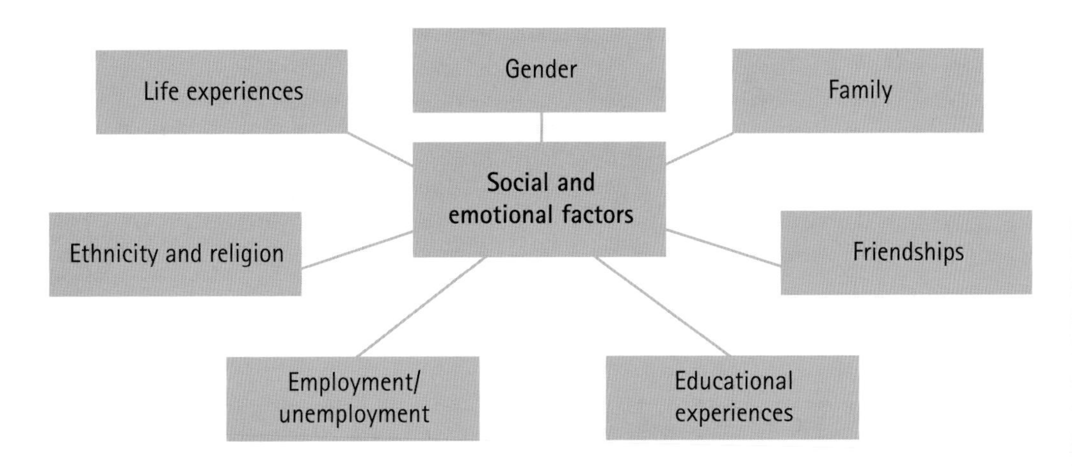

Primary socialization occurs as a result of our home life and the people that we meet first in our lives: our parents, our immediate family, our extended family.

Secondary socialization refers to those things that affect us as we grow and develop, for example, the things we learn from the wider society.

Group Activity

Work with another person and think about when you went to playgroup, nursery school or a childminder. Were you given specific toys to play with that were considered to be more suitable for you because of your gender?

Did you ever want to do something that was considered more suitable for the opposite gender? What was it? Were you allowed to do it? How did you feel when you were originally prevented from doing it?

How does gender affect growth and development?

Gender is not the same as sex. An individual's sex depends on their genes. Gender is about the way society expects people of each sex to behave. In other words, gender affects an individual's life opportunities because some jobs, sports or activities will be seen as being appropriate for males, and others for females.

It is difficult for people to be different if everybody around expects them to behave in certain ways according to their gender. For example, a boy may be provided with different toys from a girl. They may be given a train while a girl is given a doll. The child will have no choice about some of the toys they are given. Since part of their intellectual and social development happens through play, their development will be affected because they will start to think that dolls are only for girls to play with and trains are specifically for boys. This is known as '**stereotyping**'.

▲ Stereotyping.

Gender socialization is also associated with culture. It is the way in which we learn the roles that we are to take for the future, for example, male and female roles. It is thought that gender roles are learnt depending on what is taught as being acceptable to the male and female. The roles of males and females are no longer clearly defined and are often merged.

12 Why is it important to encourage boys and girls to play with toys that interest them when at nursery school?

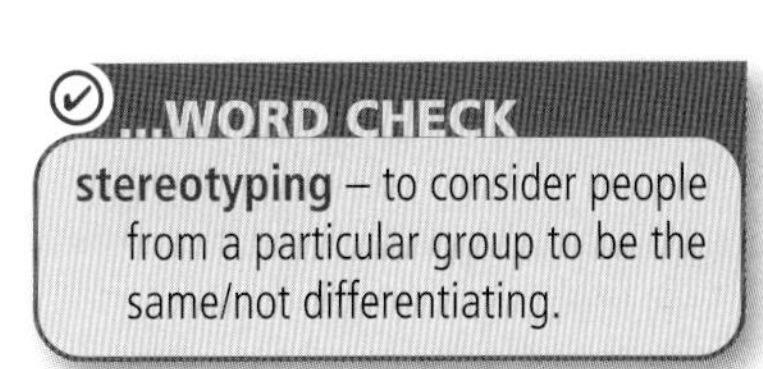

...WORD CHECK

stereotyping – to consider people from a particular group to be the same/not differentiating.

Does gender affect employment opportunities?

There are laws against **discrimination** in employment on the grounds of sex, but some people still believe that some jobs are more suitable for men or for women. At one time, nearly all doctors were men and nearly all nurses were women. This has now changed and there are a lot of women doctors and male nurses. The caring profession was once seen as exclusive to women, but more men are now entering it. Many people are still put off applying for jobs, though, if they see them as not appropriate for their sex.

While attitudes to women have changed since women obtained the right to vote in 1918, there are many men who still consider that a woman's place is in the home, carrying out domestic and child-rearing responsibilities. It is only fairly recently that women have begun to be promoted within large organizations, even though they have long demonstrated the ability take control and be planners and organizers. The 'glass ceiling' effect still exists to a certain degree.

What do you think is meant by the term 'glass ceiling'?

How do family relationships affect growth and development?

...WORD CHECK

discrimination – to show a bias or intolerance.

nuclear – a group of people comprising of mother, father and children.

inferior – lower in standing/value.

The home is the first place where an individual is socialized. This is known as primary socialization. Socialization is almost like having a series of lessons that prepare a child for its adult role. Whether the family is a **nuclear** unit where mother, father, brothers, sisters and extended family exist or whether it is a single parent family or commune, it is the family who are the main people that contribute to learnt attitudes and beliefs. It is in this context that a child will learn the way of behaving according to the particular culture of the family with whom they live. The values and norms of the society in which the child is being brought up become the accepted way for the child. The family develops the 'conscience' of new members. Once a bond has been formed between a child and its parent or main carer, any threat to that bond will cause the child anxiety. Therefore, rather than losing the close association that it has with its parent or main carer, the child will adopt the norms and values taught by them. This includes the young child's learning and experiences of prejudice, gender roles and the skills of language. For example, if the family has the attitude that some people are **inferior** to their own family, then the children in the family are likely to follow their example.

Families are very important and can be a major influence on life opportunities. A child's social class depends on their parents. The class we are in will influence the opportunities that we have in some ways. Our social class is often based on economic factors and the job we do. For example, a GP will be considered to be in a higher social class than a lorry driver. The economic status of the person enables them to have opportunities that others may not get. For example, a GP may be better at encouraging their children to succeed in education than someone who is working as a lorry driver. This could be partly due to the fact that the GP has had experience of further and higher education and will know of the advantages it can bring. They may also be better able to afford the cost of putting a child through further education. Our social class will therefore have an influence on our growth and development.

In Britain, the system is known as the 'class system'. The differences between the classes are in terms of educational success, the type of work that is being undertaken and the money earned. A person's occupation is therefore used to assess the 'importance' of people.

CASE STUDY Mandy and Greg

Mandy is training to be a lawyer like her father. Both her mother and father are encouraging her to go to university and study for a degree in Law.

Greg's father and mother have their own business and hope that Greg will join the firm when he has finished his A2 qualifications in Business.

1. How is the family affecting the development of Mandy and Greg?
2. Explain how social class can influence development.
3. Look up the Registrar General's Class Scale and the Hall-Jones Scale. What are the similarities and differences?
4. Why do you think some working-class families would encourage their children to go on to higher education?

Our position in the family can be an influence on our development. If we are the youngest family member, brothers and sisters might protect us from others. Or, on the other hand, we could be blamed for all their wrong doing!

How does our position in the family affect our development? Why?

The views and opinions that we hear within our own family when we are sharing and talking together may also influence our growth and development. Many people tend to adopt these family views and opinions in their own lives. Examples are our family's views on politics, religion, punishment, law and order, and how services should be run. We may hear these views many times within our homes and may agree with them. We could even support a football team because this is the team that members of our family support. In other words we often follow family tradition.

Friendships

Friendships are important to people's growth and development in all life stages. Most people have close friends. These are people that we share personal things with. Then we have other friends who we like doing things with. Our friends give us emotional and social support. They are the people:

- With whom we share activities and interests
- Who listen when we have a problem
- Who we share our happy times with

Hopefully we are there when they need us as well!

Sometimes friends can be a bad influence on us. We may do things that we know are wrong because we do not want to 'let our friends down'. We are 'led' by our friends. It could be that our friends want us to stay away from school or encourage us to drink alcohol to get drunk. Our friends influence us because we do not want to be 'different' and we will want to keep their friendship. Sometimes it is very hard to say 'no'.

Whether our friends influence us for good or for bad, it has to be remembered that anything that results from the actions that we take could influence our growth and development. For example, if a friend persuaded us to vandalize people's houses on a regular basis, and if we were caught, one possible effect on our development would be that we could be sent to a young offenders institution or receive an ASBO, depending on our age and the severity of the crime. The effect on our development could be that we lose our freedom, are taken away from our family, who support us, or that we lose our job and other friends. Our friends can influence our development positively or negatively.

15 How can friends have a negative effect on our development?

Most of our friends will have a positive effect on our development. Some of the features of a positive friendship are:

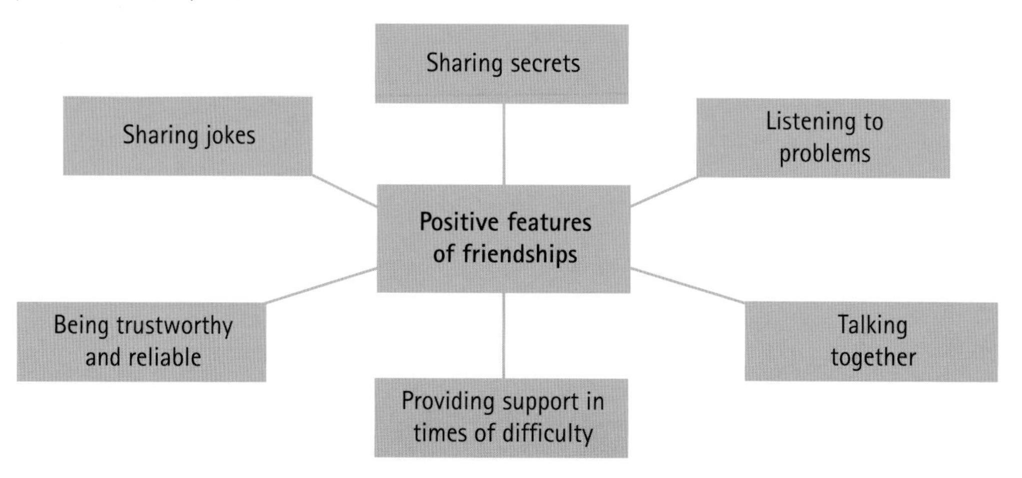

CASE STUDY Wes and Christiano

Wes is 15. He has been going out with Katy for three months. He was very happy and looked forward to their dates. Recently, Katy texted Wes during the lunch hour at school. On reading the text, Wes discovered Katy had dumped him.

Wes was very upset. Christiano, Wes' friend, had noticed the text and guessed from Wes' expression what had happened. He went over to Wes and asked him if he would go with him down to the local shop.

On the way there, Christiano asked Wes what the trouble was. Wes told him what had happened. They talked. Christiano suggested that they meet that evening to talk some more. He also offered to talk to Katy to find out what the problem was.

This is an example of a positive effect on development because of a friendship. Christiano saw that his friend was upset. He provided support and a chance for Wes to talk about his problems. He didn't want his friend to be alone that evening so he offered practical support by asking to meet him. He also tried to give support by talking to Wes' ex-girlfriend.

The effect was probably that Wes felt that someone cared about his situation. He trusted his friend and was willing to share his secrets with him.

How can educational experiences affect development?

Within the education system children and young people have the opportunity to learn new skills, gather information and pass a number of national examinations. Such examinations are important because they allow the individual to access employment, which in turn can lead to a consistent income. While in the education system, children and young people learn about their past history, the world around them, and different cultures and attitudes. It is through exposure to such topics and through the people met while being educated that secondary socialization takes place. Attitudes and opinions can change quite drastically as a result.

The educational experience → Parent and toddler groups → Playgroups/ nursery schools → Infant schools → Secondary schools → Further education → Higher education → Lifelong learning courses

Educational achievement can, however, be influenced by particular factors, some of which are genetic, and others that are **environmental**. Intelligence is an inherited factor passed down from parents, while environmental factors are linked to where you live. Both genetic and environmental factors can affect educational success. One of the current debates is 'what causes underachievement' in education. Research has shown that gender, race and social class can all affect educational success.

▲ Education influences our intellectual and social development.

Secondary socialization is also learnt from teachers and **peers**. If you were to observe the same students with two different teachers, it is possible that behaviour changes would be apparent in each class. Some teachers allow students to talk within class and to have more freedom. Others do not permit talking and demand 100 per cent concentration. Through this tolerant/non-tolerant approach, children are being socialized, albeit in different ways.

Research indicates that low income can also influence educational success.

16 How can parental attitudes influence achievement in the learning environment?

17 How can social class influence educational success?

18 How can low income influence adolescents when considering further or higher education?

Employment/unemployment – how can these influence development?

Employment is important as it provides an income, security in that a house, flat or some other form of accommodation can be purchased, as well as helping an individual to feel that they have succeeded and, therefore, fulfilled. It can have physical, intellectual, emotional and social benefits. Learning new tasks also provides intellectual stimulation. What someone does for a living has an emotional aspect as it is an important part of their **self-concept**, that is the picture they have of themselves. They will **subconsciously** compare themselves with other role models.

It is human nature to compare ourselves to other people and also for other people to compare themselves to us. Parts of our self-concept will only make sense if they are considered in relation to other people.

Unemployment can affect a person by lowering their self-esteem and they may also feel socially isolated as a result. Self-esteem could be raised through hobbies or voluntary work.

...WORD CHECK

environmental – to do with the surroundings.

peers – people who are the same age.

self-concept – how we think about ourselves.

subconsciously – without thinking about it.

Ethnicity and religion – how can these factors affect development?

▲ Religious belief is an important part of some people's identity.

Ethnicity and religion are part of someone's **culture**. Ethnic groups share common cultural traditions. This might, for example, include dress or diet. Nationality, religion, language and race all play a part in determining our ethnicity. For instance, the inhabitants of a country may be of the same race, and speak the same language, but if they have a different religion they may consider themselves as different ethnic groups.

If a number of people of the same ethnic group live in a country where the culture is different, they are called an 'ethnic minority' group. Asian people from the Indian sub-continent think of themselves as Sikhs, Bangladeshis, Pakistanis or Indians. These are all different ethnic minority groups in Britain.

Religion is often, but not always, part of ethnicity and is a system of beliefs about the spiritual aspects of life. The main religion in this country is Christianity, although only a minority of people go to church. Other major religions practised by ethnic minorities in this country are Islam, Sikhism, Hinduism, Buddhism and Judaism.

When people are members of ethnic minority groups, their growth and development is often influenced by **discrimination**. This means being treated unfairly because of your race, religion or some other characteristic.

WORD CHECK

ethnicity – to be related to a culture or race.

culture – common values, beliefs and customs.

discrimination – to show a bias or intolerance.

indirect – not directly responsible/ not obvious.

direct – straight to the person/ openly; to be responsible for a person's care.

mutual support – a two way sharing.

19 What does ethnic minority mean?

Discrimination is considering a race, culture or type of person to be of less value than one's own. To favour one group above another or to deliberately act against a group of people is to discriminate against them.

Society is made up of different types of people, each having their own traditions, beliefs and culture. Some people consider their own race or culture to be superior or better than others. They have a narrow view and think the beliefs and values they hold are the only correct ones to have. They are not prepared to be open to the values and beliefs of people from other cultures. There are two main forms of discrimination. These are:

- **indirect** discrimination, for example, only printing information in one language, which could exclude a number of people from accessing it
- **direct** discrimination, for example, talking to someone disrespectfully.

Indirect discrimination is less obvious and more subtle. Sometimes it is unintentional, arising because a person has not given a situation sufficient thought.

Direct discrimination is where individuals are treated differently in an open manner because of their race, colour, gender, sexual orientation, age, class or disability. Obvious unfair treatment shows prejudice and is intentional.

20 How are indirect and direct discrimination likely to be shown in a residential home or nursery class?

Whether discrimination is direct or indirect, it can have serious physical, emotional, intellectual and social effects on an individual, particularly if the discrimination is regular and systematic. It can lead to depression, low self-esteem and can completely destroy a person's belief in themselves.

Discrimination may affect people's life opportunities in a number of ways.

Type of discrimination	How individuals can be discriminated against
Education	People may have low expectations of people from some ethnic minority groups. As a result, they may not achieve as much in education as they could.
Access to employment	If employers discriminate against them, people may find it more difficult to get a job. If they have a job, they might find it more difficult to get a promotion.
Access to health, social care and early years services	Information about services may not be provided in a person's chosen or preferred language, which could create barriers. Health, social care or early years services may not be provided in a way that meets with a person's custom or beliefs. For instance, they may have special dietary needs, or a cultural objection to being examined by a member of the opposite sex.

CASE STUDY Cass

Cass is a Muslim who lives in England. He is 18 and is the eldest child in a family of five. He has stayed on at college to get his qualifications so that he can become a primary school teacher. His family are very supportive and have encouraged Cass as much as possible.

Cass has a small group of friends at the college with whom he gets on well. He does not go out with them at the weekend, however, because of his family and religious commitments. He would very much like to go with them sometimes but thinks that some of the friends they meet might not accept him because of his culture.

Cass is very pleased when he passes his examinations and is accepted for teacher training. He starts to worry, however, about having to move away from home.

1. What are the social and emotional factors that are affecting Cass' growth and development?
2. In what ways are Cass' friends not being sensitive to his cultural and religious needs?
3. Explain how Cass could help his friends to understand his cultural and religious needs.
4. How are Cass' educational experiences going to affect his growth and development?
5. Explain how ethnicity and religion could influence an individual's development.

Life experiences – how can these factors affect development?

These are experiences such as birth, marriage, divorce and death. Birth and death are our entry into the world and exit from it. Between the two we will have other experiences that will affect growth and development. Quite a large number of people will marry. When this event happens, a person becomes legally joined to the person they are marrying. They become responsible for one another and any children that they have together.

A successful marriage promotes the development of both individuals because they offer each other **mutual support**. Some relationships are abusive, with one partner trying to control the other, or using violence against them. These relationships can be very damaging to an individual's development.

Not all marriages are successful. If a marriage fails, because it is a formal contract, there has to be another formal process for bringing it to an end. This is called divorce. Divorce may have positive effects on an individual's development if they are freed from a relationship that was making them unhappy. It may also have negative effects. Some people may find it very

▲ In a happy marriage couples offer each other mutual support.

difficult to adjust to being single again. They may feel lonely and isolated. They may also feel that they have 'failed' in the relationship and this could lead to them having a low self-esteem. They may feel that they are not able to trust another person again and this could prevent them from forming new relationships.

Currently, more people are living together as 'partners' instead of getting married. Some individuals prefer having a partner to having a legal agreement such as marriage. Often they are as happy as a married couple. Some partners are same sex partners, while others are opposite sex partners.

Group Activity

Work with another person in the group to think about why quite a number of couples prefer to remain as 'partners' rather than getting married.

Make a list of the possible advantages and disadvantages.

Take part in a whole-class discussion on this topic using some of the items included in the lists you have made.

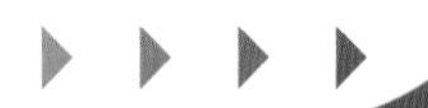

ASSESSMENT PRACTICE

Robert is the youngest of three children. His father, Ian, is manager of a bank and his mother is a teacher. The family live in a small village, which is five miles from the town where his parents work. The family live in a detached four-bedroomed house that has a large garden.

Robert has just started at the local primary school. He has frequent epileptic fits. Some of the children in his class are calling him names and refusing to sit next to him.

1. Explain how a caring home life can affect Robert's socialization. [5]
2. Identify **two** secondary socialization factors that could influence Robert's development. Explain how each is likely to influence him. [5]
3. Identify **one** form of discrimination experienced by Robert. Give two examples to illustrate how this occurs. [3]
4. Identify **two** likely effects of this discrimination on Robert. Explain how each is likely to affect him. [6]
5. Explain the difference between 'direct' and 'indirect' discrimination. Give **two** examples to illustrate how each could occur. [5]
6. Explain what is meant by the term 'self-esteem'. Explain **two** ways that Robert's self-esteem is likely to be affected positively and **two** ways it is likely to be affected negatively. [5]
7. How could Ian help Robert to understand why others were discriminating against him? [5]

HOW CAN ECONOMIC FACTORS AFFECT GROWTH AND DEVELOPMENT?

Economic influences can have a major effect on our development. When we talk about economic factors, we mean 'to do with money'. Our health and well-being is affected by the amount of money we have. Economic factors are:

Income, which is usually from wages, private pensions, or state benefits, such as child benefit, jobseeker's allowance, sickness and disability benefits, and the state retirement pension.

Savings, which people have because they had more money than they needed to meet all their commitments and were able to put some of it away.

The **essential bills** people have to pay, such as rent for their housing, council tax, gas, electricity and water bills, and transport costs.

Debts, caused by borrowing money to buy a house (a mortgage) or an expensive piece of household equipment. Sometimes people have debts because they have had problems and not paid essential bills in the past.

Material possessions, or all the things that people need to live comfortably.

These are all very important for human growth and development. The more money someone has, the more choices they have, and the better they are able to meet their physical, intellectual, emotional and social needs.

People with a high income can afford good quality clothing, and will not have to worry about fuel bills. This means that they can meet their own physical needs and the needs of the people dependent on them. A person who has a low income may have to be careful about the amount of gas and electricity that they use. They may not be able to keep their home as warm as they would like it. This may be particularly important for families with young children, and for older people who are more vulnerable to the cold.

If a person on a high income is ill, and there is a waiting list for treatment under the National Health Service, then they may be able to afford private health care. People with lower incomes do not usually have the choice of private health care; they have to wait their turn on the waiting list.

Savings are important because they help people meet their needs. If people have some money in a bank or building society, then they are prepared when something happens. If a child needs an expensive new pair of shoes, or a vacuum cleaner breaks and has to be replaced, this is much easier to do when someone has some savings. If they do not, and don't have enough income to pay for the things, they either have to go without or borrow money to get them.

Debts are important because they have to be paid, and the more debt someone has, the smaller the amount of their income there is available to spend on things they need now. Many people are drawn into debt through advertisements that encourage individuals and families to put all their outstanding debt on one account. In the long run, the amount paid back could be far more.

Material possessions are also important for meeting physical needs. Life is much more pleasant for adolescents and young adults with MP3 players, the newest mobile phones, high definition TVs and the latest in console games. People who have been able to buy these things may have spent thousands of pounds on them over a period of time and may have much pleasure in showing them to their friends. People on low incomes would be unable to do this.

Economic factors affect the way that people can meet their physical needs, but they also affect their intellectual, emotional and social needs. This is because being able to afford things can make individuals happy. Not being able to buy the things they need can make people unhappy and resentful. Individuals may not want to invite people to their homes because they are ashamed of the age and condition of their furniture. This could mean that they have few friends and could become socially isolated.

A parent on a low income might not be able to afford school trips or books and equipment that a parent on a high income could afford. People with higher incomes can also afford to help their children through higher education, but parents from lower-income families may have to go into debt to pay for their child's higher education. Parents' income can affect how well a child succeeds in education, and success in education improves a person's chance of getting a good job.

CASE STUDY Roger

Roger is 14. He lives with his family in rented council accommodation on an estate. Most of the families on the estate have low incomes.

Roger has three sisters all between the ages of five and eleven. His father works in a car factory but recently his hours have been reduced as cars are not selling very well. His mother works in a bingo hall during the afternoons, which is also part time.

Roger's parents are very short of money. They have to pay the rent and they are in debt. They have to pay off some of what they owe for a car they once had. This leaves very little left for bills such as gas and electricity, or for food.

Roger has asked if he can have an iPod for his birthday but his family cannot afford to get him this.

1. Give **two** economic factors that are affecting Roger's growth and development.
2. Identify **three** essential items of expenditure for Roger's family.
3. Roger's classmates can afford good clothes and equipment for school while Roger does not have all the things he needs. How do you think this may affect Roger's growth and development?
4. Explain how poor housing and low income could affect Roger's development.
5. Explain how not being able to have an MP3 player could affect Roger's intellectual, emotional and social development.

ENVIRONMENTAL FACTORS – HOW CAN THESE AFFECT DEVELOPMENT?

▲ Different types of housing.

Theorists such as John B. Watson have argued that environmental influences have the greater impact on the development of our personality, rather than hereditary (inborn) factors. Environmental factors relate to the conditions people live in. They include:

Housing
Pollution
Access to health and welfare services

Housing

Housing and the location where people live can strongly influence the development of individuals, particularly children. For example, if a person lives in a rural area, this could determine the number of health, social care and early years services they are able to access, and the recreational activities they can join could be limited. Visiting friends and extended family members may be more difficult and they may have to travel to receive their education. However, living in a rural area could provide easier access to natural environments, which can enhance learning and development and provide the opportunity for walking, for example, or for community activities.

Children and people living in an **urban** area could experience **social deprivation** as they could be exposed to higher crime rates and vandalism, and may be fearful of going out. Access to services may be easier when living in a town or city though and there may be more activities in which to participate.

Housing in inner cities and towns may take the form of flats, for which there are no gardens, whereas in rural areas, houses are more likely to be detached, semi-detached or terraced, having their own gardens. There is likely to be less traffic in a rural area and, consequently, pollution is likely to be less of a problem.

Cold and damp conditions within the home can aggravate chest conditions and conditions such as arthritis and rheumatism. Overcrowded housing conditions can also affect the spread of disease, as where people live closely together, infection can spread more quickly. Illnesses such as the common cold can easily be spread through families and, in the past, tuberculosis (TB), cholera and typhoid often reached epidemic proportions.

What are the effects on development likely to be?

...WORD CHECK

urban – town area/heavily populated.

social deprivation – not being able to mix with others, for example, through lack of money or location.

Effects of living in a rural area	Effects of living in an urban area
Promotes good health because of natural open areas	Illness treated quickly because services are easier to access
May be reserved as social activities may be restricted	Could be more comfortable in social situations and with people
May be physically fitter as open countryside enables walking, cycling, and so on	Could be less fit as there are fewer open spaces or these may be more difficult to reach
May be more economically aware as money is needed to reach urban areas for shopping, leisure activities, and so on	May be able to spend more money on wants as travelling costs do not have to be taken into account

ACTIVITY Where would you live?

You have been given the opportunity to decide where you will live, for example, a rural or urban area.

1. Which would you choose? Give advantages and disadvantages.
2. What are the likely effects on development?

Good quality housing will usually have a positive effect on people and poor quality housing is more likely to have a negative effect. For instance, a high-rise flat may suit a single person, a couple without children, or adults who do not want a garden. It would not be suitable for a single parent or two people with young children, or for older people who could find access difficult.

21 What is meant by inadequate housing?

An infant or child being brought up in cold damp conditions in a flat or house may suffer physical effects, because if the home is damp and difficult to heat, the infant or child will be more likely to get respiratory illnesses, which will affect their development as they will not be fit and healthy.

There may also be intellectual effects on an infant or child, particularly if the home is cramped, and it is not easy to get outside, as there may not be a stimulating environment to explore. The parents of children who live in such conditions will probably be under stress because of the conditions they live in, and this may affect the way they provide for the infant or child; they could become angry and frustrated more easily. A child living in a high-rise flat, with a lift that is broken, for example, will also not have as many opportunities to meet other children and their social development may be affected.

Older people often have less resistance to infection and have more difficulty maintaining their body temperature if their homes are not adequately heated. A bungalow is also considered to be more suitable for some, as mobility problems may make it more difficult to access upstairs levels.

CASE STUDY Elaine and family

Elaine is a lone parent with three children, Olivia, aged one, Rebekah, aged four, and Benjamin aged six. They live in an upstairs flat in an old house with no access to a garden. The flat has been badly converted, has poor heating and the windows don't fit properly. The cooker is not working as only one ring heats and the oven tends to burn food if put on the recommended temperature, so the family often eat takeaway food.

The house is on a busy road, and the nearest play area is some distance away. Elaine has put up with these conditions for a long time because she has no alternative solution and has become frustrated, angry and depressed. The children are boisterous and she is always yelling and shouting at them. Sometimes she hits them. Benjamin has missed a lot of school through illness. When he does go to school, his teacher often complains that he is unable to concentrate.

1. Think about Elaine. How is her physical, intellectual, emotional and social development being affected by their environment?
2. What would be the advantages and disadvantages to Elaine and the family if they lived in a rural area?
3. How will Benjamin's development be affected if he is being physically punished?
4. How is Olivia's development likely to be affected by the living conditions?
5. Suggest ways in which Elaine could have support to help the family in their present living conditions.

Pollution – how can this factor affect development?

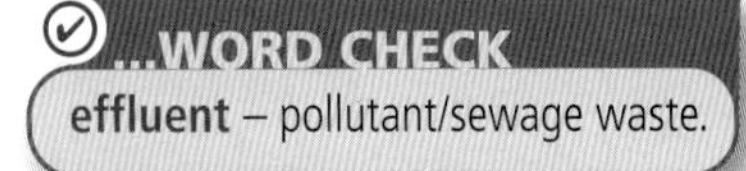

effluent – pollutant/sewage waste.

Pollution means the release of harmful elements into the environment. By the environment, we mean the earth, air and water. Clean water is essential for healthy living. This particularly applies to drinking water, which is a need for all individuals. The main source of freshwater pollution is from the discharge of untreated waste and dumping of industrial **effluent**. Waterborne infectious diseases include hepatitis, cholera, dysentery and typhoid. Exposure to polluted water can also cause diarrhoea and skin irritation.

Air pollution can cause conditions such as asthma, irritation to the eyes, bronchitis, pneumonia and other respiratory problems. This is because the pollutants in the air cause a reaction in the lungs, making airways constrict. As a result, breathing becomes more difficult.

The effect on the individual can be:

- poor health
- low self-esteem
- social isolation
- depression.

There are three sorts of pollution that people are most concerned about. These are:

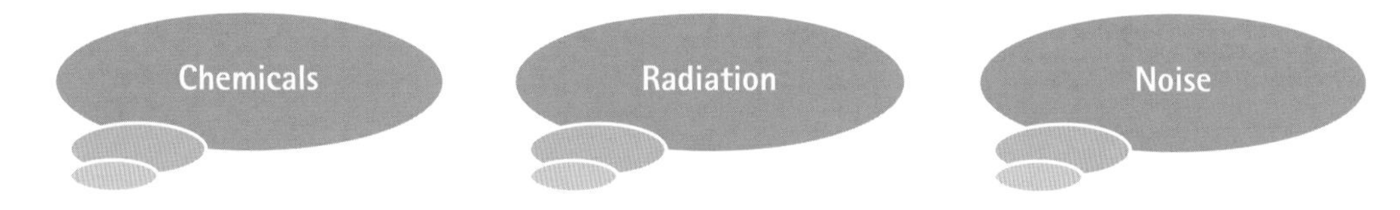

Cause	Facts
Chemicals	• There are strict laws about chemicals. The agriculture industry uses large quantities of fertilizers and pesticides, and some of these are washed by rain into the water supply. Some may remain on the food we eat, which is why it is sensible to wash fruit and vegetables. Some people eat organic foods to avoid these chemicals. • A form of pollution that affects a lot of people is the exhaust emissions from cars, buses and lorries. Engines release chemicals and tiny particles that cause respiratory problems. People who live in built-up areas where there is a lot of traffic will be most affected.
Radiation	• Radiation can affect development if it should leak from a nuclear power station so that people who live nearby or are working within the building are affected by it. There are strict rules that govern the building and maintenance of such power stations. Leukaemia is one illness that results.
Noise	• Noise is not often thought of as a type of pollution, but it can be very harmful. Exposure to loud noise can cause deafness, and there are laws about how much noise a person can be exposed to in the workplace. • Noise is produced by industry, transport and people going about their everyday lives. People who live near airports often complain about the noise of aircraft taking off. Busy roads and railway lines can be very noisy for people who live near them. Noise can be caused by inconsiderate neighbours playing loud music or having late night parties. People may be particularly harmed by noise in their homes. It causes stress and may prevent them sleeping properly.

22 How can chemicals harm us?

23 Carry out research to find out more about radiation and the illnesses and conditions it can cause.

24 Why can noise be harmful?

Access to health and welfare services – how can this affect development?

Access to health and welfare services is very important for people's health and well-being. A person who lives close to health, social care and early years services will be able to visit a GP, hospital, dentist or other service easily when there is a need. Costs of transport will not have to be considered, nor time for travel. Therefore, a person is less likely to be significantly affected by illness.

Also, if a person knows or is aware of the services that are available, they will be able to access them when needed. A person may not be able to access a service either because the language used to advertise the service is not that person's own or preferred language, or because the person needs the help of an advocate to help them understand what is available and where.

Look back at Unit 1 to read about access to services and possible barriers. This can be found on pages 20–35.

25 What may prevent people from accessing health and social care services?

HOW CAN FACTORS INTERRELATE (WORK TOGETHER) TO AFFECT AN INDIVIDUAL'S DEVELOPMENT?

It is not often that any one single factor will affect development for a long period of time. It is only when several factors join together that an individual may be more permanently affected by them.

Which types of factors could interrelate?

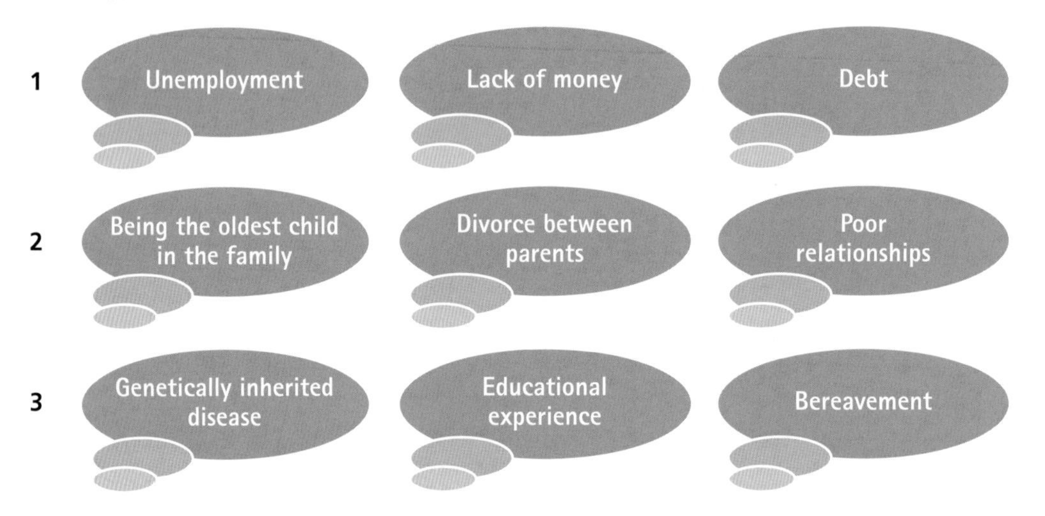

Let us consider the first combination of three factors: unemployment, lack of money and debt.

CASE STUDY Angus

Angus works in an estate agent's office and has done so since he left school ten years ago. He is now the deputy manager, and also enjoys spending time going out with his many friends. Suddenly houses are not selling very well and he is eventually made redundant. He has a large mortgage on his house, a loan on his car and money that he owes the bank for a holiday.

At first, he manages to keep up all his payments as he was given some redundancy money. He tries hard to find another job but without any luck. He gradually uses up all his money and is very anxious about what is going to happen next as his credit cards are used up to the limit. His friends have stopped asking him out as they realize he has no money.

Unemployment was the first factor that affected Angus. He had been used to a steady income each month and was not at all worried about money, so he spent what he had, was very happy and had lots of friends who he often went out with. When he was made redundant he felt quite confident that he would get another job, but as time passed he found he couldn't get one. He used his redundancy money to pay his mortgage, loans and for everyday living such as food, heating and clothes. Gradually the money ran out and Angus used his credit cards until he was up to his credit limit.

From being a happy and independent individual who did not have to think before spending, and having a high self-esteem because he was in a good job, he found himself, within a short period of time, worried about what he was going to eat, how to pay the mortgage and loans, and the outstanding amount on his credit cards. He was unable to afford to go out with his friends and so felt isolated. His self-esteem was low and he didn't feel valued. He was extremely worried. One event led to, or interrelated with, another to get Angus into this position for which it is very difficult to find a solution.

Group Activity

Work with another person to write a case study for links 2 and 3 on the previous page.

On a separate sheet of paper, write down how the three factors are linked and give the effect on development for each.

Exchange the case study with that of another pair (not the answers). Find the links and the effects on development.

Exchange work back and mark the answers.

Discuss your findings as a group of four.

How can these factors affect an individual's development?

When factors that have a positive effect on us occur, we will feel happy and pleased. When the factors are negative, the effect will be to make us have low self-esteem and, possibly, not feel valued.

Effects on our development could be positive:

happy confident fulfilled valued
high self-esteem high self-worth positive
pleased elated responsible

Effects on development could be negative:

worthless worried low self-esteem unhappy
undervalued depressed disheartened gloomy
having no authority or influence insignificant sad dejected

Group Activity

Work with another person in the group to find out the meaning of the words in both the positive and negative text boxes.

Write a sentence for each to show that you have understood the effect on development. One example has been done for you:

Angela had a low self-esteem when she was not given the promotion at work as she felt she was useless.

It should be remembered that factors can cause an individual to:

- have high or low self-esteem
- have good mental and physical health or poor mental and physical health
- have excellent employment prospects or a poor chance of gaining employment
- achieve well in education if they are feeling content and happy, or not succeed if they are worried, anxious or have poor mental and physical health.

THE EFFECT OF ABUSE AND NEGLECT ON AN INDIVIDUAL

Abuse and neglect can take various forms, which could be:

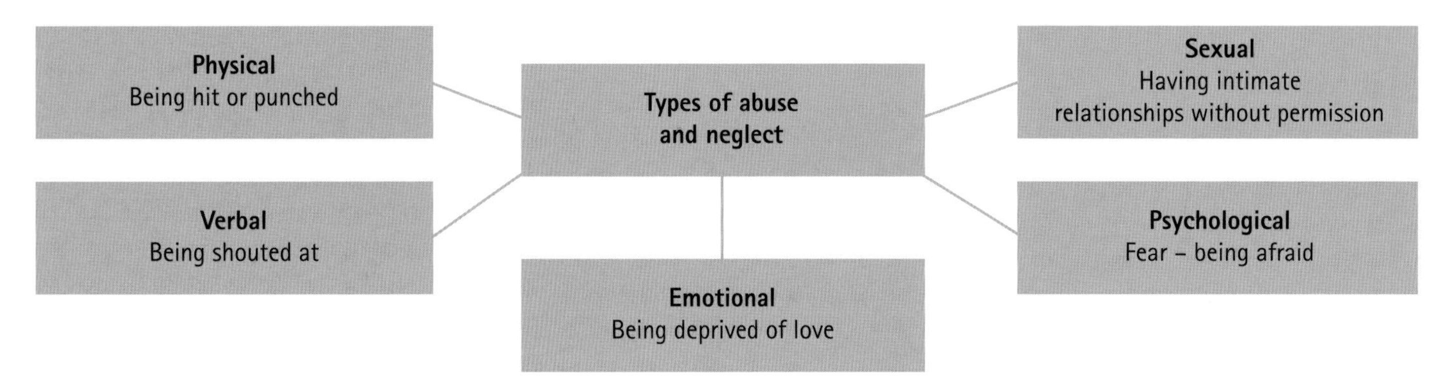

When an individual is abused or neglected in any way, they will probably have very negative feelings and a very poor opinion of themselves, for example, low self-esteem. It is likely that the person concerned will not be able to form good relationships with others. They may be affected by becoming withdrawn, quiet, unsociable, angry and resentful. It is likely that they will not cooperate with others and may start bullying other people who are weaker than themselves. Such behaviour is likely to make friends and other people dislike the individual and they may do their best to avoid them. Without the support of parents, friends, teachers, employers, partners and professional care workers, such individuals are more likely not to be able to form positive relationships.

CASE STUDY Alan

Alan is 13. He is always quarrelling with his family. He never seems to be able to please them. His examination results are never good enough, they don't like his friends and his mother does not approve of the clothes he chooses.

Alan stays out late at night in order to avoid his father's sexual advances, but for three out of seven nights his father forces him to have sex with him. He is then tired at school and avoids people who used to be his friends.

His teacher notices the change in Alan and tries to talk with him to find out what the problem is, but Alan will not say.

The next time Alan's father entered his room at night, Alan hit him over the head with a cricket bat. He then picked up a bag that he had packed before the event and left home.

1. Alan's relationship with his father is unacceptable. Describe the effect that this is likely to have on his personal development.
2. How could Alan's friends have helped more in this situation?
3. Carry out research to find out the procedures the teacher should have followed in this situation.
4. How do you think Alan felt after he left home?
5. Invite a child protection officer to your centre (with your tutor's permission) to talk about the different types of abuse and neglect that they are required to deal with. After the visit, discuss, as a whole class, the effects that the different types of abuse could have on an individual.
6. Write a case study for psychological or emotional abuse or neglect. On a separate sheet of paper, write how the person might be affected. Exchange the case study with another person and write down what you think are the effects for their particular case study.

   Discuss your answers.

Some clients, particularly older adults, could feel vulnerable when they meet with professional care workers and view any proposed communication as a threat to their self-esteem, as they are not in control of the situation they find themselves in. This could be because of what they learnt when they were growing up or could be the result of a negative past experience. Viewing the client as being 'equal' is an important aspect of any communication when working in health, social care or early years settings. The client will need to feel safe and will know from the care worker's tone of voice and body language whether they are being sincere and honest.

Clients will not feel valued if the care worker:

- tries to exert power over them
- does not give their full attention
- uses an unfriendly tone of voice
- does not address the client by their preferred name
- appears too busy
- shouts or uses verbal abuse.

What is meant by the phrase 'clients may feel vulnerable'?

ASSESSMENT PRACTICE

1. Explain what is meant by the term 'genetic factors'. [3]
2. Give **two** examples of genetic factors. [2]
3. Give **two** examples of social factors. [2]
4. Paula and Suzie are identical twins. Their parents read them stories, played with them quite a lot and taught them to play musical instruments. They both went to playgroup and enjoyed meeting other children. When she was six years old, Suzie was very ill with meningitis and missed two months of school. This put her very much behind her sister and she found it hard to make progress. Their father spent a lot of time with both girls teaching them to use the computer. Paula and Suzie are 18 years old and now have jobs working with computers. They still both like to read and enjoy activities such as badminton, swimming and dancing. They go out quite a lot with their friends.

   a Explain **four** factors, other than genetics, that have influenced the development of the twins. [8]

   b Explain how the emotional development of the twins has been affected. [3]
5. Amir is 18 years old and is a Muslim who lives in England. He is studying at a sixth form college to get qualifications that will help him train as a doctor. His family are very supportive. Amir has a small group of friends at college. He does not go out with them at the weekends because of his religious commitments. His friends often try to persuade Amir to go out with them but he is reluctant to do so in case he is not accepted by others.

   a Explain **three** ways that educational experiences could affect Amir's development. [6]

   b Other factors that have influenced Amir's development are:
   - being the eldest in a family with four other children
   - his father being unemployed
   - living in an urban area with lots of pollution.

   Explain how these factors could interrelate (work together) to affect Amir's development. [8]
6. Explain **three** ways that ethnicity and religion could affect development. [6]
7. List three different types of abuse that could take place, explaining how each could affect development. [12]

The development of self-concept and different types of relationships

What factors influence the development of a person's self-concept and what effect do relationships have on an individual's personal development?

Getting started

All people have a view of themselves, known as their self-concept. This is based on the beliefs that they have about themselves as a person and also on what they believe others think about them. You should know how a person's self-concept is affected by factors such as their:

- age
- appearance
- gender
- culture
- emotional development
- education
- relationships with others
- sexual orientation.

You need to be aware of how self-concept can impact on development.

Throughout their lives, people have many different sorts of relationship. These include:

- family relationships (for example, with parents, siblings and as parents)
- friendships
- intimate personal sexual relationships
- working relationships (including teacher/candidate, employer/employee, peers, colleagues).

You should know which relationships play a key part in an individual's intellectual, emotional and social development during each life stage. You should be able to identify how these relationships can have a positive or negative effect on personal development.

SELF-CONCEPT

Self-concept is the way we see ourselves. It is the picture we have of ourself. This picture is made up of three parts:

1 **Self-image:** based on a description of who we are. This includes knowledge from our social roles, for example, mother, father, aunt; the personality traits we have, for example, whether we are clever, have a sense of humour; and how we see our body, for example, brunette, tall, fat.

2 **Self-esteem:** an evaluation of how we see ourselves, which includes how much we like ourselves.

3 **Ideal self:** the sort of person we would like to be. The person we admire.

ACTIVITY Who am I?

Self-image Write a description of yourself.

Self-esteem Evaluate how much you like yourself.
What do you like?
What don't you like?

Ideal self How would you like to be?

Think about the facts you have written and keep them to develop further in this section.

In this activity you may have considered your physical appearance, your intellectual strengths, your personality, thoughts, hopes or fears. Everything that you considered has been evaluated through how you have been reflected back to yourself through other people's actions. Cooley (1902) called this 'the looking glass self'. This means that if people tell you that you are attractive or clever or good at netball enough times, you believe them and take on that role. This is particularly so if you are given this information by 'significant others' who are people like parents, teachers and best friends, whose opinions you trust and value. This does, of course, work with negative aspects of your self-concept as well, hence the effects of labelling of the 'naughty' girl, the 'uncooperative' boy or even the person who is 'useless at maths'!

▲ Babies cannot know where they stop and where their mother begins.

Self-concept develops as a person grows. Babies do not distinguish themselves from their mother or primary carer. They do not have any understanding of where their mother ends and they begin. An infant will put their fingers into their mother's mouth or bite their mother's finger, having no concern for how their mother will feel. It is not until an infant is around 18 months old that they begin to realize that they exist as a separate entity to anyone else.

Our self-concept is important because it affects all our relationships and interactions with others. It is only through having a good opinion of ourselves, holding ourselves in **high regard**, that we are able to value ourselves and to enjoy good relationships with others. If we have a poor self-concept, it is likely to impact on our behaviour, for example, we could become withdrawn from others, not achieve in examinations or become a bully towards others. Having a high self-concept is, therefore, a very important feature of development.

Unless a person values themselves and has a sense that other people value them, they are not likely to function very well. A person who does not place any value on themselves will not like or 'love' themselves. For some of the time, most people are often in a muddle about whether they like themselves or whether they don't. People are often unclear about how they see themselves or how others view them, particularly in adolescence.

27 Why do you value yourself or why do you not value yourself? How has this affected your behaviour?

...WORD CHECK

high regard – being well thought of; being valued.

fluid – flexible/having no boundaries.

Self-concept is also **fluid**, meaning that it can change as we grow older, meet new situations and people, and take on new roles. As individuals we are part of a cultural group and we will not want to be too far away from the values held by that group. To do so would produce an uncomfortable feeling, a feeling that you do not belong or fit in.

We all need to have a realistic view of ourselves. We need to feel comfortable with people with whom we work or enjoy leisure time. When this happens, we feel secure enough to allow other people's perspectives of us to have an influence on the way we see ourselves.

ACTIVITY Introducing a friend

1. As a whole group, sit in a circle. One at a time, stand behind a chair and, from the notes produced at the start of the work on self-concept, introduce the person who is sitting in that chair. (Only use the parts of self-concept that people are happy to share.)
2. Prepare a presentation about the development of self-concept and the factors that influence development. Present this to the rest of the class.
3. Evaluate your own performance using your tutor's comments and/or peer-evaluation.

How other people react towards us is very significant in how we view ourselves. As young children, it is our parents to whom we look and we admire, and this is a very important aspect of our development. Later, as we meet others, for example, teachers and peers, they too become significant and influence our own self-concept, as we emulate the characteristics that we value in them and adopt them for ourselves. The effect of parenting on self-esteem lasts with us throughout life.

How does age affect self-concept?

George Mead, a theorist, thought that children's behaviour developed because of their ability to imitate adult behaviour and because they had the ability to imagine characters. A child of two might pretend to be a cat or a dog in their play. They do not need to understand what cats and dogs are, they just copy the actions and sounds they have seen them make.

In later development, around four years, a child might begin to imitate adult behaviour. For example, Isobel, aged four, was given some dolls and a pushchair for her birthday. She dressed the dolls in coats and put on their shoes, gloves and hats. She put them in the pushchair and strapped them in. Then she put on her own coat and pretended to leave the house with a shopping bag and the pushchair with the dolls in. Isobel was just copying what she had seen her parents do. She was imagining a character or person. Mead believed that this was the beginning of the character of 'me' – Isobel's own self-image.

28 How does Mead think children start to develop self-awareness?

▲ Copying adult behaviour.

A newborn baby has no concept of themselves as a person, or any understanding that there is any such thing as a person. They need to develop intellectually before they can understand that they are an individual, and that there are other people in the world. They need to develop emotionally before they can understand that other people have feelings of their own. Until they understand this, they can't understand that other individuals have opinions about them. This is why young children cannot play cooperatively with others, and why the infant having a tantrum in the street is not embarrassed to lie on the floor kicking and screaming.

For a very young baby, their main carer is their world. They are helpless and depend on their carers to meet all their needs. Whether they are treated kindly, neglectfully or harshly affects how they think about the world and how it values them.

As children get older, they meet a wider range of people. These people will start to influence the picture they are forming of themselves, their self-portrait. They will be strongly influenced by their family and the friends they make. They will also learn that they have to fit in with others, and acquire basic social rules and values.

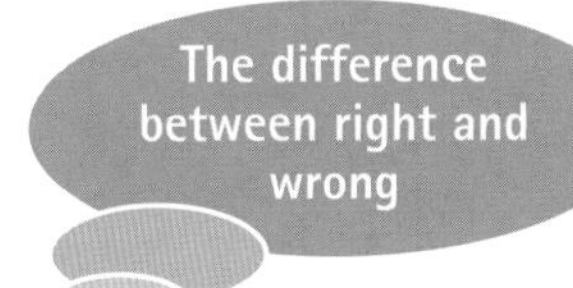

When a child does something well, they are usually praised. When they do something that is unacceptable, they usually get a good telling off. In this way the child will add to the picture they are developing of themselves.

Children do not just do the things they are taught to do or the things they see happening around them. They will think about what is happening and decide what their own values are to be. This is called '**internalizing**' or examining within themselves the experiences they are having.

...WORD CHECK

internalizing – to absorb into the self-conscious, to understand and then to be able to discuss the subject with understanding.

29 How does a child add to the picture they have of themselves?

A child's self-concept is also affected by what society expects from them. We take it for granted that being a child involves certain things. For instance:

- going to school
- not being expected to work
- not being legally responsible for their actions
- being protected from certain things, for example, alcohol, tobacco and having sex.

An adolescent sense of self is very strong. An adolescent wants more independence. They want to make their own decisions. They may not feel very secure in making these decisions but they have an internal picture of themselves and they try to project this picture so that others can see

▲ Individual identity.

who they are. Adolescents often identify themselves by their membership of particular groups. In the past, such groups have included Mods and Rockers, Hippies, Skinheads, Punks, Goths and, more currently, Emos. These groups have always identified themselves by hairstyle, clothing, tattoos, body piercings and the type of music they like. This has been a way of expressing their self-concept. It is a way of demonstrating rebellion and rejection of adult values, and independence, showing that they are no longer children.

A good self-awareness will help adolescents develop a secure sense of self. They will need this to be able to:

- make difficult decisions
- form social and sexual relationships
- develop confidence in work roles or in a chosen college course.

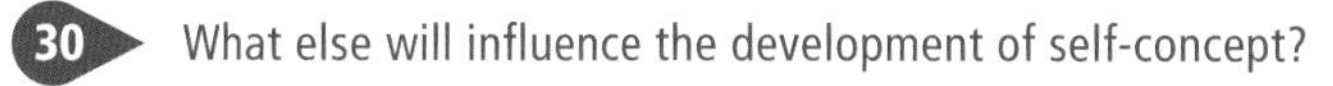

30 What else will influence the development of self-concept?

How we learn to value ourselves in childhood and during adolescence can affect us as adults. Adults are recognized by society as being fully independent. Unlike children, they are fully responsible for all their actions. We are surrounded by images of young, attractive people in advertisements, newspapers and other forms of the media. This will greatly influence our internal image of how we think we should be.

In older adulthood it is important that we still keep a clear sense of our self-concept. The image that we have of ourselves will be influenced by the life events we have experienced. Such events that influence self-concept could be getting married, starting a family or experiencing divorce, for example. Some of these life events will reinforce the positive image we may have of ourselves. Others may have a negative effect on our development. A few people may have experience of accidents that have changed lives from being 'able bodied' to 'disabled'. This can be very challenging for the person and it can be very hard to keep a positive self-image in these circumstances.

31 Why may it be hard to keep a positive self-image if disabled as a result of an accident?

CASE STUDY Sedu

Sedu is 37 and is a college lecturer. He has a wife and three children who are seven, five and three. Sedu's wife works part time as a teacher. The family are always very busy taking the children to and from school, and to their various clubs and activities during the evenings and at the weekend. They are happy.

Sedu always cycles to college to make sure he gets enough exercise. On the way home one day he is knocked off his bicycle by a car. He is taken to hospital with spinal injuries. He has a three-hour operation to remove pieces of bone from his spinal cord.

Three months after the accident, Sedu is told that he will never be able to work again. He can shuffle around the downstairs rooms at home but he cannot walk properly. He cannot get upstairs and he is in pain most of the time. He cannot work at his computer for longer than ten minutes because of the pain. The worst thing is that he is unable to help his wife with the daily chores and he cannot play with the children. Sedu becomes very depressed about his state of health.

1. How has Sedu's intellectual development been affected by the accident?
2. How do you think Sedu's self-concept has been affected as a result of the accident?
3. How do you think the accident will affect Sedu's wife's self-concept?
4. Explain how the self-concept of Sedu's children could be affected as a result of the accident.
5. Assess the possible effects that Sedu's accident could have on his self-concept in the future.

From the age of 50, many people could experience discrimination in the workplace. They may find that employers prefer younger staff that they may see as more flexible and adaptable. People over 50 may feel that they are not as valued as younger people. A person with a strong self-concept will probably be able to find other areas of their lives where they are valued, such as being a member of a club or the leader of a committee. They could be affected in some way by the discrimination, however. For example they may feel:

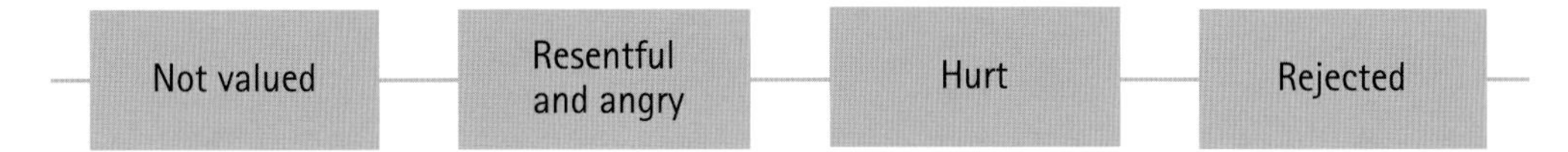

When our self-concept has been lowered the effect may be that we withdraw from social activities because we are afraid we may get hurt again. We may not want to trust people again. We may find that we communicate less with people. In some circumstances, people become so angry that they physically hurt the person with whom they live. Such actions are going to contribute to developing a negative self-concept. We may need help to see ourselves in a different way and to cope with the situation we find ourselves in.

In later adulthood some people may feel that they are not valued, particularly as they have lost their work role. The effect may cause them to become withdrawn and depressed. They may feel that others think they have nothing to contribute.

CASE STUDY Malcolm

Malcolm is 63. He has worked as a salesman in a furniture store for 30 years. Malcolm loves his work. He lives on his own so he enjoys meeting the customers and chatting to his colleagues. Sometimes he goes out with his work colleagues for a drink and a game of darts. This is his main social life.

He is called in to see the manager when he arrives at work one day. The manager tells Malcolm that the firm would like him to take early retirement. This is because they are going to introduce a number of changes and feel that he would benefit financially if he were to leave at the end of the month. The manager makes it clear that he expects Malcolm to accept the package being offered.

1. How will Malcolm's social development be affected by taking early retirement?
2. How do you think Malcolm's self-concept may be affected by taking early retirement?
3. List **three** negative social aspects of retirement. Describe how each could affect Malcolm's self-concept.

Appearance

Appearance is an important aspect of our lives. Faces are part of our appearance and are important to us because they are a main way that we recognize others and communicate with them. The very first thing that an infant recognizes is the shape of a face. They will stare for a long time at anything that looks like a face. Recognizing their carer's face is an important part of bonding. An infant will smile at a carer and copy their facial expressions long before they can talk to them.

Even when an individual is able to talk, our facial expressions are an important way of communicating. They tell other people about our feelings, and facial expressions often show a more honest picture of our inner thoughts than the words that are spoken.

▲ What does this girl's facial expression tell you about how she is feeling?

...WORD CHECK

congenital – inborn/inbred.

Our face is important because:

- it is a part of our identity – it is how we recognize ourselves and other people
- it is the focal point when communicating with other people
- it is usually possible to tell someone's sex from their face, and faces are an important part of sexual attraction.

If something happens to an individual's face, it often has very emotional consequences. Sometimes someone's face is changed, perhaps because they are badly burnt or have an operation, or a stroke stops them making facial expressions. People who have experienced this often say that they do not feel like the same person. For similar reasons, any **congenital** defect that affects someone's face, such as a birthmark, can have serious emotional effects. A common problem for adolescents, which often makes them very self-conscious, is acne.

One way we judge people's ages is from their faces. Many people are quite happy with their appearance as they age. However, sometimes a person's age has a negative effect on their self-concept. They may want to try to remove the signs of ageing. There are a large number of expensive cosmetic products that claim to do this. Often people are prepared to spend large sums of money on altering their appearance. Some people are prepared to go even further and have face lifts or other types of surgery to remove the signs of ageing from their faces. This helps their inward portrait of themselves – their self-concept.

32 How does the appearance of our face influence self-concept?

▼ An ideal of beauty?

Body shape can be very important to self-concept. Adolescent girls, particularly, often think that they have to be thin to be attractive. Very thin actresses and models are often presented as ideals of beauty. Some adolescents think of themselves as fat and unattractive because they do not meet these ideals. In some cases, their image of themselves becomes so distorted that they develop eating disorders, such as anorexia nervosa. People with this disorder become unhealthily thin but cannot see this because they have a distorted body image. There are signs that some boys may be developing similar anxieties about their bodies, and are starting to exercise to change their body shape.

People with a poor self-concept may fix on a particular part of their body, and think that they would be happier and more successful if only they were thinner, had bigger breasts or their nose was a different shape. They are not satisfied with their internal picture or self-concept.

We do have some control over the appearance of our bodies. Diet and exercise can change our body shape and this gives us some control over our self-concept. There are other aspects of our appearance over which we have much more control. These are things like the clothes we wear, the cosmetics we use, the way we have our hair, and more permanent things like tattoos and body piercings.

Adults will say a lot about their self-concept by the way they dress, and may not feel comfortable if they think they are not dressed properly for a particular occasion, for example, a wedding or special work event. People will use their clothing to show their power or sexuality.

33 How would you dress to go clubbing?

34 How would you feel if you went clubbing in the clothes you would normally wear for college or work?

35 How can clothes influence our self-concept?

How can gender affect self-concept?

Gender has been discussed previously when considering factors affecting self-concept. Look back to pages 115–116 to remind yourself of the points made.

Gender is about the way society expects individuals of each sex to behave. Gender affects self-concept because individuals have to learn how other people expect someone of their sex to behave. This is called a **gender role**. There are two ways that children learn what is expected of individuals of their gender. The first way is by watching and copying the people around them. This is called **role modelling**. Secondly, they learn from seeing how people react to their behaviour. They learn that some things are approved of, and some are not. Children are more likely to repeat behaviour when they are praised, and less likely to repeat it when they are punished. This explanation is called the **behaviourist theory**.

Gender roles were often reinforced in education in past years. Boys learnt that they were not supposed to be interested in arts subjects, and girls learnt that they should not be interested in science. Gender therefore influenced the development of self-concept.

What children learn in this way will affect their lives in adulthood. For instance, there are fewer male teachers in primary education. Both boys and girls may be learning that primary school teaching is a job for women. This may affect their career choices in later life.

...WORD CHECK

gender – whether you are male or female.

gender role – how men and women are expected to act in particular situations.

role modelling – looking at someone else to copy/set an example.

behaviourist theory – the theory that people learn how to behave through rewards and punishments.

Children learn about gender through:

Observation

Copying

How does gender affect adult behaviour?

Adults are also affected by gender. In the past, there were clear gender roles. Men went out to work and earned money, and women stayed at home, caring for the children and the home. Only certain careers, like teaching and nursing, were considered suitable for women. Women were often expected to give up work when they married, even before they had children. It was, in the past, easy to have a clear self-concept based on gender.

Today, people have more choice and it is not so easy to be exact when defining gender roles. Some women who stay at home and look after children believe that they are looked down upon by some women who work. Some women who have careers have a positive self-concept of themselves as working women, but others feel guilty that they are not spending more time with their children. Some women who put their career before having children worry about whether they will have children at all.

▲ A house husband.

Men are also affected by changes in gender roles. Some men are happy to play a greater part in caring for their children. Others work long hours and hardly see their children. Someone with traditional ideas will think this is how men should behave. Others may feel guilty that they do not have more time for their children. Some men are happy to stay at home and look after the children, while others may think that an important part of being a man is to be the breadwinner. They may find their self-concept threatened because their partner earns more than they do.

Our self-concept, therefore, is influenced by the attitudes of those living around us. If we do not conform to these attitudes, views and opinions, we may feel that we are not as good as others, or be unhappy because we are not doing what is normally accepted practice.

Culture

Culture is shared beliefs, customs and values.

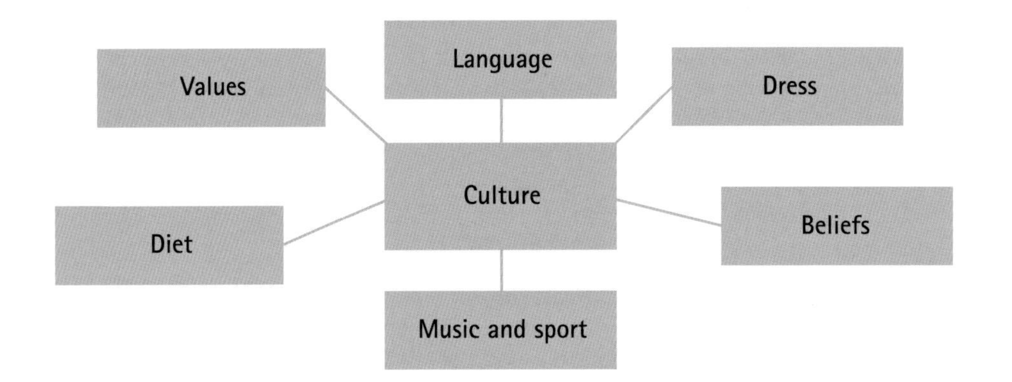

...WORD CHECK

multicultural – made up of many different people from a wide range of races.

stereotyped – to consider people from a particular group to be the same/not differentiating.

Culture binds societies together. It gives people a shared identity and a sense of belonging. This is why it is important for someone's self-concept.

Understanding culture is quite simple when there is only one culture in a society. Things are more complicated in a **multicultural** society. People from minority cultures may not feel that their differences are respected. They may feel that they are **stereotyped**, and that people are not treating them as individuals. People from minority cultures can suffer discrimination in this country, even though there are laws, such as the Race Relations Act, to protect them.

36 How does our culture affect our self-concept?

A person's self-concept can be affected if health and social services are not provided in a way that is appropriate for them. They may not get information about services in their preferred language. Their dietary needs may not be met, or their ideas about personal modesty may be ignored. They may feel that the people providing the services do not think that they are important or valuable.

These attitudes may affect the development of a person's self-concept. Their image of themselves may contribute to having low self-esteem. They may feel angry that no one has made the effort to find out what they want or what is best for them. They may become aggressive in order to draw attention to the real 'me'.

CASE STUDY Kaz

Kaz lives in a residential home. He is not able to eat the food provided because of his faith. Kaz needs a place set aside for him to pray several times each day and where he can follow the needs of his faith, but no one has responded to his request for this. Kaz has become angry because of the discrimination. He has started shouting at other residents and at some of the care staff. He also cries a lot.

1. Explain how the residential home could meet the cultural needs of Kaz.
2. How is Kaz's self-concept likely to be affected by the discrimination?
3. Explain how the discrimination could affect Kaz's relationship with the other residents.
4. Explain the effect on Kaz's self-concept if the care workers meet his cultural needs.

How is self-concept affected by emotional development?

Emotional development is very important to an individual's self-concept because it determines how an individual thinks about themselves, and what they believe others think about them. Positive emotional development includes:

Emotional characteristics	Effect on development
Forming relationships	The ability to make relationships with others later in life is often influenced by the relationships they have formed during infancy and early childhood. This is because these early experiences affect how we feel about ourselves and how we believe others feel about us
Ability to love and return love	Showing affection for others is easier if an individual has received affection
Feeling safe and secure	Being free from fear
Feeling able to trust others	Being able to rely on what others say and their actions
Praise	Genuine praise is essential. An individual needs rewards when they have done well

If these early experiences are good, then the individual will feel good about themselves and expect other people to value them.

Sometimes early experiences are not good. A child may be neglected or abused by carers. This child may have low self-esteem and feel worthless or not valued. They may not expect other people to like them. Their emotional development has been harmed.

The way parents discipline infants, children and young people will affect their emotional development and self-concept.

A four-year-old child has hit his friend with a toy and made him cry.
Working with another person, explain **two** different positive ways of disciplining the child, giving reasons for the actions suggested.

CASE STUDY Praise or punish?

Carer A tries not to punish a young child unless it is absolutely necessary. When their child is doing something dangerous or naughty, they distract them by offering them something interesting to do. When the child does something good, they are praised and rewarded. The child is often praised.

A child is shouted at and sometimes hit when they do something that Carer B thinks is wrong. They are often criticized and told they are naughty or a nuisance. They are never praised for things they do. They are often put to bed hungry as a punishment.

Discuss: Which is the best option? Why?

For each child, state how the individual's self-concept is likely to be affected.

Someone who has had a positive experience in their emotional development will have a strong self-concept. If someone is confident that they are valuable, then they will believe in themselves and won't depend on the approval of others. They will have more confidence in everything they do, whether it is sitting an examination, asking someone out or applying for a job. They will be able to accept that sometimes things go wrong, and it is not necessarily their fault. When they are criticized, they will be able to accept it, if it is justified, and learn from it. They will be optimistic about life. They will be able to present themselves confidently and have a realistic view of their abilities.

Someone with poor emotional development will have a negative self-concept. They will feel anxious about taking risks. This may make them shy and self-conscious. They may find it difficult to make friends because they are not sure what they have to offer. They may find it difficult to get a partner because they are reluctant to take the risk of asking someone out. They may feel guilty and responsible when things go wrong, even when it is not their fault. They will be afraid of confrontation with others because they will not be confident in their own opinions. They may put themselves down. They may not be able to react positively to criticism and will either resent it or see it as a personal attack. They will not have a very good opinion about life and may undervalue their abilities.

How can education affect self-concept?

Education is the process by which individuals are taught. This usually takes place in schools, colleges and universities. It can also involve learning while 'on the job' as new knowledge and skills are being developed, for example, NVQs.

Educational experiences are very important and can be a major influence on the development of self-concept. The way children are treated by their teachers and the relationships children form with other students can affect self-image, not only in childhood but throughout adolescence and adulthood as well. If children are encouraged in what they do well, they will be more confident and achieve more than if they are criticized for what they do poorly. Educational achievement is a positive influence on self-concept because it makes people feel good about themselves.

How can relationships with others affect self-concept?

▲ Close friendships can have a positive effect on self-concept.

An important part of someone's self-concept is what they believe others think about them. Communication is an important part of all relationships. Good communication skills can help us to form positive relationships with others. It is in relationships that individuals find out what others think about them. Intimate relationships are particularly important for someone's self-concept because honesty is an important part of intimacy. It is in intimate relationships, such as marriage and partnership, that we really find out what others think about us.

If an individual has a trusting and honest relationship with another person, such as a friend, they may learn from them that others have a higher opinion of them than they thought, and this will improve their self-esteem. If, on the other hand, a person has poor relationships, particularly within their family, they will lack confidence and will probably feel that they are not loved or valued. This could mean the person not being able to form lasting relationships in adolescence and adulthood. Because they find relationships difficult, a person who has experienced poor family relationships may find it difficult to make friends. They will have low self-esteem and will probably not achieve their full potential either at school or when they get a job.

Why is it that a person who has experienced poor family relationships is likely to have a poor self-concept?

Each of us has more than one social role. For example, a mother has a social role within the family, but also has a different social role when she is a member of a charity group. As individuals, we have a number of social roles at any one time. If an individual has had the experience of meeting others and interacting with others when they were children, for example, attending playgroup or attending sports clubs, they will probably have a positive self-concept and be quite confident. They will have had the opportunity of comparing themselves with others, however simplistic the comparison.

CASE STUDY Chantelle

Chantelle is aged five and lives with her mother and older brothers, Ethan, aged ten, and Mark, aged 13. Chantelle cried a great deal during the first few months of her life and constantly disrupted family life. Her father left home because of this and her mother blames Chantelle.

As a toddler, Chantelle spent a lot of time playing on her own, as her mother was too depressed to play with her. As a result, she is a quiet, withdrawn child who does not speak very much to others in the reception class.

Chantelle's mother compares her with her brothers, whom she praises a lot. She often tells Chantelle that she is a nuisance and that having to look after her prevents her from having any life of her own.

Chantelle's father takes both boys to football matches at the weekend but she is not invited to go with them. Her brothers often tease her and tell her that it's her fault that her father left and that he doesn't want to know her.

When at school, Chantelle does not make any effort to make friends and spends a lot of time just day dreaming.

1. Explain the factors that have influenced Chantelle's development of self-concept.
2. How do you think Chantelle identifies herself? What has influenced this?
3. How do you think Chantelle compares herself to others? What has influenced this?

How can sexual orientation affect self-concept?

From adolescence onwards, people experience sexual feelings towards others. During adolescence, many people experience sexual feelings towards others of the same sex. This is a common part of their development. Most people go on to develop sexual feelings for people of the opposite sex. A significant minority continue to be sexually attracted to people of their own sex. Whether you are attracted to individuals of the same or the opposite sex dictates your sexual orientation. It is an important part of self-concept.

Males who are attracted to other males and females who are attracted to other females are homosexual. Male homosexuals usually prefer to be called 'gay', and female homosexuals usually prefer to be called 'lesbian'. People who are attracted to the opposite sex are called 'heterosexual'.

Gay and lesbian people are usually in a minority in the community. The effect of sexual orientation on self-concept is similar in many ways to that of a minority culture. If you are a member of the dominant group, in this case heterosexuals, it is quite easy to see your sexuality as a valuable part of your self-concept. It is more difficult if you are gay or lesbian.

Same sex partners are now legally able to marry. As society becomes less **prejudiced** and discriminatory towards gay or lesbian people, it is becoming easier for them to be open about their sexuality and accept it as a positive part of their self-concept.

...WORD CHECK

prejudiced – being biased; making up one's mind about someone or something before really knowing what they are like.

▼ Sir Elton John and David Furnish celebrate their civil partnership.

CASE STUDY Sandy and Max

Sandy and Max, same sex partners, have been living together in a stable relationship for 25 years. They are now both in their 70s and are finding it difficult to cope.

After visiting the Swallows Residential Home with their social worker, Sandy and Max decide to move in. They have requested that they have a double bedroom, just like any married couple.

Some of the care workers and a few of the residents are not happy about the arrangement.

1. What should happen at the residential home in response to this situation?
2. What could be influencing the attitude of the care workers and clients who have objections to Sandy and Max having a double bedroom?
3. How is this type of discrimination likely to affect Sandy and Max?

ASSESSMENT PRACTICE

1. Patricia had a car accident while she was on the way to work one morning. She was badly hurt and needed to have an arm amputated.
   a Explain **three** effects that Patricia's physical disabilities may have on her self-concept. [6]
   b Patricia's husband, Andy, is a teacher.
   Explain **three** ways that Patricia's accident could affect Andy's self-concept. [6]
2. Sasha likes buying clothes and making sure that she looks good when she is out with her friends. She is a member of several recreational clubs and joins in a number of different activities.
   Explain how having nice clothes can influence self-concept. [5]
3. Kaz, 71 years of age, has recently moved to this country from India. He is now in a residential home because he is not very mobile and cannot look after himself. Kaz is a Muslim who likes to practise his faith and follow his cultural beliefs. He is the only Muslim in the residential home and the care workers do not make any different provisions for him. In fact, they talk about him to the other residents as though Kaz is not in the room and leave him out of their activities. He cannot always eat the food that is provided.
   Explain **three** ways Kaz's self-concept is likely to be affected by the discrimination he is experiencing. [6]
4. Brenda cannot look after herself any longer. The local authority have arranged for her to visit the day-care centre twice each week and for a care assistant to call three times a week. The care assistant is to help with a little tidying, ironing and doing the shopping.
   Explain **three** ways that Brenda's self-concept could be affected by visiting the day-care centre. [6]
5. Use theory to help explain how self-concept develops from childhood to the older adult life stage. [20]

RELATIONSHIPS

Family relationships

During our lifetime we have many different types of relationships.

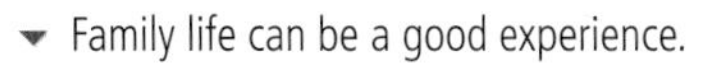
Family life can be a good experience.

Most people will, at some time in their lives, live with or in a family. The family plays an important part in the development of individuals. How we feel about and get on with members of our family will influence the way we think and relate to people throughout our lives. There are different types of family.

Lone parent families

This is where one parent, either the mother or the father, has decided to bring up a child on their own. This could be because the parents have decided to separate or divorce. Or it could be because of the death of one parent. Sometimes it is because the mother has decided that she wants to stay single and bring the child up herself, without any support from the child's father.

Nuclear families

Nuclear families live as a self-contained family unit in a single household. These consist of parents and their children. When the children in the family are young, the whole family lives together, sharing and supporting one another. When children grow up they may move away and set up their own home some distance away from their parents. This could mean the parents are only able to give them a little support because they live too far away.

Step families

Step families occur when there has been a divorce or the death of one parent, followed by re-marriage. The child (or children) will be the natural child of one person in the marriage or partnership. An example of a step family is:

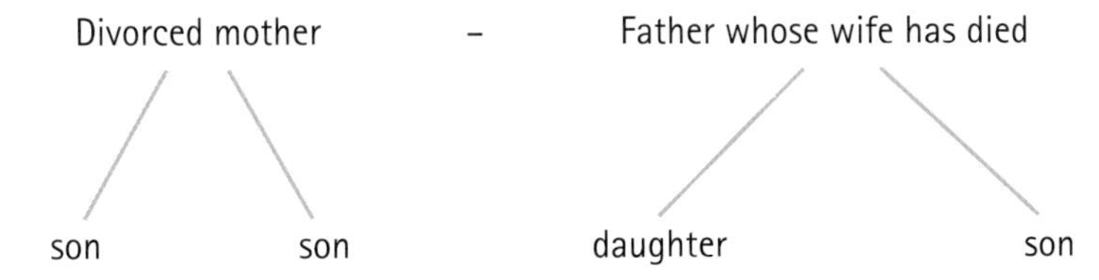

The trend in increased marriage breakdown means that families are separating at an earlier age. Re-marriages are taking place when people are younger. As a result it is likely that the new partners may have children of their own as well as children to care for from previous marriages.

Children from different families in a step family situation can find it hard to get on with one another in the early days of the new arrangement. This situation is usually resolved after the family settle down and become used to each other's ways. Sometimes problems are not resolved.

An extended family

This is a large family group that could include parents, sisters, brothers, grandparents, uncles and aunts. The members of the family all live together in the same building. Such a large group can give support to each other by helping the parent to bring up the children. They can give advice when there is a problem and will help by contributing to the daily living expenses for the group.

Extended families are not so common in Western Europe as the pattern of family life has changed in recent years, but they are common in other parts of the world.

'Looked after' families

Residential children's homes provide family life for children who cannot live with their natural parents. The care workers, or key workers, who look after the children try to make sure that the pattern of the children's life is as similar as possible to children who live in single households.

In a residential children's home there may be six or seven children living with main carers.

38 What relations could exist in a residential children's home?

39 Why do you think there are fewer extended families in Western Europe now than there were in previous years?

What is a family?

The family is a group of people of various ages who are usually related by birth or marriage. Members of a family usually feel that they have a special relationship with one another. This is often known as 'family ties'.

40 What do you think contributes to members of a family feeling they have something in common?

The members of the family will have a number of different relationships. For example:

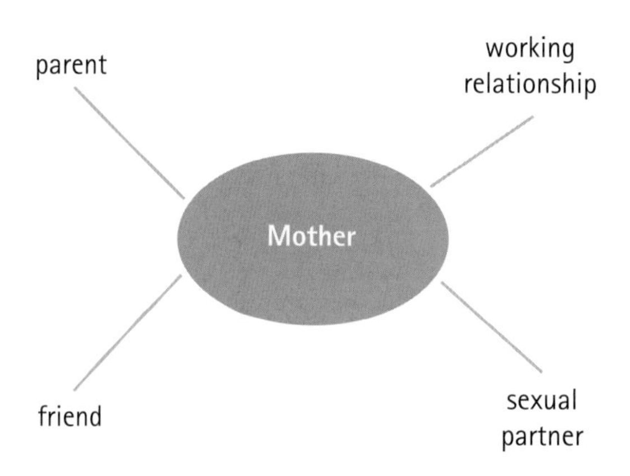

▲ Babies are dependent on their mothers.

- As parents, the mother and father will provide for and support the family. They will try to provide safe and secure surroundings for their children to grow up in. People can **biologically** become parents from the age of around 13 up to about 45–50 for women. However, most people are not ready to take on the care of another human being until they have a stable home and a strong relationship with their partner.
- As sexual partners the mother and father will develop intimate and loving relationships with one another.
- The father and/or mother may go out to work and may be an employee or an employer, and will have a working relationship with others.
- As well as providing for the family, the mother and father will be friends with their children. They will also have friends of their own age who they can talk to and share activities with.

...WORD CHECK
biologically – how we function as human beings.

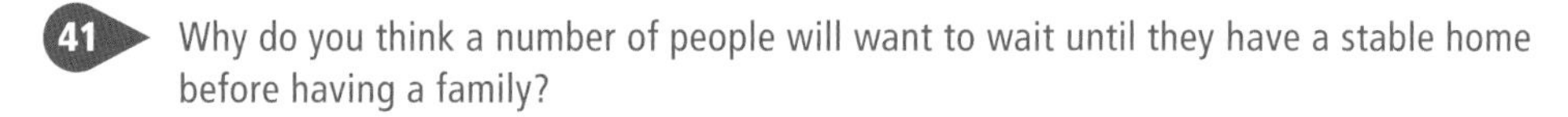

41 Why do you think a number of people will want to wait until they have a stable home before having a family?

What are the main features of a positive family relationship?

Negative family relationships can develop for a variety of reasons. Examples could include:

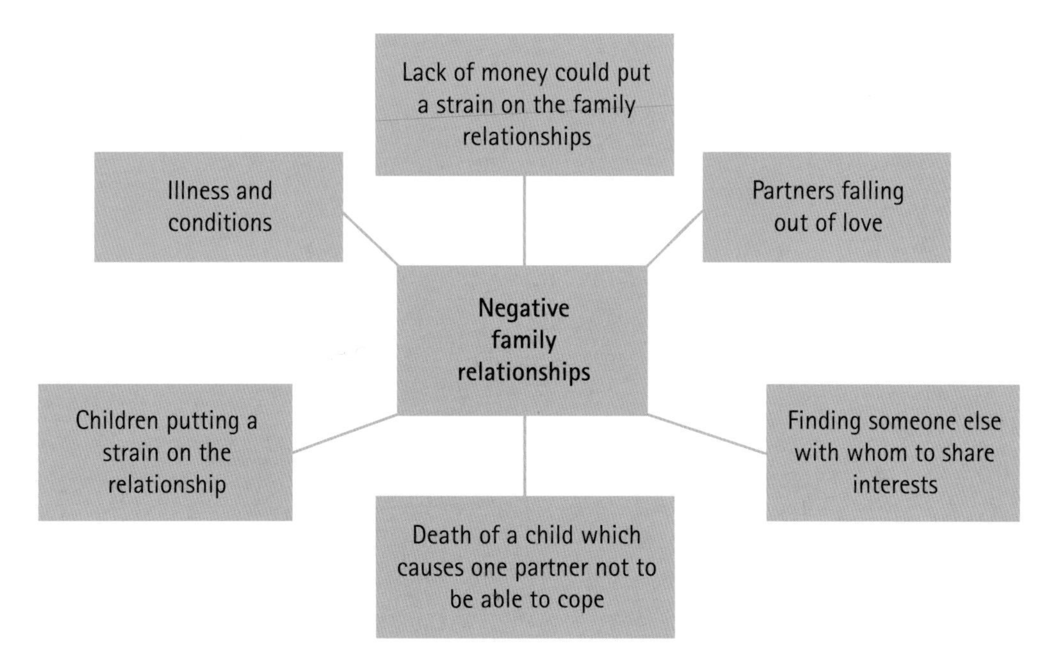

When relationships break down, whether it is between adults, children or between child and adult, the people involved get hurt.

CASE STUDY Jon and Pauline

Jon Clay works hard as an environmental health officer. He brings home a reasonable wage each month. The family are able to afford a car and they are buying their semi-detached house. Pauline, his wife, works part time as a teacher, so the money she earns helps to pay for some basic necessities, for outings for the children and holidays.

The family have bought an outdoor slide, a swing and trampoline for the children to play on. They have made sure that each play item is put up properly and is securely fixed to the ground.

After the family have had their evening meal they always spend time playing with the children. The children tell their parents what they have done during the day and Jon and Pauline tell the children something about the things they have been doing. Before they go to bed, the children have a story read to them and each parent gives them a big hug.

1. From the case study, select an example to show how Jon and Pauline showed the following features in their relationship with their children:
   - protection
   - love
   - friendship
   - providing
   - sharing.
2. Describe how Jon and Pauline are showing mutual support in their relationship.
3. Explain how a loving, caring relationship is likely to affect the development of the two children.
4. Write a short case study of your own based on a family who have a teenage son. You should make sure that you have included examples of how the family:
   - provide support
   - give protection
   - share.

   Exchange case studies with another person in the group. For the case study you have now, give examples of providing support, protection and sharing.

What are siblings?

'Siblings' is another way of saying 'brothers and sisters'. They are other children who are in the same family. Most people who have brothers and/or sisters are very protective towards them. They may quarrel from time to time but they would not want any harm to come to them.

When a new baby is born into the family, an older sibling, who has previously been either the youngest child or the only child, can become very jealous. Jealousy can be shown in many ways, such as snatching a toy away from the new arrival, behaving badly, having a temper tantrum and demanding attention. It is in these situations that parents need to remember to give love and support to the child who is jealous.

Infants (0–3 years) and children have relationships with others. When they are first born, the infant will start to develop very close relationships with their mother and then their father. As the child grows and develops it will form relationships with a much wider group of people.

◂ 'Why are they bringing him here?'

Relationships experienced by infants

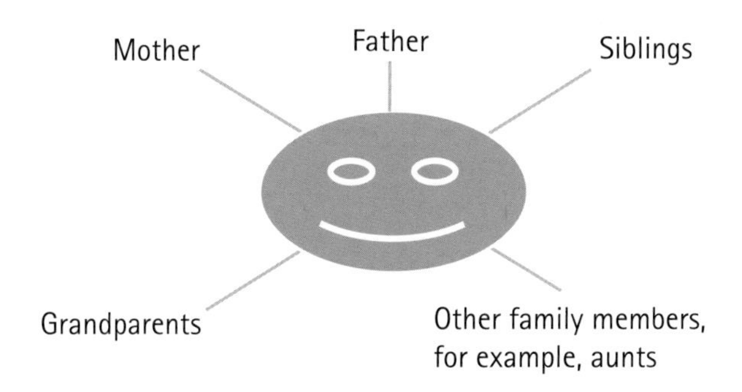

By the time the child reaches the age of eight years the relationships it has with others will have widened quite a lot. For example:

Mother and father Siblings Grandparents Other family members
Playgroup leaders Other children Teachers Neighbours
Parents of their friends

What will be the features of some of these relationships?

CASE STUDY Brittany

Brittany is eight years of age. She plays with her four-year-old brother while her mother gets their breakfast. She can dress herself for school. On some mornings she quarrels with her mother because she wants to take dolls and toys to school with her. She wants to take far too many.

Brittany's mother walks with her to school each day. As soon as they reach the school gate, she runs off to meet her friends. She enjoys school and likes the work she has to do. Her teacher is pleased with what she does. Brittany cooperates well with her teacher and tries hard to follow her instructions.

After school, Brittany, her mum and brother call at the local shop. Brittany has her own pocket money to spend and likes to choose her own sweets. Sometimes she shares them with her brother.

Let us consider some of Brittany's relationships. She has a relationship with:

- her mother
- her sibling
- her friends at school
- her teacher
- the shop assistant.

Some of the benefits of these relationships are:

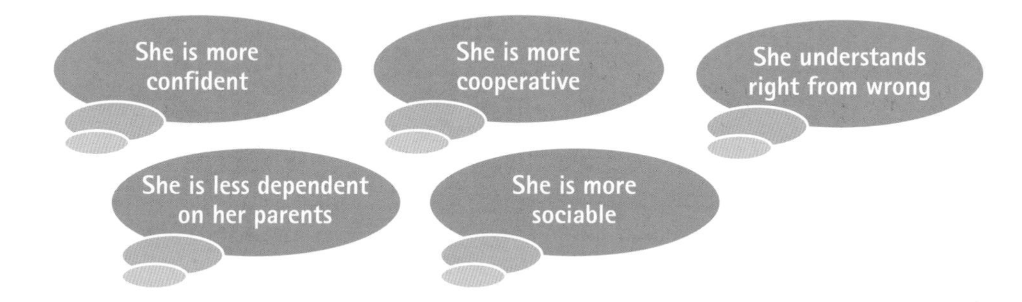

ACTIVITY Relationships

1. Carry out research to find out the meaning of the following benefits of a relationship:
   - confidence
   - being more sociable
   - being less dependent.
2. Explain how a mother still provides protection for an eight-year-old child.
3. Describe the relationship between an individual and a teacher.
4. Describe **two** features of a relationship between an eight year old and their grandparents.
5. Describe **three** ways that a child's relationship with her friends could affect development.
6. How is going to school likely to affect an individual's development?

Friendships

Group Activity

Work with another person in the group and try to list the features of a close friendship. One has been given for you to get you started: trust.

Now list the features of an acquaintance relationship.

Share your findings with another pair in the group.

...WORD CHECK

acquaintances – people who are known to us on a casual basis.

personality – a person's character.

Friendships support our need to have companionship and self-esteem. There can be different types of friendships from close friends, who you will trust and share secrets with, to **acquaintances** who you might say 'hello' to.

When do friendships start?

Can you remember who was your first 'best friend' and at what age you made this friendship? Close friendships can help fill a 'gap' in our lives. If a person is an only child then they may need someone to share and do things with. Lots of people have one or two 'best friends' with whom they share their happy times and the times when they are sad or hurt.

Friendships are often formed when one person is attracted to another person and the way they do things. Their **personality**, their sense of humour, the fact that they are dependable or the way they are prepared to work with others on school work or hobbies, could be the attracting feature.

In friendships people communicate with one another. Communication skills enable individuals to express their feelings and emotions to each other, and to share information. Some people define friendship as 'groupings of people who come together voluntarily'.

Friendships can start quite early.

Features of friendships are:

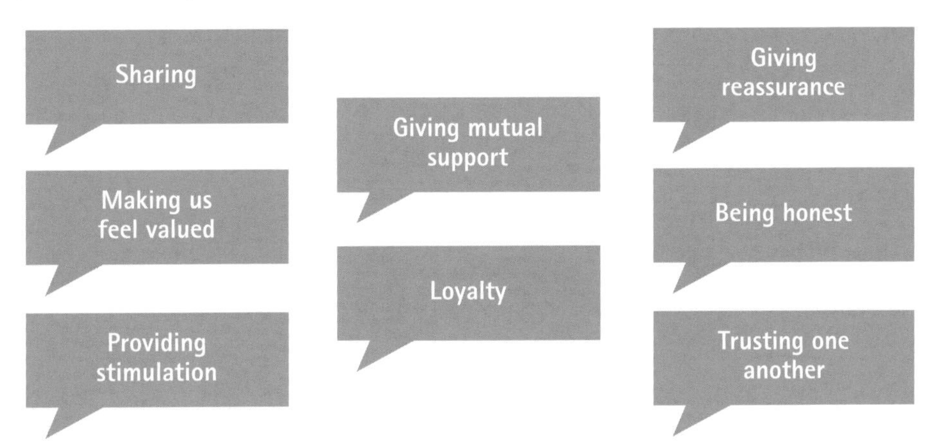

Between the ages of 14 and 17, boys and girls may be quite strongly influenced by their **peers**. For example, boys in particular will not answer a question in class if they think that this action would make them look too enthusiastic to their peers. This type of effect is known as 'peer pressure'.

'Boys like to be in larger groups of friends, and girls prefer to be with small groups of friends.' Do you think this statement is true?

Adolescents often have disagreements with their parents and appear to 'break' friends with the family. This is usually because they want to be more independent and make their own decisions. Most quarrels with parents are soon made up and are only temporary. However, some disagreements may lead to the adolescents leaving home and moving into a bedsit because the relationship between themselves and their parents has broken down beyond repair.

During adulthood we may make many friends through work. When people retire from work they often miss the company and the friendships of their work colleagues. They may decide to have a pet to keep them company. By having a dog, for example, older adults may make new friends as they are likely to take the dog out for walks. While walking the dog they may stop to speak to people. They may also take their dog to training classes and make new friends through such activities.

peers – people who are the same age.

isolated – to separate; to be considered on its own.

How are adolescent friendships different from those formed by adults?

Older adults often form friendships with their grandchildren. They may help to look after them while the parents are at work or may babysit in the evening, if they live close enough. Some grandparents have their children to stay for a holiday and firm friendships are formed that last throughout life.

Older adults may, as time passes, lose some of their friends through illness or death. This could make them feel lonely and **isolated**. As they themselves get older, they may not be able to travel as much as they used to do to meet their friends. They may also have to cope with the death of a lifelong partner who was a very close friend.

What do you think the effect of losing a lifelong partner would be?

▸ Older adults can form strong relationships with their grandchildren.

CASE STUDY Changes in relationships

Barnaby used to live with his two brothers but each has died and now he is on his own. When his brothers were alive, Barnaby did the cooking and kept the house tidy. His brothers could not help because they were ill. Barnaby used to read the newspaper to them. In the evening they would all play chess or dominoes.

Barnaby now has mobility problems himself and cannot walk very far. He used to visit his friend, Zac, every day. Zac lives two streets away. Zac cannot visit Barnaby as he has Parkinson's disease and cannot get out. When they were able to meet, they used to spend a long time chatting and would enjoy a game of cards and a pint together.

A home care assistant visits Barnaby twice a week to help keep the house tidy. A social worker has arranged for a volunteer to visit in order to chat to him on three evenings each week.

1. Think about the relationship changes that Barnaby has had in this life stage. Give **three** examples of the changes that have occurred. For each, explain the effect you think they would have had on Barnaby.
2. Barnaby used to enjoy meeting his friend, Zac. Describe **three** features of their relationship.
3. A volunteer friend is visiting Barnaby each week. Describe **three** features that could develop in this relationship.
4. Explain the effect of not being able to go out so often on Barnaby's relationships.
5. What other actions could be taken by the social worker to improve Barnaby's relationships? How would they help?

Intimate personal and sexual relationships

▲ Very much in love.

There are many different kinds of love. In fact, we use the word 'love' quite often. For example, a person might say 'I love my dog' or 'I love going on holiday' or 'I love my dad'. The love felt for a boyfriend or girlfriend is a different type of love than the love expressed for family and friends. This is because it includes a sexual attraction.

Intimate relationships involve being very close to someone. Sexual feelings start to develop during the early teens. This means that teenagers fall in and out of love quite often. These early 'first relationships' often do not last because adolescents have not matured sufficiently to be sensitive to the needs of others. Falling in and out of love, however, can be a very painful experience!

Sexual love often begins with physical attraction. Two people may find, as they get to know one another better, that they have the same interests. The relationship may deepen and sexual love develops out of a close friendship. Sexual activity is one of the most powerful expressions of intimacy that two people can share.

...WORD CHECK

intimate relationships – very close; sexual relationship.

Forming sexual relationships

Our parents are often role models on which we base our own relationships. Touch also plays an important role in sexual activity. Warm and friendly touches that show care and concern for one another are different from the very physical kissing and cuddling that happen in sexual relationships. Touch is the main language of sexual relationships when 'falling in love'. Having sexual intercourse is the expression of emotional and physical attraction.

Adults learn to be sensitive to the needs of others. As a result they are less likely to be thinking about themselves but, instead, consider the best interests of the other person. Both people in the relationship are considering the needs of the other person first. As a result the relationship is more likely to last.

Why is it necessary to be sensitive to the needs of a partner?

As two people live together they become more aware of the needs of the other partner. Interest in sexual activity does not necessarily decrease with age. Many people who have lived in partnership or marriage for a long time say that sexual activity is the result of emotional closeness and not a physical desire. The essential ingredient for a good sexual relationship is 'emotional sensitivity'.

Working relationships

Individuals spend quite a lot of adult, waking life working. The relationships that are formed with people while working are an important part of our lives. Working relationships are different from other relationships, such as friendships, because they have a specific purpose. In any working relationship, often one person is in a position of power over another.

Working relationships can include:

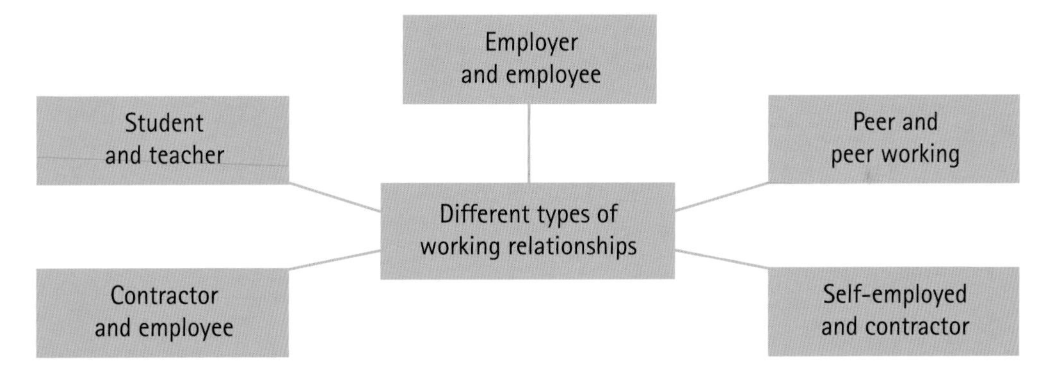

As early as five years of age, or even before if a child attends playgroup or nursery, children learn to work with others. These could be other adults or other children. Learning to work with others means learning to cooperate. The playgroup leader or teacher will ask a child to do something. The child does what has been asked and a working relationship has been formed.

Another feature of a working relationship is trust. This is particularly true when working relationships are made with children, as the child is dependent on the teacher and trusts them not to harm them in any way.

Adolescents studying for their examinations are also working with teachers and tutors. A feature of this type of relationship is a partnership. The student and the teacher will work closely together, exchanging knowledge and ideas. While there is power in the relationship, as the teacher or tutor is 'in charge', there is also a sharing of information.

Students also have working relationships with their peers. They may work on a project with one or more people in their class. In this situation, none of the people are 'in charge', although sometimes one person will take a leadership role. Peers can have a very strong effect on the actions we take. This is known as peer pressure. Peers, who are people that are usually around the same age as ourselves, can influence us in good or bad ways. This is known as having a positive or negative influence. Working relationships with teachers and lecturers can be greatly influenced by the attitudes of our peers.

46 Why do you think peers influence our behaviour?

47 Are employer and employee relationships different from other types of relationships?

▲ Following the employer's instruction is important.

Good working relationships help to keep employees and employers happy and this contributes to good health. Good communication is a feature of successful working relationships. Friendships can develop between people who are working on the same tasks or who have the same job status. It is more unusual for people who work at different levels or who have a different status within an organization to make deep friendships. This is because there is often an 'invisible barrier' between staff levels. For example, a manager or supervisor who is friendly with a care assistant could not easily reprimand the care assistant if this became necessary. It is not often that a person in charge of a department shares a problem they may have with a junior member of staff. This is because they may feel that the junior will think they are not able to cope. Not many people are able to 'choose' the people they work with.

A good atmosphere in the workplace depends on mutual tolerance and valuing the contribution that others are making. An employee who shows respect for another employee is likely to be respected in return. An employee who shows respect for the employer is likely to receive back that respect.

Some employees may feel that an employer has power over them. They may desperately need the work because they have a large mortgage or bills to pay. They may feel that they have to do whatever their employer asks, because if they don't, they will not keep their job. If they don't keep their job then they will not be able to pay the bills. This type of attitude does not help to make good working relationships.

Good working relationships depend on:

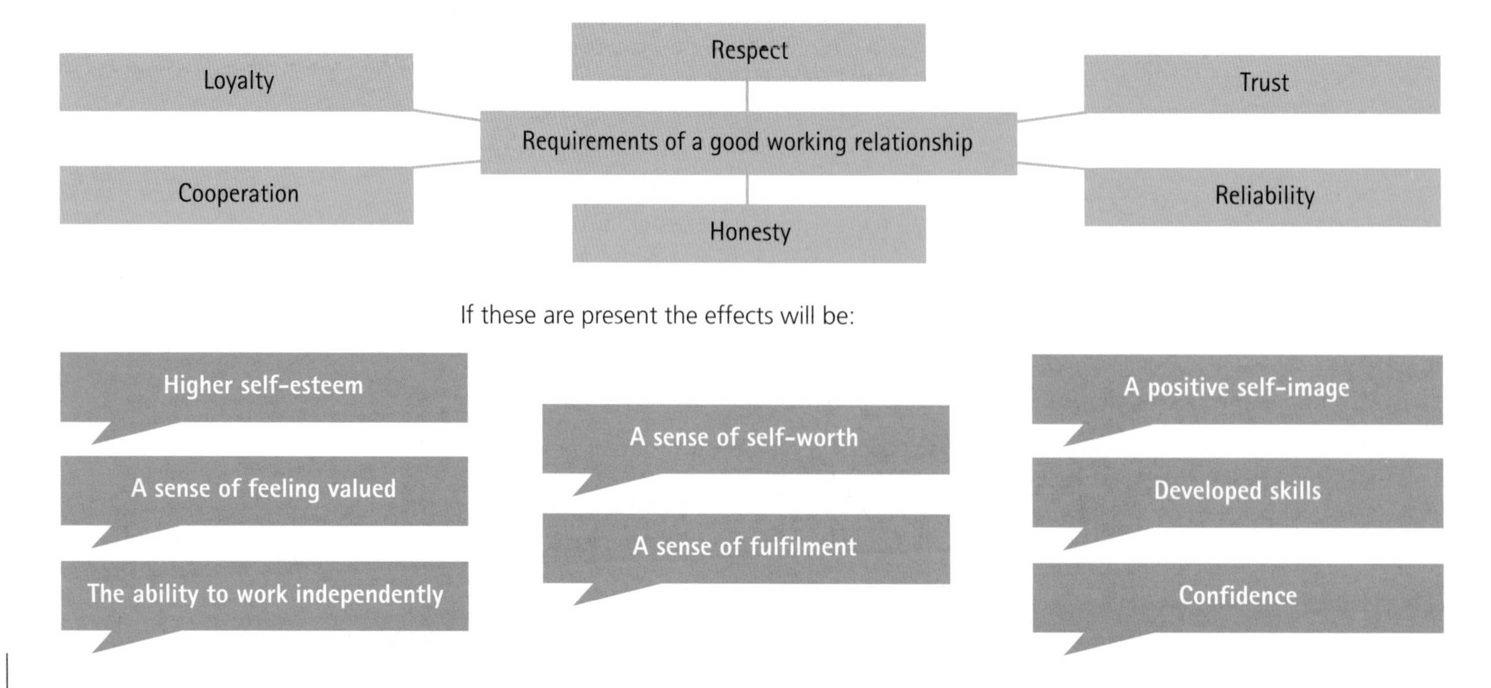

CASE STUDY Samera

Samera has worked at the hospital for 20 years. She used to like work, but now she finds it quite hard as so much is expected of her. She never seems to have enough staff, equipment or materials. She has made lots of requests for more equipment and materials and even more staff, but her line manager has not been able to provide them.

When she first started at the hospital, Samera really enjoyed the work. She also liked the people she worked with, as they were able to talk about things together. Sometimes they went out as a group in the evenings or at weekends. They always had a good time and seemed to laugh a lot. At work they would help one another, particularly if one person needed help to manage their workload. They all helped one another.

Now she is a sister in charge of a ward, Samera feels that she cannot be quite so friendly with the other nurses. She expects them to do a good job and will not allow standards on her ward to be lowered. There are one or two staff that she would, if she could choose, prefer not to work with. Samera knows, however, that in her professional role she needs to treat her staff equally.

Samera has to work as she is divorced and has a mortgage to pay. Her children are at university and they always need more books or help to pay for their accommodation.

1. From the case study show how Samera demonstrates the following features in her relationships:
   - mutual support
   - sharing
   - dependency
   - loyalty
   - respect.
2. Explain how Samera showed that she valued those with whom she worked.
3. What effect could financial pressures be having on Samera's relationships at work and with her family?
4. If Samera gave up work, how could her relationships with her children change? How do you think this would affect Samera?

It is likely that in each day of our lives we will experience both positive and negative relationships and these will affect us in some way. Positive relationships will help us to have a good self-image of ourselves. A negative relationship is likely to lower our self-esteem and make us have doubts and a lack of confidence.

A positive relationship can mean:

- having someone to share an interest with
- knowing that you are loved and liked
- having someone for whom you can provide support in times of stress
- having someone to support you when you need help.

Positive relationships are essential if we are to have high self-esteem. We need to feel good about ourselves. This happens when we feel we are valued. For example, we feel valued when we have done a job well and someone tells us so. We will also feel good in ourselves because we know we have achieved the task that has been set and this will give us a good feeling of self-worth.

Good relationships contribute to our own sense of identity and help us to know about the direction in which we are going. Positive relationships often lead to other activities. People who relate well may have a good social life, doing things together. They will enjoy being together and sharing one another's company. There are always times when we will want to be on our own but if we have positive relationships with others, there will be a good balance in our lives of being with other people and choosing when to have time to ourselves.

We will be able to:

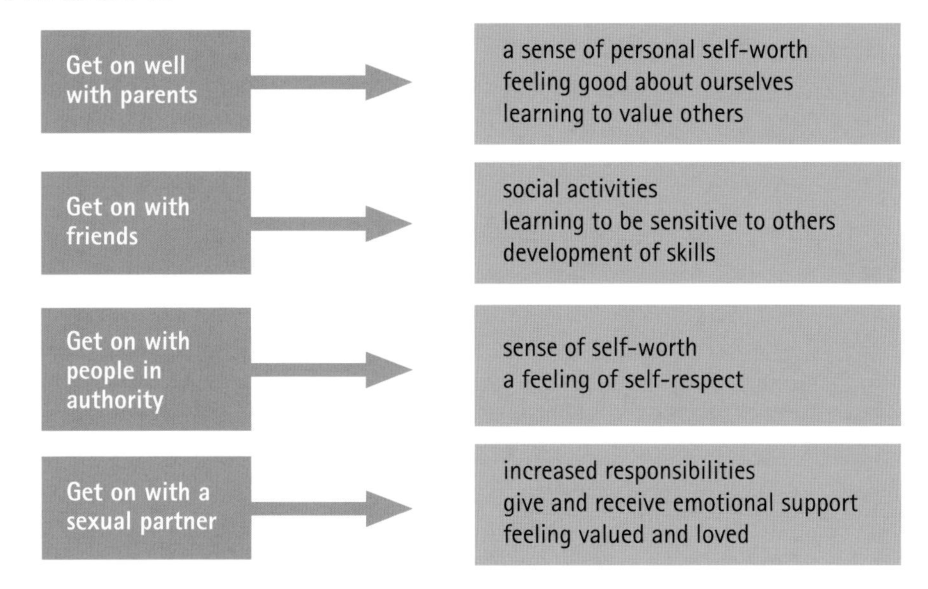

Negative or poor relationships are likely, after a period of time, to contribute to poor health. Negative relationships mean not being able to get on with other people. An individual may find it difficult to get on with their family or friends or with people in authority. It may be that a person finds it difficult to get on with any other people. When a person does not get on with others they are likely to become socially isolated and will not want to join in activities or meet with other people. Their sense of identity and self-esteem will be affected. An individual may find that they have a feeling of worthlessness and may fail in the tasks that they are given to do. This could lead to poor examination results or loss of a job. This, in turn, could lead to not being able to pay bills or eat properly. As a result, an individual could become homeless, have poor health and turn to crime in order to get the money that they need. None of these events are going to help anyone to be successful in their lives.

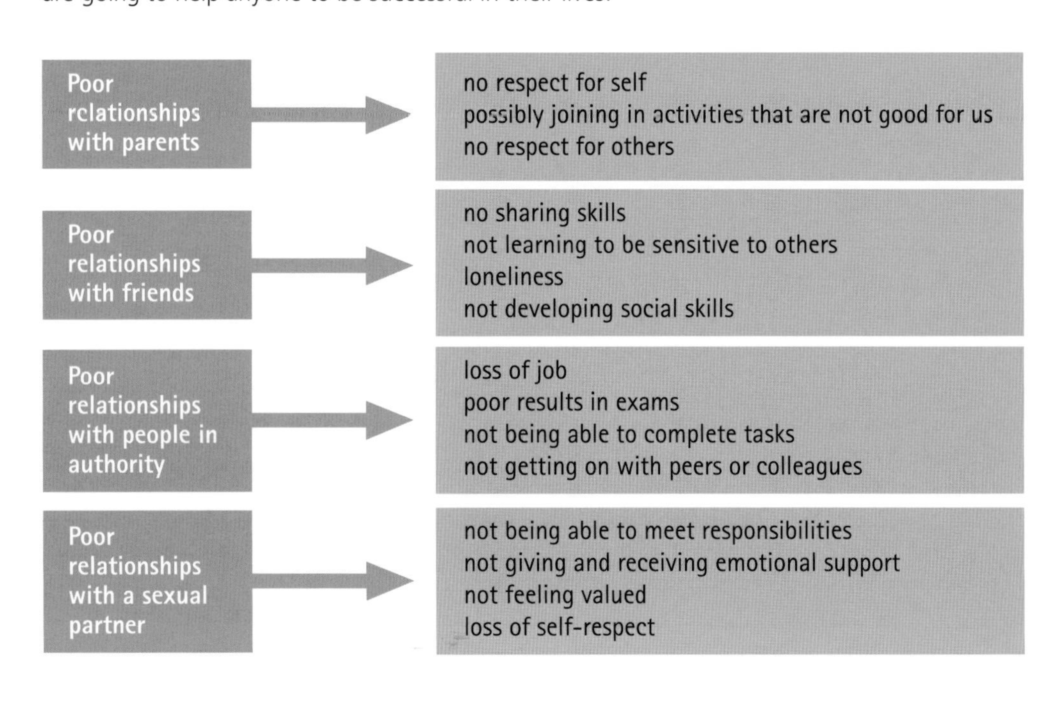

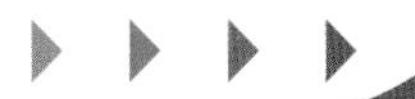

ASSESSMENT PRACTICE

1 Barry works with Mavis and Balbinder in a busy office. He enjoys his work and he has a good relationship with the people he works with.

a Explain **three** ways that a successful working relationship can affect our development. [6]

b Barry is made redundant. Explain **three** ways that redundancy and unemployment can affect development and relationships. [6]

2 dependency jealousy protection sexual relationships sharing working

a Choose the words from above to show the features of different relationships by completing the table below.

Relationship	Feature
Bibby and John serve customers in a shop	
Jack is 6 months old and is cared for by his mother	
Lucy has recently married Sean	
Martha is looking after Jo as he has been abused	
Bob has broken his friendship with Jay because Jay has a new bicycle but Bob's family can't afford to buy him one	
Greta and Sabina are working together to get information from the same book	

[6]

b Explain what is meant by the term 'mutual support' and give **one** example. [6]

3 When relationships break down, people often get hurt. Explain **three** ways that the breakdown of a relationship could affect development. [6]

Major life changes and sources of support

How can life events affect an individual's personal development and what support is available to them during these times?

Getting started

Life events can have a major impact on an individual's personal development. These may include events that result in:

- changes in relationships (for example, marriage, divorce, living with a partner, birth of a sibling or own child, death of a friend or relative)
- physical changes (for example, puberty, accident or injury, menopause)
- changes in life circumstances (for example, moving house, starting school, college or a job, retirement, redundancy or unemployment).
- You should be able to identify and describe the effects that life events can have on individuals' personal development. You should know how individuals adapt and use sources of support to cope with the effects of life events. Sources of support may include:
  - partners, family and friends
  - professional carers and services
  - voluntary (third sector) and faith-based services.

LIFE EVENTS

...WORD CHECK

expected – something you know is going to happen.

unexpected – sudden.

Life events can affect an individual's personal development and, at such times, support will be needed.

Some life events are **expected**. This means that we can be almost certain that they will happen to us. For example, everybody starts school around the age of five. Everybody goes through physical changes such as puberty. The death rate is 100 per cent and it is expected!

Other life events are **unexpected**. This means they take us by surprise, and we have no way of knowing when or if they might happen. An example of this is a serious road accident. A number of people will be killed and seriously injured on the roads each year, but we have no way of telling who it will happen to, or when.

48 Think about a life event that has occurred in your life or the life of your family. Was it expected or unexpected? How did you or the family feel at the time? Were you able to get any support?

All life events provide the opportunity for personal growth. They can also cause stress, which can have emotional effects, such as anxiety and depression. If this happens, it is a sign that changes are necessary in our lifestyle so that we can live comfortably with the new circumstances. If we can learn from the experiences, this contributes to our personal development. Stressful life events might include the death of a partner, divorce or separation, serious injury, or losing a job.

Can you think of any other major life events?

What is the difference between expected and unexpected experiences of life events?

RELATIONSHIP CHANGES

Many of the most stressful life events are to do with relationship changes. These are the events that are often most difficult to adapt to. Relationship changes can include marriage, divorce, living with a partner, the birth of a child, and death of a relative or friend.

Marriage or living with a partner

When two people get married, they are entering into a contract.

- They promise that they will be faithful to each other, which means that they will not have other sexual partners.
- They promise they will look after each other. This means that they will look after each other physically if they are unwell. It also means that they will provide for each other financially. If only one partner is working, they will be expected to support the other one financially.
- They promise that they will share the responsibility for any children that they have together.

Today, some people live together without getting married; they remain as 'partners'. They may also have children. They may decide to get married at a later date or they may not.

When two people decide to live together, they have to make changes to the way they do routine tasks. If one person insisted on having their own way all of the time, the partnership would not work and there would be a breakdown in relationships.

They also need to decide:

Where they are going to live. They might both have jobs. Will they live closer to one partner's job than another's? Near one's family or another's ?

How they are going to organize their finances. Whether they are going to keep their own money, or share it. If they have bank accounts will they have separate accounts or a joint account?

Whether or when they are going to have children, and how many.

Who is going to take responsibility for which tasks? For example, how the housework is going to be done, and who is going to do it.

These types of decisions will mean that both people have to change some of their ways or routines so that they can fit in with the needs of the other person. If people marry or have partners, they each acquire a new set of relatives, called in-laws, or in the case of partners, other people whom they need to get to know. They have to establish a relationship with the other's family members or close **associates**. These relationships can be very positive, but they can be very difficult. Having to get on with people who you have not had very much to do with or may not share the same interests with can be quite hard.

...WORD CHECK

associates – people we meet regularly who we may work with but who are not friends.

stigma – something that does not present a good image of the person.

regressing – to go back.

51 How is living with a partner or getting married likely to affect development?

Divorce

Because marriage is a contract, there has to be a special arrangement to end it. This is called 'divorce'. Today, divorce is more common, and there is not the same **stigma** about it as in past years. If couples want to get a divorce, they only have to prove that the relationship has broken down. There does not have to be a guilty party. This has removed a lot of the stigma but divorce still has a major impact on people's personal development.

Marriages do not always last.

Losing a partner through divorce or separation may have many of the same social and emotional effects as bereavement. This will mean a sense of loss, grief, perhaps loneliness. There are also other effects.

Divorce usually has financial effects and people are often worse off afterwards. It is much more expensive for two people to live separately than together because they will have separate homes. This means they have two lots of rent to pay, and two lots of heating bills and so on. They will probably have less income as well. Before they divorced, both parents may have been working and sharing the care of children or paying for child care. This is more difficult after divorce.

How does divorce affect the family?

Divorce has many other effects on the development of family members, especially if there are children. One partner has to leave the home after divorce. The parent that stays behind is usually the one that has the main responsibility for the children. If they have no partner to help care for the children, they may have to give up work. If they can't afford to stay in the house, they have all the extra problems of moving house.

It is often more stressful to bring up children alone. Young children do not have the emotional development to understand what is going on, and may react by exhibiting behavioural problems or **regressing**. This means going backwards in their development. Children are usually left with their mother when parents separate. Many fathers have access to children for a weekend, for example. This will affect the personal development of both the children and their parents. Children may lack a role model. Children often have difficulties in adjusting when their parents get new partners.

For some people, the completion of the divorce will bring some relief. It may mean the end of arguments and tension within the home.

52 How can divorce have a positive effect on development?

Birth of a sibling or own child

For a young child the birth of a sibling can often be a **traumatic** life event. If they are the first child they will be used to having all of their parents' attention. When the new baby arrives, they have to get used to having less attention. They have to adjust to this. If they are well prepared for the new baby, made to feel important and reassured that they are still loved, then it can be a very positive experience. Some children, if they are not prepared for the arrival, can be jealous and spiteful to the new baby. Sometimes they **regress** in their development to get attention. They might behave like they did at an earlier stage, for example, start having tantrums again, or have accidents although they have been toilet trained.

...WORD CHECK

traumatic – causing deep shock or upset.

regress – to go back.

bereavement – a death of a friend or relative.

The experience of having a new baby brother or sister could affect a child's development during adolescence and adulthood. It could mean that the eldest child always wants to be first, always wants to lead, because they feel that they will be pushed out or ignored if they are not seen to be the leader. Or it could mean that the person becomes withdrawn and feels guilty because they think they were not good enough, not valued.

A good experience of having brothers and sisters can mean that a person develops a positive sense of their own worth. They will be able to share and enjoy being with others. They don't always have to be first and can give support when it is required or take the lead when necessary. Their development will be 'balanced'.

People who are having difficulties in a relationship often think that having a child will bring them closer together. This is not usually true. Having a child puts extra strain on a relationship. This is not to say that having a child is a negative experience. It is usually very rewarding, but people have to be prepared for the strains it can impose. Adults have to adjust when their first child is born. Babies demand a lot of care and attention, and it is often necessary to put the baby's needs before the needs of a partner. This can make the partner feel left out.

53 How can the arrival of a sibling have a negative effect on the development of a previous 'only child'?

Death of a friend or relative

When someone dies suddenly, it is called **bereavement**. The most difficult common life event to deal with is the death of a partner or of one's own child. Bereavement has physical, intellectual, emotional and social effects. People have to adjust to these.

P.I.E.S.	How P.I.E.S. are affected
Physical	A bereaved person may lose their appetite, be unable to sleep, and lose the will to look after themselves properly.
Intellectual	They may lose interest in things around them. They may not be able to concentrate on a task.
Emotional	The person could feel a sense of grief, loss, depression, and possibly shock, if the death was unexpected. They may feel isolated and alone.
Social	The person could have lost the companionship and support of their partner. They have also lost their role, for example, as someone's partner. They may have to adapt to a new way of life as a single person.

The loss of a parent is something that most of us experience, and the adaptation required will depend on the life stage when it happens. Although bereavement of an adult is a serious life event, the loss of a child is much more stressful. We do not expect to live longer than our children. One of the worst experiences a parent can have is the death of a child.

Grief is normal and a necessary response to the death of a loved one or friend. Sometimes grief can last a long time and on other occasions it will be short lived. Grief has several stages. These are:

- shock and disbelief
- denial
- a growing awareness of the loss
- acceptance of the loss.

It is important that people are allowed to work through their feelings, and to give the bereaved person as much support as possible. If a person does not work through their grief, they can develop feelings of guilt, blaming themselves for the death. This could lead to them feeling angry, resentful and to having a sense of loneliness. Physically they may become depressed or they could become aggressive.

◂ Loss.

ACTIVITY Stages of grief

Work with another person to find out about the 'stages of grief'.

Make a handout to tell others about these stages.

CASE STUDY Hanan

Hanan and her partner, Mike, have three children. All are healthy and appear to be happy. Erin, the youngest child, appears to have a cold, but soon she develops a fever. Purple spots appear and Erin can't bear any light near her eyes. Her parents become quite worried and call the GP.

The GP immediately arranges for Erin to be admitted to hospital. She is given a great deal of medical help, but unfortunately Erin dies. The doctors tell her parents that the cause of death is meningitis.

1. What is the term used to describe this sudden death?
2. How are the parents likely to express their grief?
3. How is the loss of a child likely to affect the development of the parents?

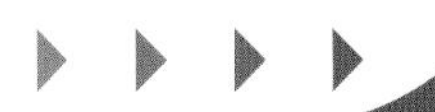

ASSESSMENT PRACTICE

1. List **three** relationship changes that could occur as life events. [3]
2. For each relationship change given for Question 1, describe how the change could affect the development of an individual. [3]
3. Explain how divorce could have both a positive and negative effect on personal development. [5]
4. Anita is four years old and runs out into the road. She is killed by a passing car. Is Anita's death an expected or unexpected life event? Give an explanation for your answer. [3]
5. Explain the difference between 'marriage' and having a 'partner'. Explain how marriage or having a partner could affect development. [6]
6. Melissa has to move into a residential home because she can no longer look after herself. How is moving into a residential home likely to affect Melissa's development? [8]
7. Explain how the birth of a sibling could affect the development of an only child. [5]

PHYSICAL CHANGES

Puberty

Puberty is a time of physical and emotional changes. It is the stage between childhood and adulthood, the attainment of sexual maturity. Both boys and girls experience puberty. There are changes in body size and shape. The reproductive organs develop. Boys usually experience a sudden voice change and both sexes start to grow more hair on the body. Weight problems sometimes occur during this period. These could be due to natural changes or they could be the result of over- or under-eating in response to emotional problems. Some teenagers develop skin problems such as acne or eczema as a result of rapid changes in hormone levels. Concern about appearance can lead to a lowering of self-confidence in teenagers.

These changes will not occur at exactly the same time in all adolescents. Some will experience the changes very early in their teenage years. For others, changes will occur more gradually. Changes during puberty are considered to be main life events as they can affect the development of individuals, having positive and negative effects.

▲ Puberty is a time of changes.

54 Why does puberty not occur at exactly the same time in all adolescents?

CASE STUDY Jackie

Jackie is 13. She thinks there may be something wrong with her. All her friends have developed very shapely bodies and are dating boyfriends. No one of the opposite sex seems to be at all interested in Jackie. She feels left out of conversations because everyone else is talking about their boyfriends and where they are going out at the weekend.

Jackie cannot understand why her body has not developed like her friends' bodies. She wonders if dieting would help, but she didn't think she was overweight. She becomes very depressed and stops trying to join in any of the group conversations.

1. Explain what is meant by the term 'puberty'.
2. What advice would you give to Jackie about her physical development?
3. How is Jackie's emotional and social development likely to be affected by the delayed onset of puberty?
4. Describe **four** physical developments of males during puberty.

Accident or injury

Becoming physically disabled through accident, injury or illness is a major life event. It is not usually expected. A person who becomes disabled will have to adapt their lifestyle, depending on the degree of disability. They may lose some of their independence, and they may have to rely on others for daily living tasks that they were once able to do for themselves. An extreme example is someone who becomes completely paralysed and requires help with all their bodily functions. Perhaps the biggest problem that many people have to face in adapting to disability is the prejudice of others. People with disabilities often complain that they are treated like children. They say that people often speak to their carers rather than to them. This makes the person who is not able-bodied feel inferior and as though they do not count. It is almost as though they are not present in the conversation.

Becoming disabled may involve losing a job and having to retrain. It may involve a loss of income or moving to more appropriate accommodation. It may also require changes in hobbies or interests.

The menopause

The menopause is the end of a woman's reproductive life. She may have to come to terms with the fact that she can no longer have children. The menopause can be a main life event for some women. It will affect their development differently. Some will be pleased that they no longer have to worry about having children, others may feel a sense of loss.

Why might a woman feel a sense of loss when the menopause occurs?

CHANGES IN LIFE CIRCUMSTANCES

All changes in life circumstances have some common features. The most important is that they involve changes in existing relationships, and a need to develop new ones. Moving house, changing schools and changing or losing a job all involve leaving some relationships behind – neighbours, friends, teachers, bosses and colleagues. To adapt successfully to the change, the individual must make new relationships, sometimes in a new role.

Moving house and starting college

When someone moves house or moves away to start a new job or college, they leave behind familiar friends, neighbours and neighbourhoods.

Leaving friends and neighbours matters because you lose the physical, emotional and social support they offer. Life is much easier with these networks to help. Parents, for instance, have to know who they can trust to babysit for them. Good neighbours can help in all sorts of ways, for example, by watching the house when you are away on holiday, or helping you when you are ill. When you move house you have to build new relationships to replace these.

A person will know a lot about where they live if they have been there for a period of time. They know where shops and services are, what buses to catch and their location. When moving to a new area, everything is new and has to be learnt again. New friends, new teachers or employers will be introduced and you will need to learn how to get on with new neighbours.

This can be a very threatening experience, even if the person has been looking forward to it for some time. The result of having to move could be isolation and a sense of grief and loss, or it could bring feelings of joy and satisfaction, as well as mental stimulation due to the new challenges being presented.

CASE STUDY Lindsey

Lindsey has been successful in her examinations. She is moving away from home to go to university to study midwifery. She has lived with her family in a rural area all her life. None of her friends are going to the same university and she is sure she will miss them.

At university, Lindsey will be sharing a house with three other girls who she has not met before. She is very nervous and anxious about the move, but it is something that she wants to do.

1. Describe the difficulties Lindsey might have to cope with when she moves to university.
2. List **four** ways that Lindsey could help to prepare herself for the move.
3. Explain how Lindsey's development is likely to be affected by moving away from home.
4. If Lindsey has an accident that affects her ability to walk, how is her development likely to be affected?
5. How is Lindsey's leaving home to go to university likely to affect her parents' development?

Starting school

Starting school may be the first time that a child has been away from their main carer for a whole day. It means that the child has to become more independent of their parents, and form relationships with other children. This could be quite a frightening experience for the child if careful preparations are not made. Parents who have previously been close at hand will no longer be available. Relationships with new adults and new children will be formed. Rules will have to be followed. All these changes can have a negative effect on the child's development.

A child may become very 'clingy' to the parent and make a fuss when it is time for them to leave. They may become withdrawn and sit in a corner away from the other children, refusing to join in the activities. The child may behave like this because they do not understand what is happening. They may think they have been abandoned or that they are being punished. This may lead to the child having nightmares or bedwetting. They may become aggressive towards their parents. It could lead to the child disliking school and underachieving in their work.

If the child is prepared before having to start school, they are more likely to have a positive experience. The parent could talk to the child about school, read them stories about school or take them to meet someone from school. Most schools invite children to attend for a morning or two before the child has to do an all day session. This can help the child to prepare for longer school hours.

56 Why is it important to prepare a child for starting school?

Starting school can be frightening.

Starting work

Starting work involves intellectual development because a person will have to learn what the job involves so that it can be done properly. They will have to learn both new skills and knowledge. Emotional development will also take place when starting work. This is particularly true if working in the health, social care or early years sector. For example, as a carer, when working with someone who is rude and bad-tempered or very slow, it will be necessary to deal with your own anger or impatience in a mature way. At work, an individual will meet new colleagues and have the opportunity to make more friends. Social development will, therefore, also be affected.

As working means earning money, an individual will become financially independent. This means they may no longer be totally dependent on parents for money. Managing finances is an important aspect of intellectual development. Physically, work may also be more challenging.

Starting work is usually considered an 'expected' life event as most people at some time during their life will have the opportunity to do this. If the job is something a person likes doing, they will be mentally stimulated and happy, and will have a sense of fulfilment. Work can give a positive direction to our lives.

Adults are likely to spend many hours at work. If they do not like the work they do, they could become depressed and physically ill. Many people today suffer from stress as a result of work. This could be because they are asked to do too much, they find the work too difficult or because the work does not suit their characteristics. Whatever the reason, the negative effects can make a person feel that they are a failure.

Why is it important to like the work we do?

Retirement

...WORD CHECK

occupational – associated with the job.

Group Activity

Work with another person to make a list of three negative effects of retirement. Describe the likely impact of these negative effects on individuals.

Share your results with others.

Retirement is when a person stops working. Some people are entitled to an **occupational** pension, while everyone is entitled to a state pension. When an individual retires, they could lose the physical, intellectual, emotional and social stimulation provided by work. Some people are very sad when their working lives come to an end. Others are very happy. Whether retirement is a positive or negative development depends upon how people deal with it. People who are happy to retire are those who find other ways of getting the stimulation that they used to get from work. This might involve:

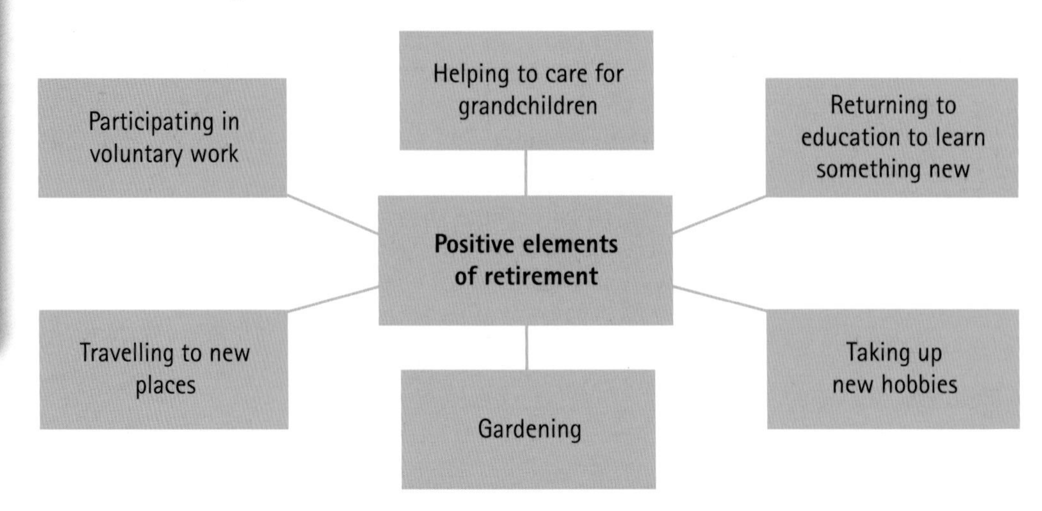

Redundancy and unemployment

Unlike retirement, redundancy and unemployment are often unexpected life events. Unemployment means not having a job. Redundancy means losing your job because the job has disappeared, perhaps because a company has closed down.

Like retirement, unemployment and redundancy mean losing physical, intellectual, emotional and social stimulation provided by work. Redundancy is different from retirement because it often happens unexpectedly and without warning. It can affect development because people worry about how they are going to manage financially. Too much worry can make us ill, both physically and mentally, through stress.

Some people who are made redundant, particularly older workers, find it very difficult to get another job before they reach retirement age. This may make them feel undervalued and lack confidence in themselves.

58 What is the difference between retirement and redundancy?

Many people who are unemployed will feel bored because they do not have enough to do to fill their time. They may get depressed if working is very important to their sense of identity. They may find it difficult in their relationship with their partner. This may be especially true for men who are used to providing for their family. They may find it very difficult to be dependent on their partner or on benefits.

59 How can unemployment affect development?

Life events do not come along one at a time. One life event may be related to several others. For instance, someone who is in a relationship and has children is offered a promotion at work that involves moving house. They will have to learn new skills and their partner may have a job of their own that they have to give up. The children will have to change schools and everyone in the family will leave friends behind when they move.

...WORD CHECK

informal carers – those who look after individuals but who do not hold the qualifications to do so, for example, parents, spouses, partners, family.

SOURCES OF SUPPORT

Partners, family and friends

Partners, family and friends are often called **informal carers**. They can help by providing physical, emotional and social support to make it possible for us to cope with the effects of life events. By talking about our problems with others, they sometimes appear to be smaller than we thought. Sometimes talking to someone can bring clarity to the situation.

Most people who have a partner will turn to the partner first when they are ill or upset about something. Emotional support is one of the most important things that occurs in a partnership. It is very important to people that their partner understands how they feel about things and responds to them.

Other relatives and friends are important informal carers. They may offer physical support, such as cooking, washing or housework. This support may be short term – for example, someone who has had a baby will often need help after the birth. Friends may help out when we are ill.

Informal carers also give emotional support. Friends are important because they are people who individuals can share problems with, and will listen and understand why a person is upset. Social support is also important. For example, after a divorce or bereavement, an individual or a family may be lonely and isolated. Friends may visit and encourage the person to go out. This is very important if they are to meet new people and rebuild their lives.

▸ Friends and neighbours can help us to cope.

60 Who are informal carers?

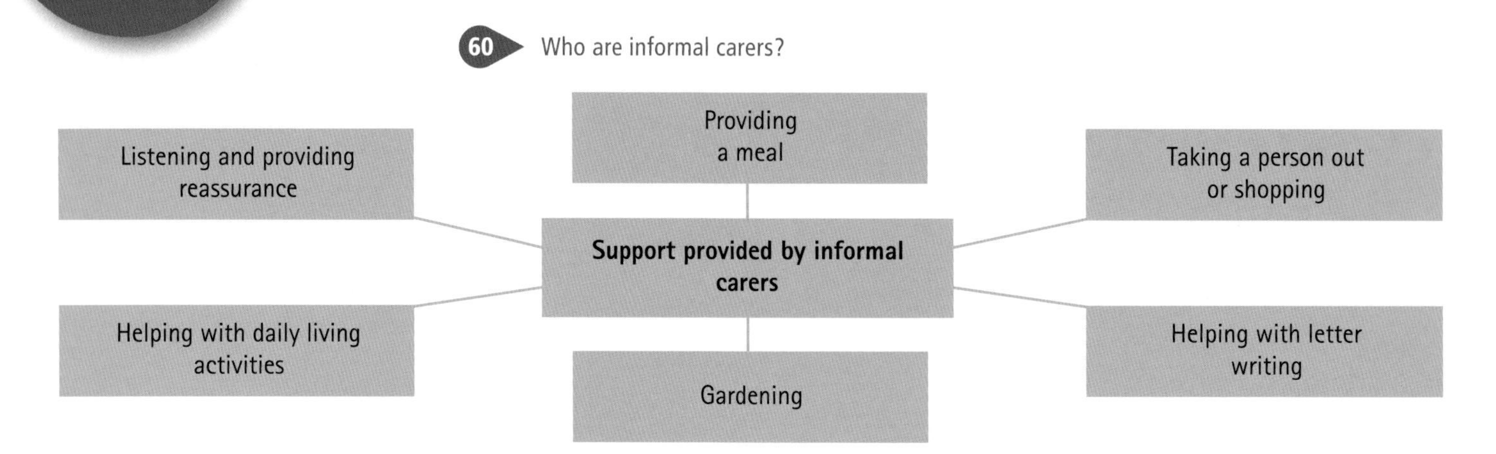

Informal carers can help a person to face up to the changes in their life. They can do this by setting short- and long-term goals or targets. Informal carers can encourage the individual to spend time in a positive way, for example, helping with charity work or learning a new hobby. Making practical suggestions is particularly helpful as the person can be involved in doing something positive to help.

How can informal carers help people to cope with change?

Professional carers and services

▲ Providing professional help.

Professional carers are people who are paid to look after individuals when they need help. This is particularly so when a life event has changed people's lives.

The role of a GP

- make an assessment of need
- talk about needs
- listen
- provide medication/sleeping tablets
- monitor health
- provide advice
- liaise with other agencies/professionals
- write a report
- provide information about all options available.

The role of a counsellor

- listen to individuals
- draw information from individuals
- clarify points
- help an individual to reflect on what
- has happened
- write reports
- liaise with other agencies/professionals.

Unit 1 provides more information about the different types of professional care workers but other examples are:

Professional	The help they provide
Home-care assistant	Helps with shopping, cleaning and preparing meals.
Midwife	Helps with the delivery of babies. Gives advice.
Social worker	Makes an assessment of a person's needs. Liaises with other professionals.
Occupational therapist	Assesses the adaptations needed to a person's home.

Group Activity

Work with another person to find out information about:

- three different health professionals
- three different social care professionals
- three different early years professionals.

Find out how each would help in the case of a life event.

How would each help an individual to cope?

Share your research as a whole group.

Group Activity

Work with another person to research the differences between informal carers and professional care workers. What different tasks are each likely to do? Compare the two.

Share your findings as a whole group.

While informal carers will do their best to help and provide support, sometimes professional help will be required. People who are professional care workers are trained to deal with some of the complex situations and life events that individuals and families have to cope with.

Voluntary and faith-based services

Many voluntary organizations provide information, support and services to help people cope with the effects of life events. Examples are:

Organization	How they would help
Citizens Advice Bureau	Refers people to specialist organizations
National Childbirth Trust	Helps people who are becoming parents
Relate	Helps people who are having marriage/relationship problems
CRUSE	Helps people who have suffered bereavement
Gingerbread	Is a self-help organization to support single parents
The Compassionate Friends	Helps people who are trying to come to terms with the loss of a child
Age Concern	Helps older people adapt to changes in their circumstances
Alzheimer's Disease Society and Dementia Care Trust	Provide support for carers of people with Alzheimer's disease and dementia
ChildLine and Kidscape	Gives advice and support to children in trouble or danger. This may be because of violence from their parents. It also includes problems at school, such as bullying

Group Activity

Work with another person to find out exactly how three of the voluntary groups in this table help individuals. How does each help the individual to cope?

Find out about two other voluntary groups not in the table.

What do they do? How do they help an individual to cope?

There are many religious faiths represented in Britain today. All faiths have ceremonies that help people through some of the most important life events. The majority religion in Britain is Christianity, although most people who are nominally Christian do not go to church. Even people who do not have a strong faith turn to the Church to help them through life events.

Having a faith or belief gives emotional and social support. Priests and other church workers, such as volunteers, can be very important in advising and comforting people during important life events.

62 How can having a faith or belief help us to cope with life events?

Without receiving help with life event changes some people may not be able to cope, because the life event will have had a major effect on their personal development. The result may be that they have very low self-esteem, become depressed or even suicidal. They may need medication to help them manage their depression or their inability to sleep. Without help, the situation could get worse. We all need to remember that we may need help when life events overtake us. We should not be afraid of asking for that help.

CASE STUDY Christopher

Christopher had a wife and a daughter aged five. He worked on a building site for 15 years. Christopher earned good money. The family lived in a semi-detached house but Christopher was still paying the mortgage and the family were reasonably well off.

One morning, Christopher was told that he was being made redundant as there was a credit crunch and orders for new houses were not coming in.

Christopher tried to get another job but so many other people also wanted jobs. He applied for 65 jobs but didn't get any of them. He became depressed. The money he had been given for redundancy started to run out and arguments broke out between Christopher and his wife. They became so bad that Christopher just walked out and only came back when he knew the family were in bed. Then he started going into the pub when he received his dole money and drank so much that there was no money left for food.

His wife decided that she could not put up with things any longer, so she left Christopher and went back to her mother, taking their little girl with her. Christopher continued to drink. He didn't pay the mortgage on the house or the bills. Eventually the house was re-possessed by the mortgage company. Christopher was homeless. He had lost everything!

1. Explain what is meant by 'being made redundant'.
2. How do you think that being made redundant affected Christopher's emotional and social development?
3. When Christopher was made redundant, which voluntary service could he have visited to get support? How would this service have provided help?
4. How could family and friends have helped when he was made redundant?
5. Explain the effect that the redundancy might have had on Christopher's wife.
6. How can faith-based organizations help people like Christopher cope with life changes?
7. Christopher had a child of five. How would the child's personal development be affected by the changes in the family circumstances?
8. What professional support could have helped Christopher to cope with the changes in his life? Explain how each would help.

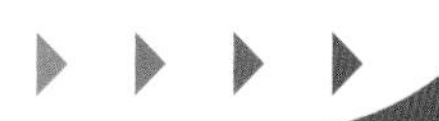

ASSESSMENT PRACTICE

1. Richard and Christine's child, aged four, dies from meningitis. They are provided with support to try and help them cope with the death of their child. The parents are supported by:
   - a counsellor
   - a GP
   - a health visitor.

   Describe how each could provide support for Richard and Christine. Explain how the actions of each professional care worker could help the family to cope. [10]

2. While out shopping, Mandy is hit by a car. She remains in hospital for several weeks as she is paralysed in her legs. Eventually, she is allowed home. She is provided with support by:
   - a physiotherapist
   - an occupational therapist
   - a health care assistant.

   Describe how each could provide support for Mandy. Explain how their actions could help her to cope. [10]

3. Describe how a hospital social worker and her family could provide support for Mandy, after her serious accident, to assist her through any changes necessary when she returns home. Explain how they will help her to cope. [10]

4. Lenny suddenly has a heart attack after which he finds it difficult to move. Since his heart attack, Lenny has been in hospital, but it is agreed that he will move home. Different formal and informal carers will help his recovery.

   Identify **three** different types of informal carers who could provide support for Lenny. Describe how each could provide different types of support. Then explain how the support could help him to cope. [10]

5. Sunny had broken ribs and two broken legs after a car accident.

   Identify **five** professional health and social care workers who could provide support for Sunny in his own home. Explain the support each would give and how they would help him to cope. [15]

3 Promoting Health and Well-being

Contents

About this unit

Well-being is the absence of disease and having good health. The term covers physical, intellectual, emotional and social factors showing that individuals are not prone to illness.

In this unit you will be asked to investigate the health and well-being of either yourself or another person, and to consider the feelings and pressures that the person chosen is likely to experience.

It is recommended that you select someone other than yourself to investigate, as this will enable you to consider the health of the individual, without having a personal bias. However, the person chosen must be someone who is accessible in order to obtain the information, as an interview or a survey will be needed to find out the facts about the person's health and well-being, and to explore positive and negative factors concerning the individual's health.

You will be asked to produce **two** plans. These include:

- a plan showing how you will conduct the investigation
- a health plan that will give details about how the individual can improve or maintain their health and well-being.

The information collected will need to be kept confidential so you will need to change the name of the individual for whom you are producing a health promotion plan.

The unit will be assessed internally by the staff in your centre and externally by OCR.

In this unit you will:

- Define the health and well-being of individuals.
- Interpret physical measures of health for individuals.
- Consider factors that contribute positively to health and well-being throughout a person's life.
- Consider the risks to health and well-being.
- Investigate health promotion and health promotion methods.

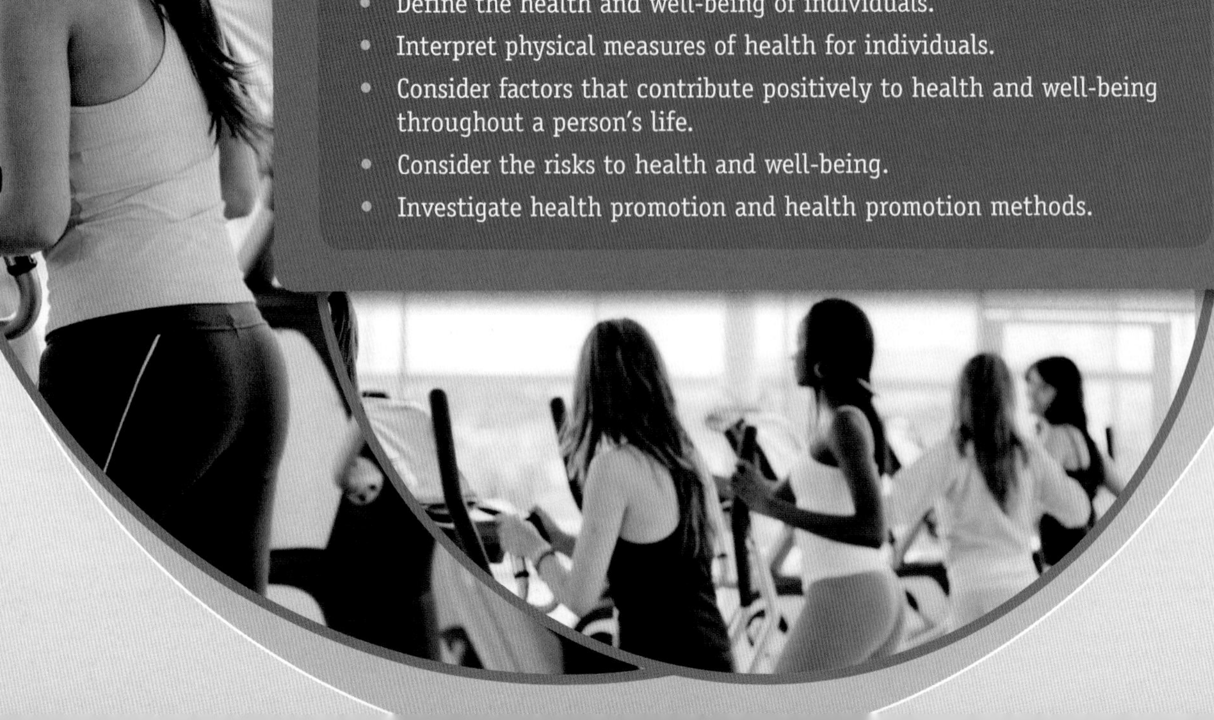

Introducing this unit

Imagine you have been asked to design a health promotion stand for the opening of a new Health Promotion Unit. The focus of the material for the stand that you have to prepare is the health of *one* individual *before* they have received a health promotion plan and the situation *after* they have been helped to improve their health and well-being.

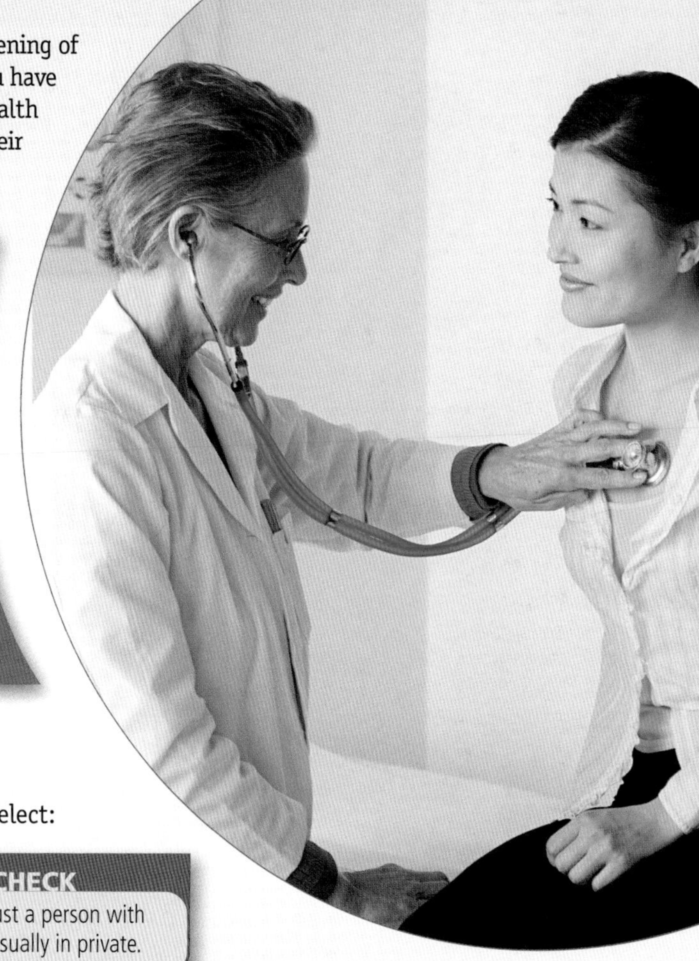

TO DO...

Before deciding who you will investigate, think about your own health.

- List **three** areas of your health that you know are strong points.
- List **three** areas of your health where you know improvements could be made.
- Share your thoughts with another person. How would you and the other person improve each of the three areas identified?
- How do you know which are the strong points about your own health?
- Have a whole-group discussion about the strong points and the improvements that could be made.

Who is going to be the focus of the health plan?

One person must be chosen as the focus of the health plan. You could select:

- a friend
- a member of your group
- a member of your immediate family
- a member of your extended family
- a neighbour
- yourself.

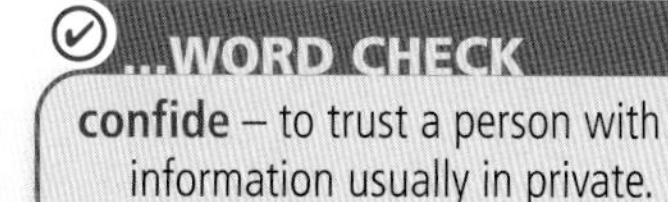

The table below shows an advantage and disadvantage for each group:

Group	Advantage	Disadvantage
A friend	You find it easy to talk to them	Your friendship may not last as long as the investigation
A member of the group	You would be with them every day so you could check on pieces of information required	The individual could get fed up with being continually questioned or they may be away for a long period of time
A member of your immediate family	There would probably be others in the family who would know the details if the person had forgotten anything	The family may not want others to know what is personal to them
A member of your extended family, for example, grandparent	They are older and would have the knowledge that you need to collect	They may not want to **confide** in you
A neighbour	You could contact them quite frequently if you had forgotten something	There may be times when they are not available due to work, holidays or other family commitments
Yourself	You will have access to all the information required	You may be biased about your own strengths and weaknesses

It will be very important to make the correct choice. You will have to ask yourself some questions before making a final decision, for example:

- Will I be able to access the individual easily?
- Will the individual have all the information I need?
- Will the individual be interested in helping with the topic?
- Does the individual need to have their health improved?
- Has the individual got the 'staying power' to see the project through to the end?

Make your choice of the person who you wish to select.

Obtain their permission, after outlining all that is involved.

Producing a plan to gather the information

In order to manage the investigation well, you will need to put a plan in place to make sure that you gather all the information that is needed. You will also need to produce a bibliography.

A plan can be made in:

- a pre-format form
- paragraphs.

A pre-format plan

A pre-format plan could look like the plan shown below:

Date	Action	Reason for action
12 October	Go to the library to look for books on health improvement	To gather information about which aspects of health could be improved, for example, diet, exercise, and so on.
14 October	Look for different definitions of health	To assemble material to write a meaningful definition for my investigation.

This plan is not complete but shows the date when certain things concerning the investigation will be done. It also indicates what actions are going to be taken, with the third column showing why they will need to be completed. The plan must show:

- the aim of the investigation
- the objectives of the investigation
- the purpose of the investigation.

...WORD CHECK

encompassing – covering or including all of an event or object.

An aim is the overall or **encompassing** outcome required. An aim could be:

'To improve the health and well-being of Fern, who is 45 years of age, by producing a health plan.'

The objectives are the steps that will be taken to achieve the aim, for example:

- to investigate Fern's current diet
- to explore where improvements are needed
- to find out how much exercise Fern does in one week and for how long
- to explore which forms of exercise Fern prefers
- to find out about Fern's intellectual health and consider how to improve it
- to explore other areas of Fern's life, such as environment, hygiene, work, finances, emotional health and well-being, and to consider how best to assist her with improvement
- to develop a plan that will help to improve Fern's health and well-being.

The purpose of the plan

The purpose of the plan in overall terms is to improve the health and well-being of the individual. Each person will have different aspects of their lives that may need to be improved. For example, for Fern, the purpose could be:

'To improve Fern's diet, her work–life balance and to make sure she has sufficient sleep.'

CASE STUDY Bartez

Bartez eats quite a lot of fatty food as he likes fish and chips, fried breakfasts and chocolate. He watches TV all evening except for Saturday evenings when he joins his neighbour for drinks at the local pub.

Bartez does not go to bed until 4:00am as he watches TV and drinks cans of beer while he does so. He is unemployed, so he does not need to get up early in the morning.

Money is short so Bartez saves by only showering once each week and wears his clothes for several days.

Work with another person to make a list of the:

- aims of a health plan for Bartez
- the objectives for the plan
- the purpose of the plan.

Making a bibliography

A **bibliography** is a record of all the sources of material that will be used during the investigation. It is sometimes also called a 'reference list' or 'sources of information'. A bibliography can include:

- primary sources of information – for example, information gained from people who may be professionals or individuals for whom the health plan is intended
- from secondary sources – from different books, magazines or journals
- from websites – for example, websites set up to give information about diet, exercise or support groups, and so on.

WORD CHECK

bibliography – a history or description of books and manuscripts, with notices of the different editions, the times when they were printed, and so on.

Work with another person to find:
- four books that would be useful to use for the investigation
- four websites that could provide useful information for the investigation
- one journal that would be useful for the investigation
- one professional organization or specialist (primary source) that could be helpful to the investigation – you may need to discuss this with others as you will need to work as a team.

Keep a bibliography of all of these.

A bibliography could be set out in a similar way to the example given below:

GCSE Health and Social Care for OCR: Double Award Student's Book, Angela Fisher, Stephen Seamons, Richard Cresswell and Mike Ancil, Folens Publishers, 2009.

Teamwork

Every day, as individuals, we work in different teams. This may be as a member of the family team, having different tasks to carry out in the home. In school we may be in a team for sports events, such as netball, or in a team when conducting an experiment in science. If we do not carry out our role well, other members of the team will be affected. If all members of the team do their very best then the team are likely to be successful.

In health, social care and early years sectors, professionals and support workers are part of a team, and the same principles apply. Professional care workers' main role is to improve the lives of those for whom they care. This cannot be achieved by just one person but through each member of the team knowing their particular tasks or roles and in working together to improve the clients' quality of life.

▲ Working as a team.

Gaining information from primary sources, that is the individuals who work in health promotion, is probably not a task that can be done individually, because professional care workers will have busy schedules and will not have time to spend talking with a large number of individuals. It will, therefore, be necessary to work as a team, allocating the work according to the skills of each person.

What information will the teams need and from whom?

Work in a group of four or five people to decide:
- Which professional organization and which professionals you could use to help gather information about the needs of individuals, how individuals may wish to improve their health and what methods could be used to do this.
- Make a plan of the tasks that the team would need to complete before meeting with the professional care worker.
- Share your decisions as a whole group.

You have probably decided that one of the organizations you could contact would be the Health Promotion Unit, as this organization works with individuals and groups to help improve health and well-being. Another professional care worker who could help with health improvement is a practice nurse in a GP's surgery or a dietician at a hospital or health centre.

Within your plan of the tasks that would need to be completed as a team would probably be:

- contacting the organization to see how they could help
- deciding which aspects of health improvements your individual is most likely to need
- drawing up questions to ask the individual of your choice about their current health
- finding out which aspects of their life need to be improved
- asking the specialist to visit your centre to answer questions about promoting the health of individuals
- producing questions to ask the professional care worker during the visit
- finding out which health promotion campaigns have been run locally
- investigating which methods have been used to promote the campaign.

These are just some of the tasks that you may have listed as a result of the discussions. There will be many more, but in order to work as a team, each person will need to be **committed** to the tasks that they have agreed to do.

Each person within the team will have **strengths**, that is, things they can do well, and there will also be things they are not so good at. The table below shows some strengths that can be found within a team.

...WORD CHECK

committed – making sure that the task/job is carried out to the highest quality.

strengths – activities or actions that a person or object is good at or good for.

Good at communicating with people	Prefers to carry out the tasks given rather than thinking of what they should do for themselves
Can draw and produce excellent artwork	Prefers to listen to the ideas of others and will make comments about them
Likes being a leader and can give clear directions	Will collect information from various sources but prefers someone else to write them up
Is reliable and will continue until the job is done	Likes to have an overview of the whole job rather than getting involved in the detail
Has good ideas to put forward	Has excellent computer skills
Writes clearly and accurately	Can take good notes and will write them up so that everyone can understand

It must be remembered that everyone in a team has some contribution to make. It is important that these strengths are identified before jobs are divided up. This way the best outcome is achieved.

ASSESSMENT PRACTICE: PREPARATION

You have been asked to produce a health plan for **one** individual to help them improve their health and well-being. A description of the individual's health and well-being, as it is currently, will need to be given; for example, their diet, exercise, and so on. Information about how to improve their health will also be needed in order to make a health plan. This information will be presented on a stall at the opening of a new Health Promotion Unit.

Before starting the project you must:

- Select the person for whom you will do the health plan. Write an outline **profile** of this person, for example, name (changed for confidentiality purposes), age, an outline of where they live and so on. This is a short profile about 'who they are'. This will not be finished but will provide a starting point for the investigation.
- Produce a plan that gives:
  - the aim
  - the objectives
  - the purpose.

  You will add to the plan as the work continues for the investigation.
- Look at a selection of resources that could be used for the investigation and start a bibliography.
- Continue with the plan, making decisions about:
  - who is to be in the team
  - which professional care workers you may contact
  - the strengths and weaknesses of those in the team so that jobs can be allocated at a later stage.

...WORD CHECK

profile – an outline or a description of an object or a person.

Define the health and well-being of individuals

What is health and well-being?

Getting started

There are several different ways of thinking about health and well-being:

- health and well-being can be described as the absence of physical illness, disease and mental distress – this is a negative definition of health and well-being
- health and well-being can be described as the achievement and maintenance of physical fitness and mental stability – this is a positive definition of health and well-being
- health and well-being can be described as being the result of a combination of physical, social, intellectual and emotional factors – this is an holistic definition of health and well-being.

You should know that ideas about health and well-being change over time and vary between different cultures.

This section could also help with Task 2 of the Assignment.

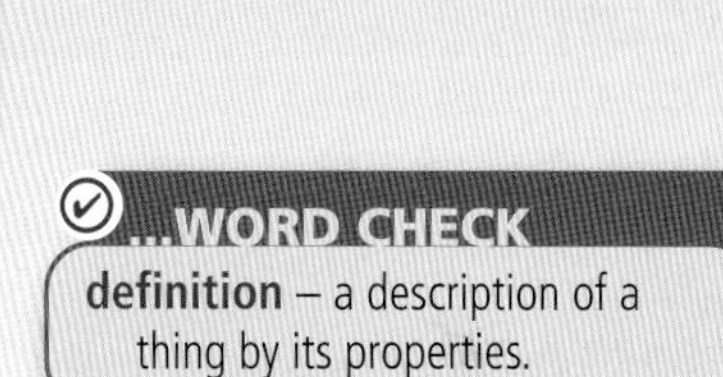

DEFINING HEALTH AND WELL-BEING

There are a number of ways to describe health. The Health Promotion Agency supports the view of the World Health Organization (WHO) whose **definition** is that health is 'a state of complete physical, mental and social well-being and not merely the absence of disease or infirmity'. Health is a fundamental human right and is placed at the highest possible level of worldwide importance. Those working to promote health view it as being a resource that is needed to support everyone in their day-to-day life.

Health is a fundamental human right.

Health is often seen differently by individuals and there are a number of ways of describing health. Health can be described as:

The absence of physical illness, diseases and mental distress.

OR

The achievement and maintenance of physical fitness and mental stability.

OR

An holistic combination of a variety of physical, intellectual, emotional and social factors that provide a person with a feeling of being healthy.

...WORD CHECK

empower – to give control to a person or group.

Health is important to everyone at every life stage, be it infancy, adolescence or later adulthood. Money cannot buy health but lifestyle choices can affect it. Although health education campaigns can be costly, they can save the NHS billions of pounds in the long term. This is because health campaigns can **empower** clients by giving them information to help them to make life-changing choices that could improve their health and well-being.

Achieving good health has many positive benefits; however, what is considered to be good health can change as people age. As people get older, they will often understand that their level of health is limited by:

- the physical condition of their body
- the understanding of their health
- their emotions and their state of mind
- their social situation.

The health of a person can be constantly changing, and maintaining health requires regular monitoring and support.

Where do health promotion campaigns originate?

Group Activity

Find out more about *'Our Healthier Nation'* and *'Choosing Health'*.

Make a handout to show the main purposes of these campaigns.

Share the information with others.

Health promotion campaigns could come from:

Local health promotion teams (from the Primary Care Trusts) – they base their campaigns around nationally set health events with local teams choosing their own particular targets, depending on the health issues within their area. Such events could include:

- no smoking day
- breastfeeding awareness
- heart week
- sexual health week
- world mental health day
- world AIDS day
- five a day

Government sources could be based on the government white papers: *'Our Healthier Nation'* (1997) and the more recent *'Choosing Health'* (2004).

The government targets for reducing illness and disease were:

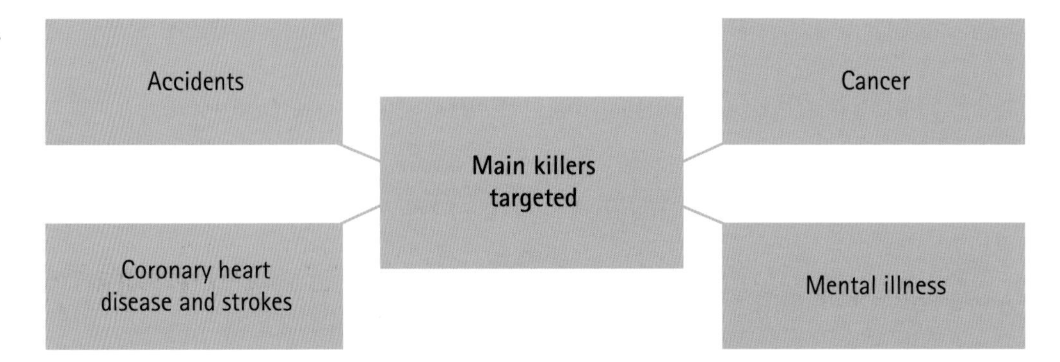

Government-targeted main killers.

If these areas were targeted, the government hoped to achieve:

Main killer of under 75s	Reduce death rate by year 2010	Actual number saved
Cancer	1/5	100,000
Coronary heart disease and strokes	2/5	200,000
Accidents	1/5 (serious surgery at least 1/10)	12,000
Mental health	1/5	4000

It was strongly considered by the government that individuals could improve their own health through:

- having a better diet, for example, a balanced diet
- taking more exercise
- giving up smoking.

To encourage individuals to achieve this, in 2004, the government introduced the white paper, '*Choosing Health: Making Choices Easier*' where the main priorities were:

- reducing the number of people who smoke
- reducing obesity and improving diet and nutrition
- encouraging sensible drinking of alcohol
- increasing exercise
- improving sexual health
- improving mental health.

It must be recognized that ideas about health and well-being will change over time although the priorities given above are still current, particularly as obesity and the abuse of alcohol is growing.

CASE STUDY Pradeep and Angelina

Pradeep

Pradeep is 25 years old and works as a financial assistant for a bank. He is studying for his examinations while he is working. At lunchtime he has a takeaway bread roll and a drink, and collects his evening meal from different takeaway shops on his way home. He watches TV most nights but goes clubbing on a Friday evening with his friends.

Angelina

Angelina is overweight and does very little exercise. She thinks she eats very little and cannot understand why she is putting on weight. She does drink quite a lot of alcohol each evening, but takes the dog for a short walk before she settles down to TV and a drink.

1. What advice would you give each individual regarding their health?
2. What type of health promotion campaign might help each of them?
3. Which professional care workers could assist each of them?

Collecting the information from the chosen person

Two of the best methods of assessing a person's needs are an interview or a questionnaire. They both have advantages and disadvantages, so your choice will depend on:

- the amount of time the chosen person will have
- the amount of time you have
- the details needed for the investigation.

Both methods have strengths and weaknesses:

Research method	Strengths	Weaknesses
Interviews	People have the freedom to give an answer in their own words and in their own time.	Time and privacy are both needed to carry out an interview. People often do not answer all of the questions because they are embarrassed.
Questionnaires	Data can be collected without intimidating the person completing the questionnaire.	May not get the questionnaires back, and also you have no control. People often do not answer all of the questions or may not tell the truth.

...WORD CHECK

status – a person's position within a society or organization.

What information do we need?

In order to produce a health plan or to make suggestions about a health plan, it will be necessary to investigate the current health **status** of the individual. Questions will need to be formed about the individual's:

- physical state of health, for example, what they eat or how much exercise they do
- intellectual state, for example, how they stimulate their mind
- emotional state of well-being, for example, if they feel valued
- social state of well-being, for example, the support they receive, friendships.

Conducting a survey is a way of gathering information about a certain subject, in this case, to find out about the health status of the person chosen so that a plan can be produced to make improvements to different aspects of their health and well-being. Before starting to collect information, the person who is conducting the survey will have to decide which data collecting tool or method(s) will be best to get the information that is needed.

There are a range of methods that could be used for the collection of information, for example:

- interviewing people
- using questionnaires
- observation of people or situations
- carrying out experiments.

Sometimes more than one method is used to gather information for a survey, depending on the subjects that information is required about. For this survey, which is based on 'current health status of an individual', the focus of information gathering is to be:

- through interviews

  and/or
- by using questionnaires.

Such methods will produce both **quantitative** and **qualitative** data. Quantitative data is numerical and can be analysed using mathematical methods. An example of a question that produces quantitative data would be, 'How many times do you take exercise each week?' This would need a **follow-on question** to find out the type of exercise the person does. When producing questions for the survey, you may need to include some follow-on questions in order to collect all the information needed and to obtain the whole picture of what is happening as far as health and well-being is concerned. Quantitative data can be displayed using graphs, charts and tables.

Qualitative data concerns attitudes and opinions and often cannot be produced in numerical form. The participants might talk about their feelings; for example, a client may say 'I feel I need to stimulate my mind more as I am bored most of the time'. Qualitative data is expressed in words and not in numbers.

Both qualitative and quantitative data can produce useful and meaningful results.

...WORD CHECK

quantitative – information that is collected through a survey/questionnaire that will lead to numerical analysis.

qualitative – information that is based on spoken or written responses from people.

follow-on question – something that is extra to or continues on from.

Interviews

An interview involves asking a person questions in a 'face-to-face' situation. The person being interviewed has probably agreed to take part beforehand. The interviewer will have prepared questions for the interview. When planning and carrying out the interviews you should:

- ask permission to carry out the interview
- arrange a mutually convenient date and time
- prepare questions to make sure you gather the required information – you may need to trial questions before use to make sure they produce the answers required
- avoid bias – do not lead the person answering in the way you ask the questions
- consider recording the interview so that you can concentrate on asking the questions and listening to the responses – you must ask the individual's permission to do this
- maintain confidentiality – do not use the full names of those involved
- prepare a transcript of the interview so that results can be analysed.

▲ 'Can you tell me … ?'

Structured interviews

A structured interview is when the person gathering the information (the researcher) meets with the participant(s) and the researcher then asks a prepared list of questions, with little help. The data (information) collected from this type of interview is likely to be quantitative, but a limited amount of qualitative data will also be gained.

The advantage of using a structured interview is that response rates are usually quite good, the researcher knows who is answering the questions and **prompts** and **probes** can be used to encourage responses.

...WORD CHECK

prompts – something that reminds you to do something.

probes – to get a response by a continuous action.

In-depth interviews

This is where the person collecting the information meets with the participant and allows them to talk freely about a particular topic. As the aim of this type of interview is to encourage the participant to get their true feelings across, only qualitative data is collected. The advantage of using in-depth interviews is that participants are able to open up on sensitive issues, as there is no structure and the researcher can explore any interesting areas that arise. The disadvantage is that the interviewer can influence the answers given.

Questionnaires

...WORD CHECK

self-completed – filled in/answered by an individual not by someone else on their behalf.

A **self-completed** questionnaire is one where the researcher hands out questionnaire forms to the participants, who then answer the questions by filling in the answers in the spaces provided. The forms are then collected by the researcher when they have been completed. This is a good way of collecting qualitative data. The advantages of using questionnaires are that it is cheap, quick, can be anonymous and a way to collect information without interviewer bias. Participants can also take their time to answer the questions.

When using a questionnaire:

- begin with easy-to-answer closed questions and work towards questions that need more thought, open questions, at the end
- include a short introduction that explains why the survey is being carried out and covers the issue of confidentiality
- ask factual response questions.

Remember:

- to make sure the questions are easy to understand
- do not use questions that allow the respondent to repeat previous answers
- do not assume the person answering has any previous knowledge of the topics you are asking about
- thank the individual for completing the questionnaire when it is finished.

Group Activity

Continue to produce the plan already started for the investigation. Decisions will need to be made about:

- which questions to ask
- how the questions will be grouped
- how the results are to be presented, for example, graphs, charts.

Ideas for the method could come from secondary research into the topic of quality practice from the work of others who have already completed similar research topics. Secondary sources can provide data that would be difficult to collect for oneself. For example, government papers, research papers and statistics completed after inspection reports may all help you to make decisions about the methods that should be used for conducting the survey.

Planning will help with the organization of thoughts and to put things into the correct sequence or order. A plan for research, for example, could look like the one given below:

Date	Action	Reason for action
6 January ½ hour	Research three secondary sources of information about health campaigns and make notes	To find out what research has been done previously and the methods used.
9 January ½ hour	Decide on aims, objectives, methods to be used, timescales, who to gather information from	To help inform the process, for example, 'What do I want to find out?'
12 January ½ hour	Letter to chosen person and/or professional carer to explain the research, with examples of questions	To get permission to use the professional care worker. To give advanced notice of the questions that will be asked.
15 January 1 hour	Plan structured interview/survey questions for the chosen person and/or professional carer, and group them together in an organized sequence	To make sure that there is full coverage of all the topics. To make sure the questions are appropriate and not ambiguous. To make sure all the questions on one particular topic are grouped together.

The sequence of the questions cannot be decided until the questions themselves are written. Before even that is done, the topics to be included in the survey must be decided.

The topics that will need to be investigated are:

Physical health

Intellectual health

Emotional health

Social health

...WORD CHECK

aspects – parts of a theory or a concept.

functioning – something that is active or working.

judgements – decisions that are made by one or more people.

These are known as **aspects** or features of health.

▲ Keeping physically fit.

Physical health

Physical health is how our body is **functioning**. If an individual is fit and healthy they can be said to be in good physical health.

Intellectual health

Intellectual health is where we show our ability to think, learn, and make decisions and **judgements**. An individual's intellectual health is maintained by everyday activities. A person is always learning from changes that happen around them and decisions that they make. Everything that is read, watched and listened to has an effect on an individual's intellectual health. Good intellectual health can help an individual to find solutions to challenging situations.

Emotional health

Emotional health involves the ability to understand and recognize personal feelings. These include happiness, anger and fear. How we feel will depend on what is happening around us. Often emotions are shown through the expression on our face or in our body language.

Social health

All human beings are involved in relationships with other people. An individual's friends and family often influence the way that they think and feel. A person will also be affected by where they live, their education, their job and how much money they have. All of these can have big or small effects on health and well-being.

1 What is your definition of health and well-being?

Health and well-being can be a complex subject. All of its components are affected by events that occur on a daily basis. It is the physical, intellectual, emotional and social aspects of the individual chosen that need to be investigated.

Each of these topics will need to be broken down into smaller parts. For example:

Physical health

1 Do you have a healthy diet?
2 Can you tell me what you have for meals each day?
3 Do you eat snacks between meals?
4 If 'yes' could you tell me what you eat?

Intellectual health

1 Do you have a job?
2 How does your job intellectually stimulate you?

Emotional health

1 Would you say you are happy for most of the time?
2 What makes you feel happy?

Social health

1 Do you have any free time to meet friends?
2 Do you have a good relationship with your family?

Once all the topics and the parts have been listed, the questions can be correctly formed. It must be remembered that the focus of the survey is on current health status, so questions must be focused on this topic. Make sure you use both 'open' and 'closed' questions.

An example of an open question is:

'Tell me why you think you have a healthy diet?'

The question allows the person being interviewed or surveyed to give their thoughts and feelings on the subject, as well as being able to talk about the facts.

An example of a closed question is:

'What is your height and weight?'

The individual can give specific facts to answer this question.

...WORD CHECK

unambiguous – uncomplicated and easy to understand.

Before putting your questions to the participant, it is always a good idea to 'trial' the questions. This means trying them on another person to see if they are **unambiguous** and that they produce the type of answers that are needed. Questions could be tried by giving them to other people in the group, relatives or friends. Being able to trial questions provides the opportunity to alter any questions that are not clear.

ACTIVITY Collecting information

You have been asked to collect information about the health status of **one** individual.

1. Work in pairs to produce **four** research questions for each of the aspects of health to find out about the physical, intellectual, emotional and social health status of an individual.
2. Share your questions with another pair within the group and ask them to try answering the questions. Did you get the type of answers you were looking for? Rewrite any questions that were **ambiguous** or were not successful.
3. As a whole group, discuss some of the issues that have arisen when producing the questions.
4. Work in a small group to think about qualitative data that you might want to collect about the individual's health status. Work out the main topics.
5. Write **five** questions that could be used in an in-depth interview with an individual, including at least one follow-on question.

Drawing conclusions

When drawing conclusions, remember they must be clearly directed to the questions asked. A summary needs to be made about how the individual views their own health for physical, intellectual, emotional and social health and well-being. For example:

'Fern views her physical health as being reasonable but does realize that she is on the borderline of obesity and that she needs to lose weight. She thinks she should eat less starchy foods and include more fruit and vegetables in her diet.'

'Fern thinks that she is basically happy but sometimes when the children keep on and on she loses her temper and shouts at them.'

In order to make definite conclusions about Fern's health status, the person conducting the interview will need to compare Fern's answers with the **norms** or **averages** of development to **calculate** how her health can be improved. The table below gives some ideas on how this can be achieved:

...WORD CHECK

norms – that which is considered normal for the majority of the population.

averages – an arithmetical mean, mean proportion, medial sum or quantity, made out of unequal sums or quantities.

calculate – to make a calculation; to forecast consequences; to estimate; to compute.

Fern's responses	Norm or average	Improvements needed
Hardly any fruit or vegetables in diet	5 portions of fruit and vegetables per day	Increase by at least 4 portions each day
Amount of exercise 10 minutes each day	30 minutes at least 5 times each week	Increase by 20 minutes each day
No real mental stimulation except TV	A good balance of work and play required	Include a mental challenge for Fern, for example, reading, crosswords, learning something new
Drinking 16 units of alcohol per week	14 units should be the upper limit	Try to reduce consumption by more than two units

Producing a table such as this from the responses will begin to help show where there is a definite need for improvement in health and well-being. A table on its own is not really enough to gain marks in the higher grades and it may be useful to discuss the table in a meaningful way. For example:

'Fern never eats more than one portion of fruit and vegetables each day and even when she does eat vegetables, it is usually peas, which only have a little vitamin C. I will need to ensure that Fern has five portions of fruit and vegetables each day as this is the government's recommendation, in '*Choosing Health*'. This could be done by varying the vegetables and introducing foods rich in vitamin C, which are oranges, blackcurrants and green vegetables.'

From this sample it can be seen that the writer has given more detail and referred to theory such as the government initiative '*Choosing Health*'.

Different theorists could be included such as Maslow and his 'pyramid of needs' (see page 5). Using such a diagram, the writer of the conclusions above could refer to the different levels of need and indicate how the chosen individual is or is not meeting those needs at the different levels. It would also help if a diary of current eating patterns and/or exercise were included, so that close comparisons could be made with the averages recommended, and the differences explained.

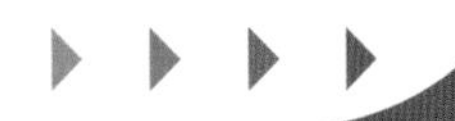

ASSESSMENT PRACTICE: PREPARATION

You have been asked to conduct a survey to find out how an individual maintains their health and to investigate any improvements needed.

1. Give a comprehensive explanation of what the terms 'good health and well-being' and 'poor health and well-being' mean. Try to give examples to explain the points made.
2. For the **one** person chosen, prepare detailed interview questions and/or a questionnaire that will help you collect the information required. Trial the questionnaire with others to make sure the questions are clear and unambiguous.
3. Draw up a recording document that groups the questions in order within the topic and gives space to record the answers given. Group the questions under physical, intellectual, emotional and social factors.
4. Write a letter to the chosen person asking if it is possible to conduct the survey. Give them a copy of the questions that you will ask during your visit.
5. Conduct the survey.
6. Analyse the results of the survey and present them in the form of a report, drawing conclusions that make accurate references to interpreting the information correctly.

Interpret physical measures of health for individuals

How can an individual's physical health be measured?

Getting started

Individuals are being encouraged to take responsibility for their own health and as a result most people are more aware of the different types of health measurements that are available. Some measurements of health can be taken in the comfort of the individual's own home, for example, height and weight or pulse. Others are taken on a regular basis by professional care staff.

▼ You will learn that some indicators of physical health can be measured. You will know how the measures listed below can be taken and are used to assess the state of an individual's physical health:

- blood pressure
- peak flow
- height and weight/body mass index
- waist to hip ratio
- resting pulse and recovery after exercise.

▼ You should know that a person's age, sex and lifestyle have to be taken into account when interpreting the measurement that is recorded.

MEASURING HEALTH

There are a variety of factors that influence an individual's health, which means there must be a variety of ways to measure health. When visiting the health clinic, GP or the hospital, there is a range of tests available to measure health. It is not only professionals that can measure health. Anyone can monitor their own health but some measurements are best made by professional care workers. Measurements of health can include:

- blood pressure
- peak flow
- height and weight/body mass index
- waist to hip ratios
- resting pulse and recovery rate (after exercise)

When health workers carry out these tasks they refer to them as clinical tests. When carrying out tests they use conventional **SI units** to calculate results. Health professionals will take **physical** and **physiological** measurements. The word physical indicates basic measurements like weight and temperature. Physical health is often measured using charts. These can be graphs or tables that provide information. Various types of charts have been produced over the years by the different health care professions. Their purpose is to show the **range** of normal readings, which helps highlight abnormal readings when they occur. These include body mass index and

...WORD CHECK

SI units – scientific units of measurement, for example, kilograms, kilojoules.

physical – relating to the body as distinguished from the mind or spirit.

physiological – actions or events relating to body function and chemical processes.

range – a differing collection of results.

height–weight charts. A health worker measures an individual and then compares the measurement to the measurement that is commonly considered to be the 'norm' across the population. One of the best examples of this is a height–weight ratio chart. This compares height against the weight of a person. This chart can be used both by health care professionals and by ourselves to monitor whether people are the correct weight for their height.

Physiological measurements show how the body **functions** and measures these functions. Examples of this are blood pressure and peak flow, which will be looked at later on page 191.

Blood pressure

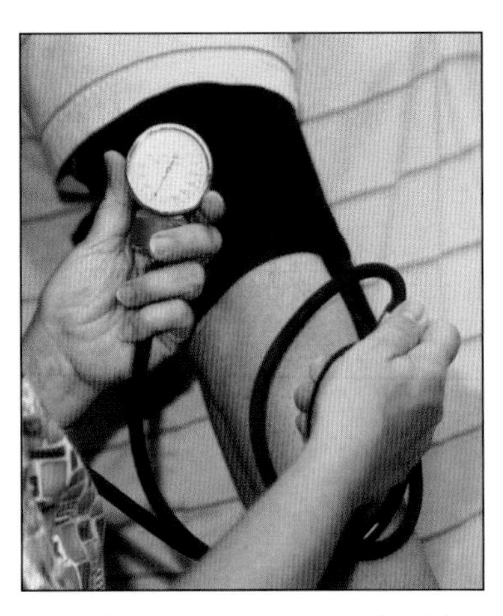

▲ A sphygmomanometer is used to take blood pressure.

Blood pressure is made up of more than one measurement. It is the measurable force on the vessels that is created when the heart pumps blood around the body. This will vary in different people due to age, weight or illness.

The two letters BP are often used to represent blood pressure. Two measurements are taken to measure blood pressure. They are known as the **systolic** pressure and the **diastolic** pressure.

The force of the blood pumping out of the heart creates the systolic pressure. The diastolic pressure is a measurement of the continuous pressure put upon the arteries as the heart relaxes.

To measure these pressures, a **sphygmomanometer** is used. It is easier to say '**sphyg**' for short.

A sphygmomanometer consists of an inflatable rubber cuff that is wrapped around the upper arm. This is connected by two tubes to a pressure gauge that has a column of mercury. There are also new sphygmomanometers with digital displays. These are often referred to as **digital osimeters**.

With a **stethoscope** the operator listens to the brachial artery in the bend of the elbow. The cuff is then pumped up until the operator can no longer hear the pulse. At this point the pressure outside equals the pressure of blood inside the artery and this is the systolic pressure. The cuff is then slowly released and the column of mercury begins to fall and the pulse returns. As the sound of the last beat disappears, the operator looks at the column of mercury or display; they now take a reading. This gives them the second reading, the diastolic pressure. Electronic blood pressure meters take the pressures in a similar way but automatically.

It must be remembered that blood pressure should only be taken by a trained person (unless using an electronic device). If it is done incorrectly it can be painful and sometimes dangerous.

The average blood pressure of a young, fit person is expected to be in the region of:

120/80 (120 = systolic, 80 = diastolic).

Doctors take into account factors that include height, weight and age when diagnosing high blood pressure. Stress can also cause blood pressure to rise. If an individual's systolic pressure is higher than 160 and/or their diastolic is over 100, then they are clinically at risk from high blood pressure. This is also known as **hypertension**. Persistent high blood pressure can lead to problems such as a **stroke (cerebro-vascular accident)**. This is when a small blood vessel in the brain bursts. This causes damage to that area of the brain. If this happens, a person can lose the ability to speak and move. A stroke can sometimes cause death.

2 What does a sphygmomanometer measure?

3 Describe how to take a person's blood pressure.

...WORD CHECK

functions – works or operates.
systolic – the force created in blood pressure.
diastolic – the rhythmical expansion or dilatation of the heart and arteries.
sphygmomanometer – a device for measuring blood pressure that is strapped to the arm.
sphyg – the shortened name for the above device.
digital osimeters – a digital blood pressure measuring device.
stethoscope – an acoustic device placed in the ears for listening to a person's breathing.
hypertension – high blood pressure.
stroke (cerebro-vascular accident) – a blood clot or a burst blood vessel in the brain.

Respiration

The body is made up from cells, which all need oxygen to function. The blood absorbs oxygen in the lungs during the action of breathing. At rest, breathing is usually at a rate of 15–20 breaths in every minute. This is the **average respiration rate**. As activity increases, so does respiration rate. This is because activity in the body uses up extra oxygen, so you have to breathe faster to replace it.

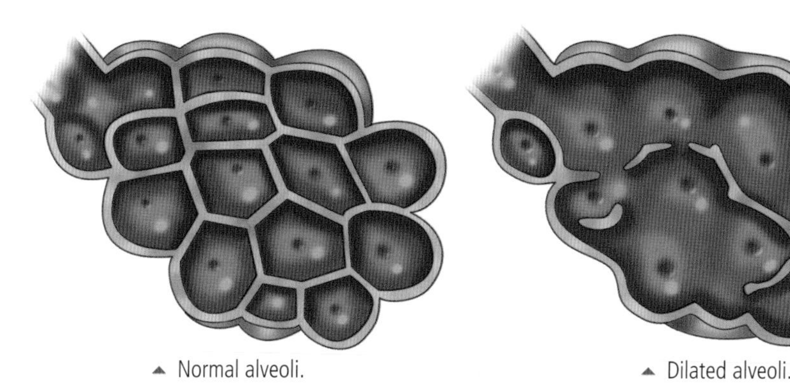

▲ Normal alveoli.

▲ Dilated alveoli.

Illness and disease can also affect respiration rate. Asthma causes a reduction in air flow to the little air sacs (alveoli) in the lungs. This will reduce the amount of air getting in and reduce the amount of oxygen being absorbed. It then causes an increase in the rate of respiration. The wheeze that can be heard when a person has a chest infection is the air being forced along narrowed airways.

These air sacs (alveoli) can also become too big because of a disease known as **emphysema**. This is not an advantage because the surface area that absorbs the oxygen decreases as they become bigger. This is because bigger air sacs take up more space, so there are fewer of them. This causes continuous gasping for air and often the only solution is an oxygen mask or **nasal cannula**.

4 What is asthma?

...WORD CHECK

average respiration rate – the normal rate at which a person breathes.

emphysema – a lung dysfunction that makes breathing very difficult and reduces activity.

nasal cannula – a tube placed into the nose.

peak flow meter – a device for measuring forced expiration of air from the lungs.

Peak flow

Watching someone breathe will only give basic information. To be more accurate, the measurement of the amount of air breathed out and the force with which it happens is required. This can be obtained by using a **peak flow meter**.

This simple machine measures the maximum rate at which a person blows out (expels) air from the lungs in one second. To do this, they just breathe out hard into the peak flow meter. The scale on the side will give the reading in millilitres per second. This can be compared to a table of expected scores.

People with chronic lung disease or bad asthma will normally score below 350, whereas a fit person will score in the region of 500–600 on the scale. Very fit athletes can almost blow the needle off the scale.

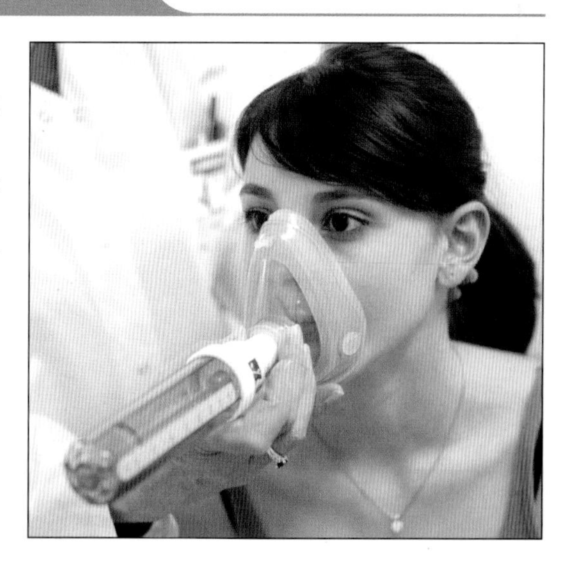

▶ Measuring breathing rate with a peak flow meter.

CASE STUDY Brad

Brad has smoked a lot since he was 15 years old and he is now 35. He is having difficulty breathing, particularly when he tries to walk anywhere. As a result, he does little exercise. He is still able to work part time as he is a telephone operator, which means he is sitting down. Brad visits his GP for some advice.

The GP advises Brad that he urgently needs to stop smoking and to adapt his lifestyle. The GP also takes some health measurements so that he can help Brad in more detail.

1. The GP does a peak flow test for Brad. Explain how this would be done and the results it would show.
2. The GP is interested to know what Brad's blood pressure is. Explain how the GP would take Brad's blood pressure and how it would be calculated.
3. What is the norm for blood pressure? How are norms calculated?

Height and weight

...WORD CHECK

proportional – related by or possessing a constant ratio.

obese – very overweight, having a body mass index of over 30.

The relationship between height and weight can be a good indicator of the state of an adult's health. As a rule, a person's weight should be **proportional** to their height. By looking at the whole population, scientists have worked out the weight a person should be for their height. A person will be considered to be **obese** when their weight is 20% or more above the normal average weight for people of the same height. To make this as accurate as possible, scientists base this on individuals with similar personal and cultural characteristics. From this they have produced a general chart that gives a range of comparisons of height against weight.

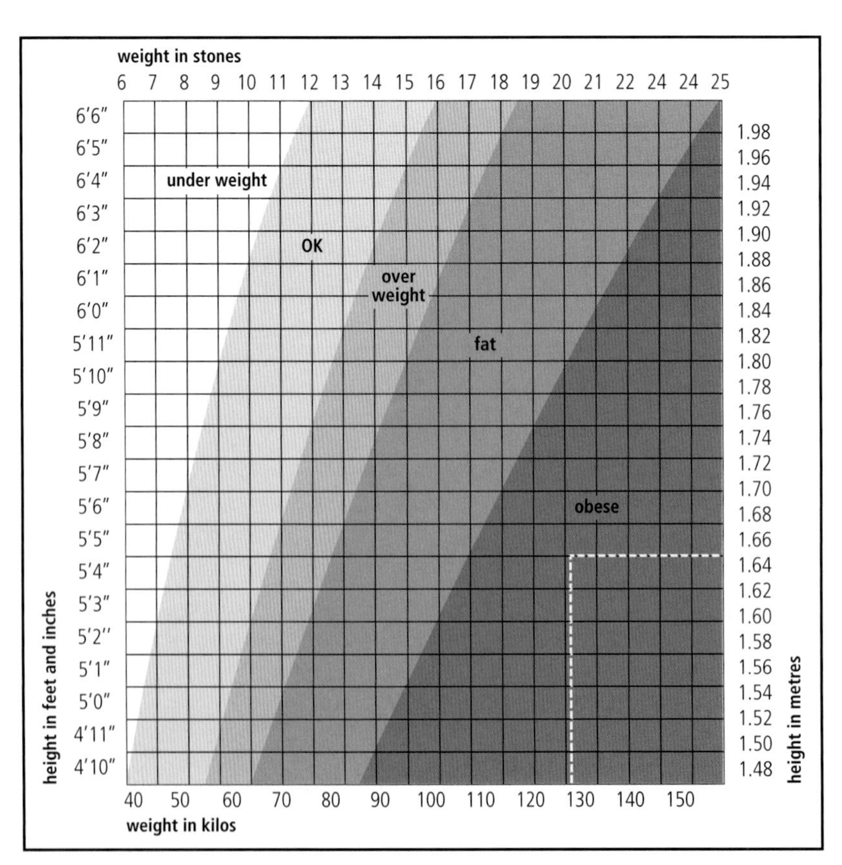

A height–weight chart.

The chart provides us with information about categories that go from underweight to obese. By reading the two measurements (height and weight) for the person from the chart, and looking at the point where the two meet, it is possible to see exactly what 'category' a person will fit, for example, obese.

ACTIVITY Weighing and measuring

1. Weigh and measure four other people who agree to it. Plot the measurements on the chart provided. What 'categories' do they fall into?
2. How can knowing height and weight measurements help when working out a health plan for a person?
3. Use the height and weight of a famous person who is overweight and draw up a diet plan for one day for this person.

It has to be remembered that this is a **generalized** system and this does not always provide an accurate result.

Let us think about an Olympic weightlifter weighing in at 100kg and 1.80m. Our chart would label him fat. He needs to be muscular for the work he is doing and this makes him heavy. So there are **exceptions**, which means that we cannot use a single method in **isolation**, as it can be inaccurate.

5 What does the word obese mean?

...WORD CHECK

generalized – not special or particular, having a relation to all.

exceptions – something that is not included and is exempt from the effects of what is happening.

isolation – to be alone or excluded.

Body mass index (BMI)

Another measurement that could be used is body mass index (BMI).

Looking at the height–weight chart, the weightlifter appears to be fat. How does he measure up using the BMI test? A BMI test is a straightforward calculation that will give an index number. Again, scientists have worked out, by using statistics, what the healthy normal range is.

The calculation looks like this:

$$\text{BMI} = \frac{\text{body weight (kg)}}{\text{height (m}^2)}$$

In the weightlifter's case he still does not fit into the scientists' category of 'normal' even though he is a picture of health.

6 Work out the weightlifter's BMI.

For the weightlifter the balance of body tissues is different to that of the average man in the street. He has very little body fat and much more muscle than normal.

With his weight being 100kg and his height being 1.80m, the calculation will look like this.

$$\text{BMI} = \frac{100}{1.8^2} = 30.9$$

His index number of 30.9 is above the normal range of 20–24 for men (19–24 for women).

Having a number over 30 puts him in the obese range, which is obviously incorrect. His body is made up of more muscle than fat, which has confused the calculation. This is because most people do not normally have such a large amount of muscle tissue.

For most people, this system works well. This is because the extra weight that is carried by many people is usually fat. The super-fit weightlifter is an exception.

ACTIVITY Calculating BMI

1. Try calculating your own BMI and compare the results with the table below:

Weight group	BMI (kg/m²)	Obesity class
Underweight	<18.5	
Normal	18.5–24.9	
Overweight	25.0–29.9	
Obese	30.0–34.9 35.0–39.9	I II
Extreme obesity	40.0+	III

2. Now try calculating the BMI for another person in the group.
3. Explain how knowing a person's BMI would help the development of a plan of exercise for the person.

Waist to hip ratio

...WORD CHECK
circumference – the line that goes round or encompasses a circular figure; a periphery.

Waist to hip ratio is one of the predictors of risk for heart disease and diabetes. So what does their shape say about that person? Waist to hip ratio (WHR) is the ratio of the **circumference** of the waist to that of the hips. It is calculated by measuring the waist circumference (located just above the upper hip bone at the joint). That measurement is then divided by the hip circumference at its widest part. WHR has been found to be a more efficient predictor of mortality in older people but is not considered totally accurate when used on its own.

Are you an apple or a pear?

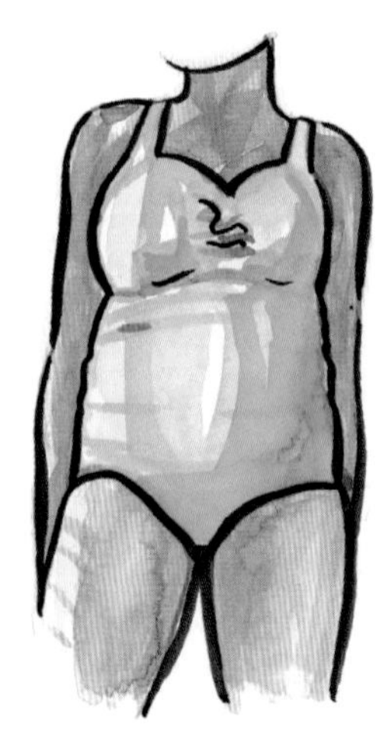

Are you an apple or a pear?

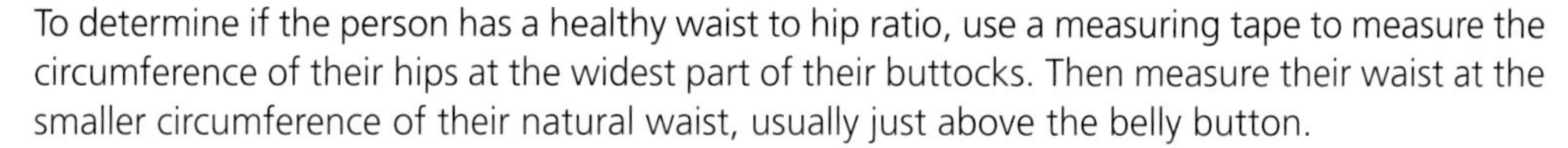

To determine if the person has a healthy waist to hip ratio, use a measuring tape to measure the circumference of their hips at the widest part of their buttocks. Then measure their waist at the smaller circumference of their natural waist, usually just above the belly button.

To determine the ratio, divide their waist measurement by their hip measurement.

For a female, a waist measurement of 75cm (30 inches) divided by a hip measurement of 90cm (36 inches) equals a WHR of 0.83.

This appears to indicate that they are close to being at an increased risk of heart disease and diabetes.

However:

A waist measurement of 70cm (28 inches) divided by hip measurement of 90cm (36 inches) equals a WHR of 0.77.

This appears to be within the healthy range.

A ratio of more than 0.95 for men and 0.85 for women may mean they have a predisposition to heart disease, and should be extra careful with their diet and lifestyle.

Research shows that people with 'apple-shaped' bodies (with more weight around the waist) face more health risks than those with 'pear-shaped' bodies who carry more weight around the hips. It's all related to the distribution of fat in the body. 'Apple-shaped' people predominantly store fat in the abdominal area and are more likely to have health-related risks than those who are 'pear-shaped'.

...WORD CHECK

pulse – the beat of the heart that can be felt by pressing against an artery.

respiration – the inhalation and exhalation of air (breathing).

ACTIVITY Calculating waist to hip ratio

1. Try calculating your own WHR and compare it to the guideline previously mentioned.
2. Now try calculating the WHR for another person in the group.
3. Explain how knowing a person's WHR would help in developing a plan of exercise and diet changes for the person.

Resting pulse and recovery after exercise

Pulse and **respiration** can provide important information. Looking at these can give a good overview of a person's health and fitness. So what is a person's pulse and how is it used it to measure health? A person's pulse can be felt at many different points on their body, for example:

- wrist
- neck.

When nurses and doctors are observed taking a patient's pulse, they usually press on the patient's wrist or neck to get the reading. What they are actually doing is pressing a blood vessel, called an artery, against something solid like a muscle or bone. The carotid artery in the neck and the radial artery in the wrist are commonly used. The force of the heart pumping blood around the arteries can be felt as a pulsing sensation. This is measured in 'beats per minute' and the only equipment needed is a watch with a second hand.

ACTIVITY Taking your pulse

Try taking your own pulse:

1. Place your first and second finger of your right hand on the edge of your left wrist, just below your left thumb (see picture).
2. Press gently until you feel the artery begin to pulse.

You are now feeling the force of the blood being pumped around the body. People who are very fit can have a slow pulse with a strong force when resting. People who are less fit may have a faster pulse when resting.

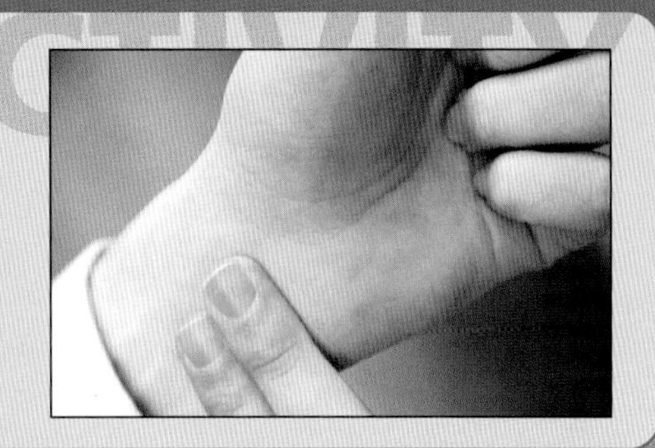

Trick of the trade

To save time, doctors and nurses don't measure your pulse for one minute. This is because the heart has a very regular beat, so they measure it for 15 seconds. Then, they multiply the number by four. This is how professionals take pulse measurements. For example:

Pulse is 18 beats in 15 seconds; now multiply both by 4.

18 beats x 4 = 72, and 15 seconds x 4 = 60 seconds (one minute).

This gives 72 beats per minute.

This is an accurate way of measuring a pulse. Now try this method on another person.

ACTIVITY Taking a pulse measurement – short method

1. Measure a person's pulse for 15 seconds at the point of the wrist. Calculate what the pulse will be for one minute.
2. Now measure their pulse over one minute; compare the two results. Are there any differences? If the difference is within five beats, the reading is reasonably accurate.
3. How would a pulse measurement be used to help plan an exercise programme for a person?

By using this method, 45 seconds are saved. This may not sound a lot but if a nurse has to check a whole ward of patients, the saving soon mounts up. The average adult pulse rate while they are resting is between 70 and 80 beats per minute. If an adult is very fit, it can be as low as 60 beats per minute. A newborn baby's pulse rate can be anything from 120 to as high as 180 beats per minute.

During exercise a person's pulse rate increases; it then returns to normal when at rest. Other events will also cause the pulse rate to increase. For example, when people are afraid, the brain orders an increase in a chemical called adrenalin. This increases the heart rate and delivers more blood to your body to allow you to act more quickly or run from danger. When the danger is over, the brain orders no adrenalin to be released; this slows the heart down again.

Pulse rate can also be affected by heart disease and lung disease, which can reduce the oxygen in the blood. An increase in the rate can be because the body is not getting enough oxygen. The brain will sense this and cause the heart to pump the oxygen-containing blood around the body much faster.

ACTIVITY Recovery rate exercise

1. Get someone in the group to take your pulse and the number of breaths for one minute while you are resting. Write them down so that the readings are not forgotten.
2. Exercise for one minute, for example, walk up and down stairs quickly.
3. Get your partner to check your pulse and number of breaths again immediately after finishing the exercise. Write down the results.
4. Now check your pulse every minute until it returns to the resting rate.
5. Record your results in a table that looks like this:

	Pulse (beats/min)	Breaths	Recovery rate
Before exercise	84	15	
Exercise finished	120	30	Time starts here
1 minute after	110	25	
2 minutes after	95	20	
5 minutes after	84	15	Time stops here 5 mins

This time span, until the pulse rate returns to normal, is known as the **recovery rate**. It will vary between different people and is related to how fit they are. The fitter they are, the shorter the recovery time will be. Recovery time can be improved by regular exercise.

...WORD CHECK

recovery rate – the time it takes the body to get back to normal respiration and pulse rates.

CASE STUDY Gina

Gina is 19 years of age and lives on her own. She has been unemployed since leaving college and has very low self-esteem as she thinks she is not wanted by anyone. When she first left college she applied for many jobs as a health care assistant but didn't get any of them, so she has now given up trying.

Gina sits on the settee all day watching TV and during the evenings she drinks several glasses of wine. Gina knows she has put on some weight as she has to use safety pins to do up her skirts and trousers.

Gina's friend Kim has talked to her and as a result Gina thinks she could benefit from a health plan to improve her health and well-being. She has given Kim permission to take the following measurements:

Height: 160cm — Weight: 68kg
BMI: 26.5 — Waist to hip ratio: 0.86
Peak flow: 380 — Blood pressure: 130/88
Resting pulse rate: 78 — Recovery rate: 24.5 mins

1. Analyse the findings, comparing Gina's measurements to the norms, taking into account Gina's age, gender and lifestyle.
2. From the results, identify two physical needs to help Gina that are to be the focus of the health plan. Explain why you have chosen these needs for her.
3. Identify two targets that will meet Gina's needs for each measurement that is to be the focus of the health plan.
4. Describe the possible impact on Gina's health if she meets these targets.
5. Explain how Gina's lifestyle is contributing to her need for a health plan.

AGE, SEX AND LIFESTYLE

Age

As people grow older, their bodies begin to change and so can all the physical values that have been talked about:

- As people grow older, if they do not maintain their fitness, their pulse rate will rise. At 18 it may be 60 at rest but by age 45 it could be 80.
- As people age, their blood pressure will begin to rise. At 18 their BP may be 110/65 but by the time they are 45 it could be 145/85.
- Peak flow may also not be as good as people get older. Owing to various medical problems it can become lower.

◂ It is important to maintain fitness in later life.

As people age, often their level of fitness decreases and this can have a negative effect on their recovery time after exercise. The tissue that makes up the blood vessels in the circulatory system can also become weaker and less elastic. This, in turn, can have an effect on their pulse and blood pressure. Respiratory illnesses, such as bronchitis and emphysema, are much more common in older people. This can lead to infections and changes in their lung structure. This may lead to their peak flow decreasing and a decrease in their ability to absorb oxygen. At this point, exercise often becomes difficult, which may cause them to put on weight.

These events show us that health and fitness is a complex collection of events that are balanced by the body, providing it is allowed the correct conditions, namely:

- exercise
- good diet
- good **immunity**.

Sex

...WORD CHECK

immunity – resistance to a disease.

gender – whether you are male or female.

Our **gender** can have an effect on our ability to do certain things. This is because the roles of males and females are often seen as different (see page 115). There are also physical differences between men and women:

- Women store fat in different places to men. This gives us our different shapes.
- Men can be more prone to heart disease and strokes.

There has been a growing recognition that the biological differences between males and females exist beyond their reproductive differences.

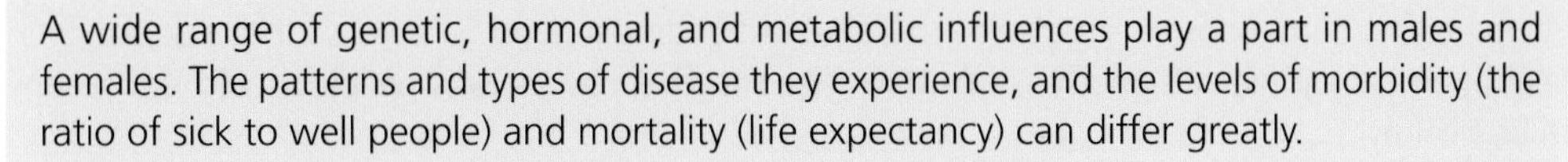

A wide range of genetic, hormonal, and metabolic influences play a part in males and females. The patterns and types of disease they experience, and the levels of morbidity (the ratio of sick to well people) and mortality (life expectancy) can differ greatly.

Gender-specific diseases, such as cancers of the cervix and prostate, are the most obvious examples. However, there is also growing evidence that both men and women can have a higher likelihood of getting certain diseases. The symptoms that they get and the outcomes of the diseases may also differ between men and women. These diseases can include:

- HIV/AIDS
- tropical infectious diseases
- tuberculosis
- autoimmune problems
- coronary heart disease
- cerebro-vascular accident (stroke).

One of the most important of these gender differences is that of men developing heart disease early in life.

Lifestyle

A healthy lifestyle simply means the way that a person lives from day to day, making them feel physically and emotionally fit and well. If they have a poor lifestyle, it can affect how their health is measured; they may:

- have high blood pressure
- be overweight
- be more prone to infection
- be unfit.

7 How does age affect blood pressure?

If an individual's lifestyle is not a healthy balance, for instance because they are:

- not exercising
- consuming drugs or alcohol
- not eating a balanced diet
- keeping worries and problems to themselves

they are more likely to become ill and have trouble concentrating at work or school, or be unhappy or depressed. Lifestyle has a big effect on how people feel and what they get out of life. This can be both now and in the future. A healthy lifestyle is important as it affects a person's:

- work
- body
- study
- play
- relationships
- happiness.

Living a healthy life is a combination of lots of different things, including:

- Exercising regularly
- Staying safe
- Coping with stress
- Eating sensibly
- Talking through your problems with people you trust

Being healthy is not about being perfect; it's all about getting a good balance, so that a person feels healthy and enjoys life. It is good to remember 'you are what you eat' and people should 'eat healthy to be healthy'.

Healthy people with a sensible lifestyle are usually:

- fitter
- less prone to disease and infection
- of normal blood pressure
- the correct weight.

ASSESSMENT PRACTICE: PREPARATION

1. For the person you have chosen, give a detailed explanation of any features of the individual's lifestyle that could affect their physical health. (You will have this information as a result of the survey that you conducted for the previous Assessment practice.)
2. Use at least **two** of the following physical measures of health to calculate your chosen individual's measurements:
   - blood pressure
   - peak flow
   - height–weight and body mass index
   - waist to hip measurements
   - resting pulse and recovery.

   Make sure you record these measurements accurately.
3. Compare each of the measures taken with the 'norms' and analyse the similarities and differences.
4. Draw some conclusions about the health status of the individual against the norms, explaining which aspects will need to be covered in the health plan and why.

Factors that have positively affected health and well-being

What factors contribute positively to health and well-being through a person's life?

Getting started

A person's health and well-being is affected by a number of different factors. You should know about factors that contribute positively to health and well-being, such as:

- a balanced diet
- regular exercise
- sufficient sleep
- personal hygiene
- supportive relationships
- adequate financial resources
- stimulating work
- education
- leisure activity
- work–life balance
- use of health monitoring and illness prevention services (such as screening and vaccination)
- use of risk management to protect individuals and promote personal safety (such as sun protection, road crossing, sexual health care).

You will learn about the importance of these factors to individuals throughout their lives and how research has been important in making us aware of these factors.

Group Activity

Decide which three factors from diet, exercise, supportive relationships, location and stress have a positive influence on your development. Why?

Share your findings with another person.

FACTORS THAT CONTRIBUTE POSITIVELY TO HEALTH AND WELL-BEING

Many factors combine to affect the health and well-being of individuals and communities. To a large extent, factors such as what people eat, where they live, the state of the environment, genetics, income and education level, and our relationships with friends and family all have considerable impact on health and well-being. Also, the more commonly considered factors, such as exercise and illness, can often have an equal impact. The way people run their lives determines their health! This also means that individuals have a responsibility to themselves to remain healthy. Individuals are unlikely to be able to directly control all of the **determinants** of health but have to accept responsibility for those that they can control.

Thinking about those factors that are positive in the lives of individuals is just as important as thinking about the risks.

...WORD CHECK

determinants – to cause to come to a conclusion or decision.

BALANCED DIET

...WORD CHECK

balanced – an even distribution or equal amounts.

essential components – parts of an object or activity that cannot be done without.

nutrients – substances that provide nourishment.

portion – a part of, or an amount of.

A **balanced** diet is essential if overall good health is to be achieved, but which are the best foods to include on a daily basis and which ones are best avoided? What is a balanced diet? A balanced diet is made up of the following seven **essential components**:

- vitamins
- protein
- fats
- fibre.
- minerals
- water
- carbohydrates

See Unit 2, page 108–109, for more information on these seven essential components.

Daily meals

A healthy diet contains all of the **nutrients** needed by the body. Scientific studies have shown that people who eat a lot of fruit and vegetables are usually healthier. They may have a lower risk of getting illnesses, such as heart disease and some cancers. For this reason, it is recommended that people eat at least five portions of fruit and vegetables every day. It doesn't matter whether they're fresh, tinned, frozen, cooked, juiced or dried.

This is one portion of the recommended five-a-day.

Portion is a word for a measure of food eaten. In everyday eating, one portion would be:

- One piece of medium-sized fruit, for example, an apple, peach, banana or orange.
- One slice of large fruit, such as melon, mango or pineapple.
- A few handfuls of grapes, or berry fruits.
- A glass (100ml) of fruit or vegetable juice.
- The vegetables (100g) served in a portion of vegetable curry, lasagne, stir fry or casserole.
- A side salad.
- A small handful of dried fruit, for example, small pack of dried apricots.
- A small tin (200g) of fruit.
- Peas, beans or carrots, served with main meal.

Group Activity

Everyone requires vitamins and minerals in their daily diet. Work with another person to find out how much of the following an individual should take in each day:

- vitamin C
- calcium
- iron
- vitamin A.

8 How many portions of fruit and vegetables do you need each day?

It is recommended that an individual also eats:

- Carbohydrates sourced from bread, cereals, pasta and potatoes. This should be roughly 30% of each day's meals.
- Sugary foods but individuals should eat less of these. It is possible to cut down on sugary foods by snacking on fresh or dried fruit rather than biscuits and chocolate.
- Government guidelines recommend that fat makes up no more than 35% of the diet. For the average woman, this means about 76g of fat per day and, for a man, this means roughly 100g of fat per day. In reality though, most of us have higher fat intakes than this.

The eatwell plate shows how much of what you eat should come from each food group.

9 Which two food groups should make up the majority of an individual's diet?

...WORD CHECK

calories – the unit of heat according to the French standard; the amount of heat required to raise the temperature of one kilogram (sometimes, one gram) of water one degree centigrade, or from 0 to 1.

kilocalories – used to measure the energy value of food.

kilojoules – a unit of work or energy expended.

What is the role of calories, kilojoules and joules?

Calories and joules are units used to measure the amount of energy the body uses. They can also be used as terms for measuring energy values of food. They are used to measure the energy we burn off in exercise.

Look at the calorie table (see Appendix 1, pages 325–326). Use this table to create healthy diets for the person you chose for carrying out the assignments. It will also help to make sure that you, too, are eating the right foods.

ACTIVITY Finding out about diet

1. Keep a diary of everything that you eat and drink in a week. Calculate the following:
   - How many portions of fruit and vegetables have you eaten?
   - How many bags of crisps (or similar) have you eaten?
   - How many calories were in the crisps? (The packet will tell you how many calories are in a bag.)
2. Copy and complete the sentences:

   Protein helps to __________ __________ and __________

   Protein foods can be found in __________, __________ and __________

   There are __________ main types of protein.
3. Maxine, aged 16, has the following for her evening meal: beefburger, chips, tomato and chocolate.

   Give the main nutrients that are in the meal and explain how Maxine could make the meal well balanced.
4. Plan a meal for Maxine that is well balanced. Explain why it is well balanced, making reference to nutritional values.

REGULAR EXERCISE

Exercise can help to keep individuals healthy.

Physical exercise is any bodily activity that **enhances** or maintains physical fitness and overall health. It is performed for many different reasons. These include:

- strengthening muscles
- strengthening the cardiovascular system
- weight loss or maintenance.

Frequent and regular physical exercise boosts the immune system, and helps prevent diseases of **affluence**, such as heart disease, cardiovascular disease, Type 2 diabetes and obesity. It also improves mental health and helps prevent depression. Childhood obesity is a growing global concern and physical exercise may help decrease the effects of childhood obesity in developed countries.

If people fail to exercise on a regular basis, they may suffer from one or more of the following:

- cardiovascular problems
- coronary heart disease
- muscle and joint problems
- obesity
- osteoporosis.

Exercise helps to maintain fitness. It strengthens the body and helps to control weight, by burning off extra energy. It has a great many other health benefits too, because it:

- helps in building up **immunity**
- improves **circulation**
- improves **stamina**
- reduces the risk of a heart attack.
- helps the heart work more efficiently
- improves **mobility**
- improves the strength in muscles

Not having any exercise can put a person's health at risk.

Exercise has other positive effects on health and well-being, such as psychological effects, for example:

- building confidence
- giving a general feeling of well-being
- helping relieve stress
- improving **self-esteem**
- it is a great way to socialize.

Babies, from the moment that they are born, begin to exercise their muscles. Children exercise in all of their activities and sport is a major part of growing up. Exercise protects our physical, as well as our emotional, well-being. It also helps protect against diseases in later life such as osteoporosis.

10 Why is exercise important?

...WORD CHECK

enhances – something that makes an item or activity better or stronger.

affluence – abundance of property; wealth.

immunity – resistance to a disease.

circulation – the movement of the blood in the blood-vascular system.

mobility – to be able to move around.

stamina – a person's continued strength during an activity.

self-esteem – how a person feels about themselves.

Aerobic exercise

Aerobic exercises include walking, jogging and swimming. They involve muscles moving through their full range over set time periods (15–20 minutes). These activities are an addition to the normal daily routines. During these activities, the heart and respiration rates will increase. This type of exercise is used to improve cardiovascular fitness. It also increases blood flow to the muscles and benefits the whole body.

Aerobic exercises are planned to increase the heart rate to 70% of its maximum. This is 220 beats per minute (bpm), minus the person's age. This provides a safety barrier that helps to reduce any danger from excessive exercise.

Aerobic exercise is the most commonly used method of increasing and maintaining fitness. It must be remembered that exercising above the safe rate can be dangerous.

▲ Swimming is one type of aerobic exercise.

Anaerobic exercise

Anaerobic exercise is the bodybuilder's method of building muscle. It involves **high intensity** activity aimed at developing the muscles. It is only done for short periods of time.

Weightlifting is a good example of an anaerobic exercise. Anaerobic activities increase the amount of muscle and strength. Benefits to the heart and the lungs are limited by using this method.

11 What is the difference between aerobic and anaerobic exercise?

...WORD CHECK

aerobic – with the use of oxygen.

anaerobic – without the use of oxygen.

high intensity – something that is strong, forceful or bright.

How can safety be maintained when exercising?

When starting exercise, beginners should ideally be supervised and should be made aware of the dangers of over-exercising, especially the strain that they can put on their heart and circulation. Making muscles work to the point of exhaustion is dangerous. Where the person's health and heart are poor, this can bring on a collapse or a heart attack.

Exercise should always be moderate and not excessive. It should also be regular. This allows the body to build up stamina and lessens the risk of injury.

Which exercises are best?

Just as certain foods are better for us than others, so are certain exercises. Exercise should start off at an easy pace. Eventually an individual should be doing 30 minutes exercise at least five times a week. Remember, exercise should not make an individual exceed 70% of their maximum heart rate.

Whether a person is young or old, fit, unfit or disabled, they can always find some form of exercise to suit their age or condition. Being fit is becoming very fashionable, which fits in with the government's health plans, as it encourages individuals to take responsibility for their own health.

Remember:

To lose one kilogram in weight, you have to burn off 8000 calories or 33,600 kilojoules (3500 calories per pound in weight).

ACTIVITY Learning about exercise

1. Carry out some research to find out about **two** other types of both aerobic and anaerobic exercise.
2. Keep a diary of how much exercise you have done during the week. What did you do? How much did you do? Make a plan to show the exercise done during the week. Draw some conclusions about how the exercise contributed to your health status. What could you do to improve your exercise programme?
3. Create a plan of regular exercise for a friend who needs to improve the amount and type of exercise taken. This plan should be for one week. Make sure the exercises can be done safely. Explain how the exercises will help to improve or maintain fitness.
4. If someone takes regular exercise and becomes fit, how will the improvements affect their health, well-being and self-esteem?

SUFFICIENT SLEEP

We all need different amounts of sleep.

Some believe that sleep gives the body a chance to **recuperate** from the day's activities but in reality, the amount of energy saved by sleeping for even eight hours is miniscule – about 50 kcal, the same amount of energy in a piece of toast. So sleep is a natural state of bodily rest.

The amount of sleep needed varies with age and is an essential part of a person's daily routine. It is well known that small babies, toddlers, pregnant mothers and some older people need to rest during the day. Sleep helps to refresh the body and **revitalize** energy reserves. Whilst asleep, the body has the opportunity to carry out repairs to its systems and restore energy.

Sleep patterns change with a person's age. Usually a newborn baby will only sleep for a few hours at any one time. By three months they often sleep through the night. When children reach six years of age, they have usually given up the daytime nap.

As a person ages, the amount of sleep they take depends on individual needs. Most adults sleep anywhere between four and eight hours a day. Many older people find that they begin to need less sleep as they get older. The average recommended amount of sleep is seven to eight hours each night.

A good night's sleep is very important. If a person does not get enough sleep, then everything they do will be affected. They become tired, irritable, confused and make mistakes in their daily routine. Also, their hearing and vision may become affected and this is why drivers are told, 'tiredness kills'.

...WORD CHECK

recuperate – to get better or recover.

revitalize – to refresh or rejuvenate.

12 Why is sleep important?

ACTIVITY Sleeping patterns

In pairs, examine each other's sleep patterns.

1. Record how much sleep each of you gets each day for a week.
2. Examine the quality – are the sleep patterns regular or broken up?
3. How does the other person feel each morning after a night's sleep?
4. Work with another pair in the group to compare findings. Draw some conclusions about how sleep can affect:
   - ability
   - perseverance
   - attitude.
5. Using your findings produce a PowerPoint® presentation with speaker's notes on the value of sleep.

PERSONAL HYGIENE

Personal hygiene may be described as the principle of maintaining cleanliness and grooming of the external body. Personal hygiene can be controlled by **sustaining** high standards of personal care. Humans have been aware of the importance of hygiene for thousands of years; for example, the Romans spent many hours in the bath, using fragrances and make-up in an effort to beautify themselves and be presentable to others.

Personal cleanliness promotes good health and well-being. Regular washing and attention to personal hygiene helps to control the growth of bacteria, viruses and fungi. Left uncontrolled, some of these **organisms** could cause disease and illness.

Lack of personal hygiene can be a difficult social problem, which can lead to exclusion from group activities. If bacteria start to build up on the skin, it can create body odour, which is socially unacceptable.

It is important to have good toilet hygiene, for example, washing hands after going to the lavatory. Otherwise, it is possible to become a carrier of certain dangerous diseases and infections.

Following good hygiene procedures can be a positive factor in the life of an individual as it will help them to have high self-esteem and will help to prevent the spread of infection.

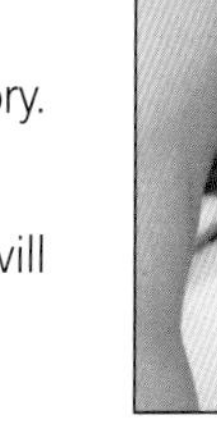

▲ Personal grooming.

13 Why is it important to wash your hands after going to the toilet?

Dental hygiene

It is quite normal to find bacteria in the mouth, as the mouth is part of the digestive process. The saliva in the mouth helps to stop bacteria building up when food is chewed. At other times, the bacteria can produce an acid, which can build up around the teeth and in food particles. When this happens, small areas of tooth enamel can be dissolved. This is how cavities are created and where tooth decay can start. If this carries on, it will break into the **pulp cavity** of the tooth. The nerve in the tooth will become irritated and the tooth will ache. By brushing teeth regularly we can give a higher level of protection.

...WORD CHECK

sustaining – to keep going.

organisms – small living creatures.

pulp cavity – the centre of a tooth where the nerve is situated.

Maintaining a good level of personal hygiene is very important. Many diseases and infections can be **eradicated** or **controlled** by good personal hygiene practice.

ACTIVITY Maintaining good hygiene practice

1. Produce a poster to inform people about the top five personal hygiene routines. This should include:
   - what the personal hygiene routines are
   - how an individual should carry them out
   - why they are important.
2. Carry out research with another person to find out how poor hygiene can cause infection to be passed to others. Produce a handout that could be used by others to help them understand how cross-infection can occur.
3. Explain the likely effects on an individual's self-concept if:
   - they do not follow good hygiene practice
   - they are being cared for by a person who does not follow good hygiene practice.

HOW CAN SUPPORTIVE RELATIONSHIPS CONTRIBUTE TO GOOD HEALTH?

...WORD CHECK

eradicated – to remove completely, as in stopping a disease.

controlled – to regulate; to govern.

gregarious – liking to mix with other people.

self-concept – how we think about ourselves.

immune system – a body system that prevents infection in that body.

Most humans tend to be **gregarious**, which means that they like mixing with other people. A person's health and well-being can be affected by the relationships that are made. Having supportive relationships at home gives security and provides a level of happiness, and feeling happy and secure is a major factor in feeling good. When a person feels good, they have pride in themselves. They then look after themselves and this helps them to remain healthy.

▲ Sharing and caring helps us to feel good about ourselves.

Supportive relationships are, therefore, very important. They can lift self-esteem and make people feel positive about themselves. This feeling of a good '**self-concept**' is needed to stay healthy. The mind is a powerful force and people will act according to how they feel about themselves. If they wake up in the morning and everything around them is good, then they will feel good all day. If they wake up and think their relationships are not working, they are more likely to have a bad day. Everyone has days when they do not feel very good about themselves. If this lasts for a long period of time, they can become depressed and this can affect their health. Their **immune system** can also be affected and they then become more prone to illness.

14 What does it mean to be gregarious?

15 Why do we need to socialize with other people?

More information about relationships with others can be found in Unit 2.

ADEQUATE FINANCIAL RESOURCES

Being able to work and earn money can be linked to health and well-being because it will influence the social activities that are possible. By earning money it is possible to buy important items that are needed and less important personal items that are wanted. Money will also allow people to socialize, so they can go out to the cinema or a nightclub and meet people.

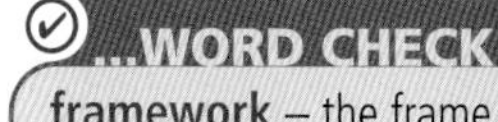

...WORD CHECK
framework – the frame or constructional part of anything; as, the framework of society.

It is possible to get a lot of social enjoyment from working and the relationships developed with work colleagues. This can have a very positive effect on health and well-being. Working gives a person's life structure. This is a **framework** that they can build everything else around. If an individual is working, they are more likely to have more confidence and self-respect. The big psychological boost is that it can give them status and make them feel important.

Not having a great deal of money can lower self-esteem and could have the effect of making an individual withdrawn, angry or violent, as they may feel they are not valued as much as those around them.

STIMULATING EMPLOYMENT

Employment can have a significant effect on people and their families. If someone is actively employed they may well feel:

- empowered
- happy
- financially secure.

They may also have:

- high self-worth
- high self-confidence
- high self-esteem.

Although single parents or the main wage earner often feel under a lot of pressure to work, it also helps to support their total health and well-being. By working, they have more control over all aspects of their lives. Their interest is stimulated and they are given a sense of purpose. They begin to feel that they have a position in the world, which provides personal value to their existence. The ability to work and to earn puts people in control, and knowing that they are in control of their lives can help them to remain healthy. When a person feels they are in control, they tend to worry less. It has been proven that continuous worry has a negative effect on the body's ability to fight off diseases. This is because it can lower a person's immunity and by doing this make them more prone to illness.

16 How does being employed affect emotional well-being?

ACTIVITY Money and work

1. In pairs or small groups, produce questions to find out how people feel when
   - they are in a safe job that they like
   - they are in a job that they do not like
   - they have been out of work for more than six weeks.
2. Draw some conclusions from the answers received.
3. How is the self-concept of each group of people likely to be affected?
4. Use the words given below to discuss, in writing, the effect of each on personal development:
   - debt
   - material possessions
   - need to make regular payments.

EDUCATION

▲ Learning can help to stimulate the mind.

Education plays an important part in health and well-being. A good all-round education has a real impact on everyone's lives. Education allows people to have greater control of their lives and to make better decisions. It can affect all decisions, whether intellectual, emotional or social.

A willingness to learn makes individuals **inquisitive** and this, in turn, helps the individual to make the best choices. These choices could include choosing a job, whether to go to university or which parts of the world to see. Life is full of choices and it is not always possible to make the best ones. People have to use their **intellect** to make decisions, if they are going to make the correct ones. Knowledge also allows us to manage risks better and helps keep us safe.

An individual who does not use their intellect will become bored and this could lead to unacceptable behaviour or crime. Intellectual activities can include:

- reading
- word puzzles/crosswords
- taking part in a quiz
- solving a crime
- helping to make decisions.

How does health education stimulate the mind?

HOW CAN LEISURE ACTIVITIES HELP HEALTH AND WELL-BEING?

▲ Joining in activities is a good boost to well-being.

Leisure and recreational activities play a vital role in keeping everyone healthy. Many of the leisure activities that are participated in involve meeting others. Well-being is increased by becoming part of a team, joining in with group activities or even just being with one other person in leisure activities. These can be a great boost to physical well-being. Leisure activities require people to either take:

- a physical role
- an intellectual role
- an emotional role
- a social role.

Often, an activity can contain a number or all of these and it can lead to further development. If a person takes up a new sport, they may become physically fitter. Their intellectual ability will increase by learning about the skills that are involved. They may become emotionally stronger by being successful in competitions. Finally, there are few sports where you are totally isolated. This means that individuals will probably mix socially with others who take part, leading to the making of friendships, which could lead to supportive relationships. One factor often leads to another to help the development of the individual.

Examples of leisure activities can include:

- chess
- drama clubs
- martial arts
- pottery
- learning a new language.

Taking part in activities is a basic part of community and family life, and helps people feel purposeful and included. **Inclusion** prevents people from experiencing **isolation** and the emotional dangers that this attracts.

...WORD CHECK

inquisitive – to be very interested and enquire.

intellect – the mind; the brain's activity.

inclusion – to be a part of or to be included in an event.

isolation – to be alone or excluded.

WORK–LIFE BALANCE

In everyone's life there must be a balance between work and leisure. It is not possible to either work or play all of the time. People must have time to themselves away from work. This is so they can relax both emotionally and socially. The pressure of work is lifted and they can enjoy the luxury of being with family and friends. This could involve activities or merely relaxing and talking together or watching television. Whatever this entails, they can then return to work feeling physically and emotionally refreshed. This will make them ready for the more intellectual stimulation that is often found during gainful employment.

The old saying still stands, 'All work and no play makes Jack a dull boy'.

ACTIVITY Improving the work–life balance

1. Find an individual who has a very active life and try to find out the following by asking questions in a sensitive way:
   - How many hours do they work each week?
   - How much time is taken up with housework and chores at home, for example, gardening?
   - How much leisure time do they have?
   - How do they use their leisure time?
2. Draw conclusions about the balance of work and leisure in their life.
3. What improvements could be made?
4. Explain how education could affect the development of an individual.
5. Explain how leisure, education and work–life balance could interrelate to affect the development of an individual.

HEALTH MONITORING AND ILLNESS PREVENTION SERVICES

Screening and vaccination

Preventing disease is a way of helping individuals to stay healthy for longer. Some diseases are not always visible and can be difficult to detect. It is possible for a person to have a disease and not know that they have got it. Diseases like tuberculosis may not show any symptoms for up to six months. For this reason, many different methods of **detection** and prevention have been developed.

Health care professionals can use tests like chest x-rays and blood tests to help detect illness and disease. These will show any changes in the person caused by the disease. The x-ray will provide a visible picture of any infection in the chest. The blood test may show chemical changes in the body. Where these tests are done on a large scale, they are known as **screening programmes**. Screening allows doctors to examine many people and to select those that need treatment because disease has been found. Screening can include:

- breast screening
- chest x-rays
- cervical smear tests
- blood tests.

These tests are all done for the purpose of screening, which is finding out if a problem exists.

18 Why do we need to test people for diseases?

...WORD CHECK

detection – the act of detecting; the laying open what was concealed or hidden; discovery.

screening programmes – large-scale testing for disease in the population with a view to stopping it.

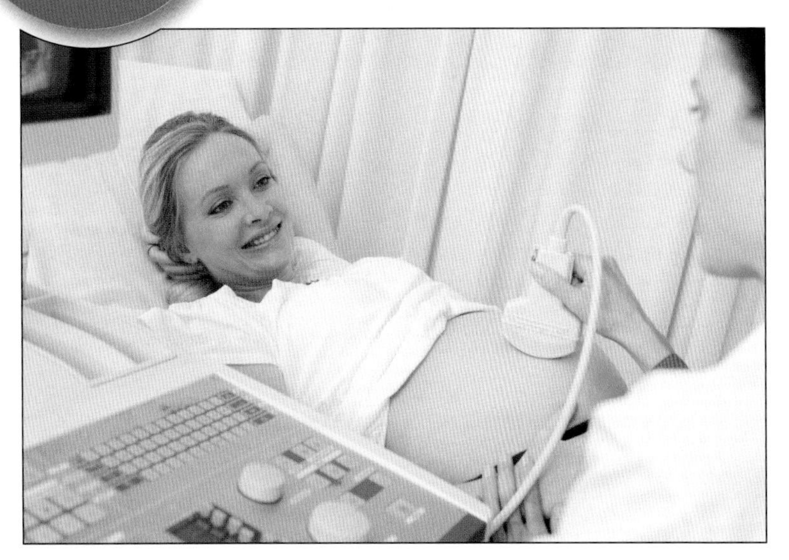

▲ Checking that the baby is healthy.

The government currently runs **vaccination** programmes. This is where people, who have a high risk of catching certain illnesses, can have medical help to prevent them from catching a disease. Some diseases are so dangerous that a method had to be found to prevent them from occurring. This is often achieved by giving vaccines by injection.

Vaccination programmes have been running in the UK for over 50 years. The killer disease called smallpox was totally **eradicated** by vaccinating everyone to prevent the disease. More recently, vaccinations against measles, mumps and rubella (MMR) and influenza have become available. These have been introduced because these diseases can be killers of children and older adults.

19 Why do we vaccinate small children?

ACTIVITY Preventing disease and illness

1. Helen is expecting her first child. Carry out research to find out which tests Helen could have to make sure that her unborn child is not going to be born with health problems.
2. Produce a leaflet or handout that gives Helen information and advice about vaccinations available for young children. Explain why screening tests are important.
3. Explain how health monitoring and vaccinations could contribute positively to an individual's development.

RISK MANAGEMENT TO PROTECT INDIVIDUALS AND PROMOTE PERSONAL SAFETY

▲ Sun protection.

Personal safety is an important aspect of lives at home, in public places or at work. Accidents are responsible for 10,000 deaths each year in England and staying safe is our responsibility. A large number of people are disabled as a result of accidents and many could be avoided.

Risk management is more likely to be applied in public services, such as hospitals, residential homes, playgroups and in businesses.

Employers are responsible for the health and safety of their employees and for those in their care. A risk assessment would be carried out to find out where there are risks. Methods for reducing the risks would then be put in place. These could include smoke detectors, fire alarms and making sure fire exits are not blocked.

More about risk assessment can be found in Unit 4.

The government has a long history of using public information films and advertisements to promote safety. Young children are taught in a variety of ways how to cross the road safely. Skincare is a big issue in respect of sunbathing. People who fail to sunbathe sensibly greatly increase their risk of damaging their skin. They also increase their risk of getting a skin cancer

...WORD CHECK

vaccination – a method of preventing disease by injection of a pathogen.

eradicated – removed completely, as in stopping a disease.

known as **melanoma**. This highly dangerous cancer can start with a small and insignificant-looking skin **lesion**. If untreated, it can grow rapidly and spread to other parts of the body. If it is not diagnosed and treated early, it can be a killer. If people behave sensibly in the sun then they should not be afraid of skin cancer. By following the suggested precautions of wearing sun block, putting on a hat and limiting their exposure, they can be safe. It is important that everyone receives sunlight as it stimulates the skin to produce vitamin D.

Over-exposure is the problem and it is important to be as safe as possible in the sun.

...WORD CHECK

melanoma – a type of skin cancer that spreads rapidly and can be fatal.

lesion – a collection of abnormal cells that grows in a part of the body where it should not.

CASE STUDY Jessica, James and auntie

Jessica and James, aged ten and eight years old, were spending a day with their auntie in her caravan by the sea. They took their swimming gear, buckets, spades and a rubber boat with them when they went to the beach at 10:00am.

It was a lovely day, with the sun shining and the sea being very calm. They swam, dug holes, went out in the rubber boat and sunbathed. They all had a picnic lunch, then went swimming again and had ice creams later in the afternoon.

When they arrived back at the caravan at about 6:00pm, their auntie noticed how burnt their skin was from head to toe. When their mother came to collect them, she was not pleased!

1. What should their auntie have done to prevent Jessica and James becoming sunburnt?
2. What was the danger to Jessica and James of becoming sunburnt?
3. How could this affect both when they are older?

ACTIVITY Risk management

1. Explain the effects on the development of clients living in a residential home if risk assessments were not carried out.
2. Work with another person to carry out research about screening that can be done for sexual health. Produce a leaflet to show which diseases are discovered by screening and explain how this approach could benefit the development of an individual.
3. Explain how screening, education and supportive relationships could interrelate to affect the development of an individual.

Sexual health care

It is important to manage the risk of sexually transmitted diseases (STDs), otherwise known as sexually transmitted infections (STIs), promptly in order to avoid long-term complications, such as infertility and ectopic pregnancy. For most people, the thought of STDs causes considerable distress and anxiety.

Looking after sexual health is an important part of health and well-being. The UK is continuing to see yearly increases in most STIs, HIV (the virus that leads to AIDS) and terminations of pregnancies, which have physical and emotional consequences for many people.

The government has recognized the importance of reducing rates of HIV, STIs and unintended pregnancies and outlined its commitment to sexual health by producing the '*National Strategy for HIV and Sexual Health*' in 2001. This was followed by '*Choosing Health*' – the purpose being to enable better access to sexual health services and support.

To help manage the risk, the government is increasing people's access to testing for HIV and STIs. This is raising awareness of services, support and symptoms of STIs, as well as continuing with prevention work. This form of risk management is helping people understand how they can protect themselves from poor sexual health.

We have a responsibility not to put ourselves or others at risk.

ACTIVITY Maintaining sexual health

Using a presentation method of your choice, demonstrate the importance of the need to reduce the spread of sexually transmitted diseases.

1. Select **one** STI and explain why it is dangerous.
2. Identify the methods used to treat it.
3. Outline the precautions that can be taken to prevent its spread.
4. How could the prevention of sexually transmitted infection affect the development of an individual?

The theorists' perspective and the interrelationship of factors

Remind yourself of Maslow's pyramid of needs in Unit 1, page 5.

Group Activity

Work with another person to find out the stages in the sequence that Piaget's theories focus on.

...WORD CHECK

sequence – the order in which events happen.

Considering the individual from a theorist's perspective is often helpful when thinking about the factors that link together or interrelate to affect the development of an individual in a positive way.

By looking at Maslow's pyramid of needs you will be able to conclude that if physical needs, for example, diet, are not met, then supportive relationships and intellectual needs are not likely to be achieved, so that the individual can feel that they are fully satisfied or, in the words of Maslow, achieve 'self-actualization'.

Maslow concentrates on a person-centred approach. He considers the person as a whole, not just the functioning parts. He also considers that the individual should be considered in the context of their family situation and that the individual's strengths and weaknesses should be used to build on strengths and to improve any weaknesses.

In the plan that you will be considering for the individual chosen, you will need to think about the individual's strengths and to build on these, and about the ways in which any weaknesses can be improved.

Piaget's theory is based on intellectual development, in particular how children develop their thinking. He considers that children's thinking occurs in the same **sequence** but not necessarily at the same time. The exact age may vary but Piaget believes the sequence is always the same.

The factors that have been discussed throughout this section often develop through infancy and childhood, although adolescent and adult experience will also contribute to the type of person we are. Adults can help move children through the various stages of development, to help them reach their full potential, by promoting learning and encouraging the individual to form supportive relationships. Therefore, taking exercise with others can be both intellectually stimulating and provide the opportunity for positive relationships or friendships to form. At the same time, the exercise is helping to keep the individual fit and healthy, so each factor relates to the other.

Another theorist, Albert Bandua, believed that individuals learn a lot by what they see and hear and that people copy the behaviour of others. Seeing someone do something that the individual thinks is good makes it likely to be copied. For example, if one person sees another gaining respect and being looked up to because they are praised for their school or sporting achievements, this could encourage the observer to try and emulate these achievements. This is known as 'imitation learning'. The local environment can influence speech, health and behaviour, linking together several factors.

Learning theories are useful in helping to explain individual differences in development but they may not be sufficient, on their own, to explain all the different factors that make us who we are.

CASE STUDY Herbie

Herbie, who is 13 years old, lives in an urban area where there are very few green spaces and there is not a lot to do. In the evenings and at weekends, he hangs around with some older boys who are not interested in improving their lives, as no one seems to encourage them or really takes an interest in them.

The group go round the estate where they live using bad language, shouting names at people and bullying individuals into giving them money, which they spend on alcohol.

Sometimes, when they have drunk a lot of alcohol, they go round the estate pulling the mirrors off cars and letting down tyres.

1. What factors are influencing Herbie's development?
2. Explain how one factor could link with another and how they could affect Herbie's development. Use theory to help explain your answer.
3. Discuss your answers as a whole group.

CASE STUDY Jana

Jana is 25 years old. She has always lived in a rural area on the outskirts of a small market town. She has one older brother and a younger sister. Jana's father is the manager of a small company and her mother works part time at the local infant school.

When she was small, Jana went to nursery school and made friends with children who lived in the area. As they grew up, they joined a gymnastic and athletics club. The equipment needed was quite expensive but her parents bought what was needed so that Jana could learn the skills needed to achieve.

Jana also had a laptop as a present for one of her birthdays, so she was able to look things up on the Internet, as well as chat to her friends. Her father used to spend time teaching her how to use the computer. She enjoyed these occasions and was able to use her skills in the schoolwork she was doing.

Jana went to college after she finished school and followed a computer course. Now, she has a job working with computers and still meets her friends for a pub meal or for leisure activities. They all talk a lot together and listen to each other's problems.

1. What factors have influenced Jana's development?
2. Explain how one factor could link with another and how they could affect Jana's development. Use theory to help explain your answer.
3. Discuss your answers as a whole group.

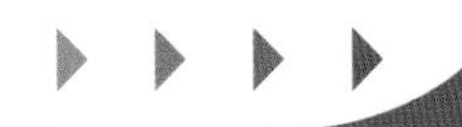

ASSESSMENT PRACTICE: PREPARATION

For the individual chosen in the previous Assessment practices:

1. Select factors that have positively affected the development of the individual. Include at least **three** factors. Describe each factor chosen.
2. Analyse how each factor has positively affected the health and well-being of the individual, using theory to help explain the positive effects.
3. Explain how the factors have interrelated (worked together) to positively affect the health and well-being of the individual.

Remember:

- update the bibliography
- make sure your plan has covered all of the topics above and includes dates, actions and reasons for the actions taken.

Risks to health and well-being

What factors are risks to health and well-being and how do they have a damaging effect?

Getting started

You should know about factors that put an individual's health and well-being at risk.

You should be able to identify the lifestyle factors over which people have control, and also the genetic, social and economic factors that people may not be able to change.

You will learn that health and well-being can be affected by:

- genetically inherited diseases and conditions
- substance misuse (including misuse of legal and illegal drugs, solvents, tobacco smoking and excessive alcohol intake)
- an unbalanced, poor quality or inadequate diet
- too much stress
- lack of personal hygiene
- lack of regular physical exercise
- lack of sleep
- unprotected sex
- social isolation
- poverty
- inadequate housing
- unemployment
- poor work–life balance
- environmental pollution.

You should understand how these factors can affect an individual's health and well-being as well as understanding how these risks can have an impact on our wider society. The wider society should include health and social care service provision, incidents of crime, economic implications, impact on families and the environment.

FACTORS THAT PUT AN INDIVIDUAL'S HEALTH AND WELL-BEING AT RISK

The individual in your health promotion plan will be faced with a number of risks to their health and well-being. These risks will have the potential to do a lot of damage to that individual, as well as causing problems for the wider society, such as higher levels of crime, economic and financial problems, and also affecting the individual's family.

To be successful in the assignment, you need to be aware of these risks. They need to be covered in Task 3: Production of the health plan, particularly in Sections 3 and 4 where you have to explain 'possible risks to the health and well-being of the individual', and analyse how each risk could 'damage the health of the individual in the short and long term'.

It is important to understand that many of the risks are linked in that an individual who is experiencing one problem is likely to be exposed to many others at the same time. This means that in society there is a group of **vulnerable** people who require a lot of help to escape the circumstances they face on a daily basis. The individuals might get caught in a **spiral** of risks, as shown by the following diagrams:

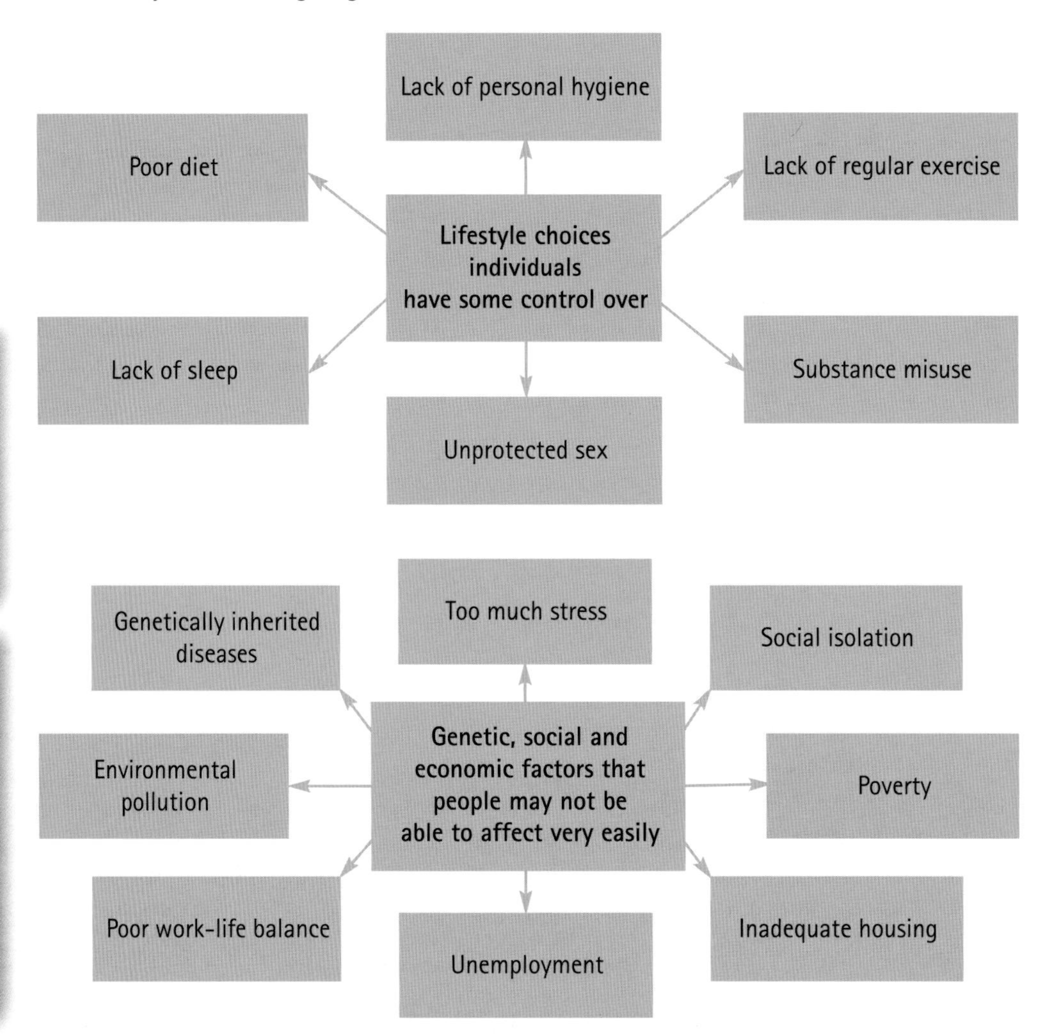

...WORD CHECK

vulnerable – to be at risk of harm; not able to cope by themselves; needing support.

spiral – anything that travels in a direction by using a circular pattern, for example, a spiral staircase.

Group Activity

Working in small groups, discuss why some risks to health are possible to affect, whilst others are more difficult. Which risks would be easier to affect than others? Why?

Share each group's ideas with the whole class.

GENETICALLY INHERITED DISEASES AND CONDITIONS

There are many diseases and physical problems that can be inherited genetically. The following are some of the main types:

- autism
- Down's syndrome
- cystic fibrosis
- Asperger's syndrome
- diabetes
- heart conditions.

Genes are units that contain the information and instructions that control the development of living organisms. Genes influence individual differences, such as sex, hair and eye colour, height and skin colour. Some medical conditions, such as 'Tourette's syndrome', also run in families. Various medical conditions are influenced by genetics, for example, autism is a condition that is associated with the development of the nervous system.

▲ Pete Bennett, winner of Big Brother series 7, has Tourette's syndrome.

Genetic disorders are likely to have serious physical, intellectual, social and emotional effects on the individual's health and well-being. For example, an individual suffering from autism is likely to have communication difficulties, such as not being able to express themselves and make up their own utterances. Their behaviour will be erratic with rapid mood swings and anger. The parents of an autistic child may feel guilty and responsible for their child's condition. People in society may find it difficult to relate to autistic children and the health and social care services will need to provide a considerable amount of long-term care and support.

In a health promotion plan for an individual with a genetically inherited condition or disease, it is important to set realistic targets for any health improvement. This will need to be resourced in terms of both finance and care workers.

It is interesting that a documentary on Channel 4 'Born with Down's Syndrome' found that more mothers are choosing to keep their Down's syndrome babies than have an abortion. Many parents found that life and society had improved for people affected by this condition. Some parents also said that their decision was influenced by the fact that they knew people with the condition. This suggests that the wider society is much more understanding and supportive than in the past, when most people were very ignorant of all such conditions and those suffering from the condition would often be isolated and **institutionalized**. Cara Boys, the Chief Executive of the Down's Syndrome Association, said: 'Now there is much greater **inclusion** and acceptance, with **mainstream education** having a huge role. We think this plays a part in the decisions parents make – there's been a baby with Down's syndrome on *Eastenders*.'

Diabetes is a condition that is increasing rapidly in society today, partly because of the increase in obesity and poor diet. There are two main types of diabetes. Type 1 occurs when the body stops making **insulin**, which is necessary to control levels of sugar. Treatment to control the blood glucose level is with insulin injections and a healthy diet. There is a genetic factor with this condition. A first degree relative (sister, brother, son, daughter) of someone with Type 1 diabetes has about a six per cent chance of developing Type 1 diabetes. This is higher than the chance of the general population, which is about one in 250. This is probably because certain people are more prone to develop autoimmune diseases, such as diabetes, and this is due to their genetic make-up, which is inherited. Type 2 diabetes is caused by the body not producing enough insulin or not using what it produces effectively. It's the most common form and accounts for around 90 per cent of all sufferers of diabetes. This form can often be controlled by improved diet and/or the use of tablets. This type of diabetes usually occurs in people over the age of 40.

Group Activity

Look up autism and the effect it will have on the individual's behaviour on www.nas.org.uk/autism.

Have a whole-group discussion about the effects autism could have on an individual.

...WORD CHECK

genes – part of a chromosome that controls a particular characteristic, for example, eye colour.

institutionalized – to become conditioned to work and live in a way designed by a large organization.

inclusion – to be a part of or to be included in an event.

mainstream education – normal education accessed by all.

insulin – a body hormone that helps the body to use glucose (sugar).

CASE STUDY Jane and Jack

Jane became diabetic when she was 23 years of age. Three years later, she went to her doctor to see about the possibility of having children. Her doctor said that it should be fine but there was an above average risk that the child would also be diabetic. Jane became pregnant and gave birth to Jack. Unfortunately, at the age of three he started to be thirsty all the time, passing a lot of urine and always felt tired. When his blood sugar level was tested, he had high blood sugar levels and, like his mother, was put onto insulin. Jane now has to inject both herself and Jack three times a day with insulin. This is the only way they can both survive.

1. How would diabetes impact upon Jane and Jack physically, emotionally, intellectually and socially?
2. Look up diabetes on www.diabetes.org.uk and find out what a health promotion plan would involve for diabetics. You will need to consider diet, weight, exercise, smoking and alcohol.
3. What health risks are diabetics more likely to suffer from?

SUBSTANCE MISUSE

Any health promotion plan for individuals over the age of 16 is likely to involve a discussion of the use of legal, and possibly illegal, substances.

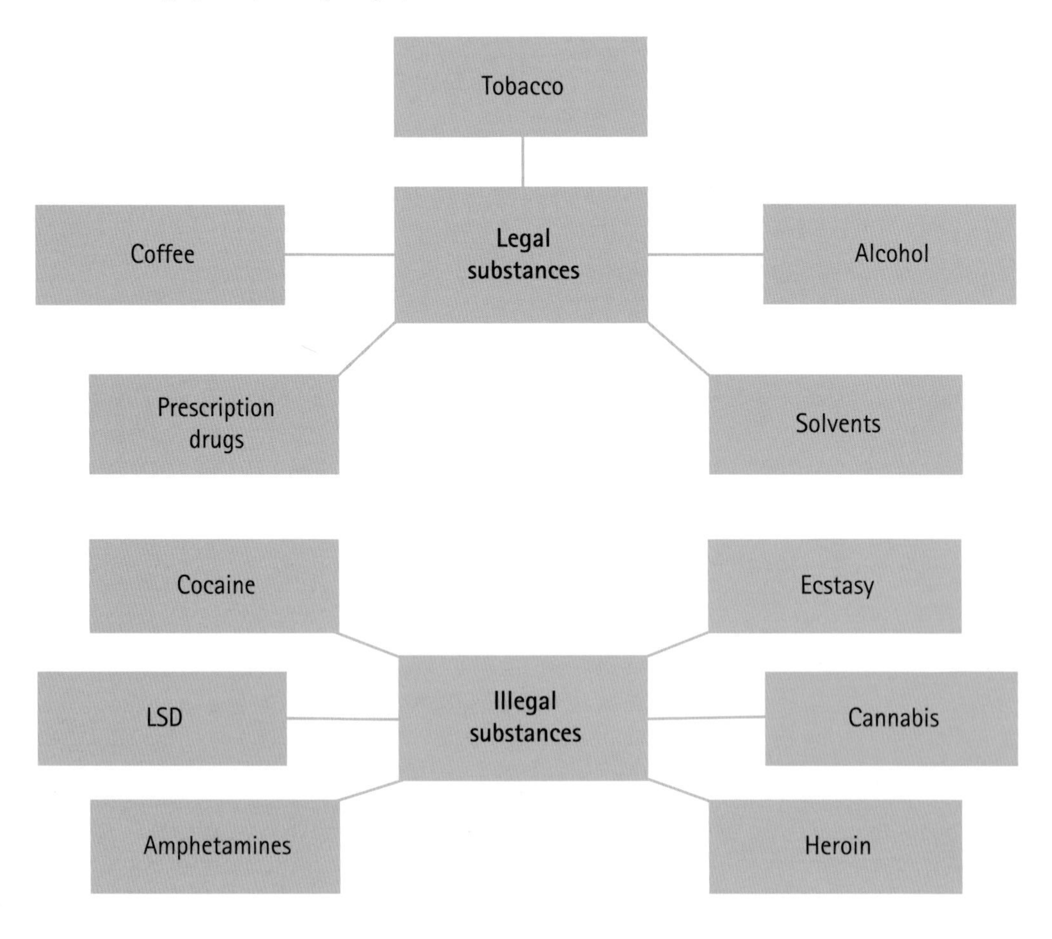

Growing numbers of the population use legal drugs for recreational and social purposes.

Smoking

Most people are aware of the health risks linked to smoking, such as:

- bronchitis and emphysema
- high blood pressure
- lung cancer
- coronary heart disease
- kidney and bladder cancer
- throat and larynx cancer.

Half of all teenagers who currently smoke will die from diseases caused by tobacco if they continue to smoke. It has been estimated that, in England, 364,000 patients are admitted to NHS hospitals each year due to smoking-related illnesses. This is equivalent to 7000 hospital admissions a week, or 1000 a day!

The government has tried health promotion campaigns to reduce smoking, such as banning smoking in public places and recently putting dramatic, shocking pictures of, for example, diseased lungs on cigarette packets. Despite this, approximately 400 children start to smoke each day! One in seven 15 year olds is already a smoker.

▲ Shock tactics to try to stop people smoking.

If the individual health plan involves pregnant women, then the advice has to be to stop smoking immediately. For other people, the plan should involve strategies to reduce and eventually give up smoking altogether. Such strategies could include:

- deciding when to quit
- keeping a smoking diary
- talking to a doctor for advice
- planning a coping strategy – use nicotine replacements, chew gum
- getting rid of all your cigarettes, lighters, tobacco and ashtrays on the day you give up
- trying in the first few weeks to stay away from people who smoke.

Look up ASH on www.ash.org.uk and find out how they campaign to stop people smoking. Their ideas might be useful if your individual health plan involves a smoker.

According to the anti-smoking group, ASH, the economic cost to society of smoking is huge. In 2008, it is estimated that smokers cost the NHS in England £2.7 billion a year, compared with £1.7 billion ten years ago.

...WORD CHECK

culture – common values, beliefs and customs.

Alcohol

Most health promotion plans for all age groups, apart from very young children and babies, will have to analyse the use of alcohol by the individual. Alcohol is the most widely used and acceptable drug in our **culture**. It is widely available and is a way of life for many people. Most soap operas on television have a pub as an essential part of the community.

For many individuals, drinking alcohol is not a major risk to their health if they stick to the recommended limits:

- For men, no more than three to four units a day, with at least two alcohol-free days a week.
- For women, no more than two to three units a day, with at least two alcohol-free days a week.

▲ In *Coronation Street* a lot of the drama happens in the local pub.

...WORD CHECK

binge – to do something to excess in a short space of time.

hazardous – dangerous or life threatening.

Group Activity

Carry out some research and find out what one unit of alcohol is for beer, wines and spirits.

The biggest risk to health at the moment is the culture of **binge** drinking. A study of people held at a police station in Plymouth revealed that many were not hardened criminals but just ordinary people who had had too much to drink. Two-thirds of people arrested were drinking at '**hazardous**' levels. The biggest drinkers were young men aged 17–24, in which group more than 1000 drank more than ten units of alcohol a day and many admitted to drinking with the express intention of getting drunk. This behaviour is increasingly being mirrored by young women.

High levels of drinking have a widespread effect upon many aspects of society:

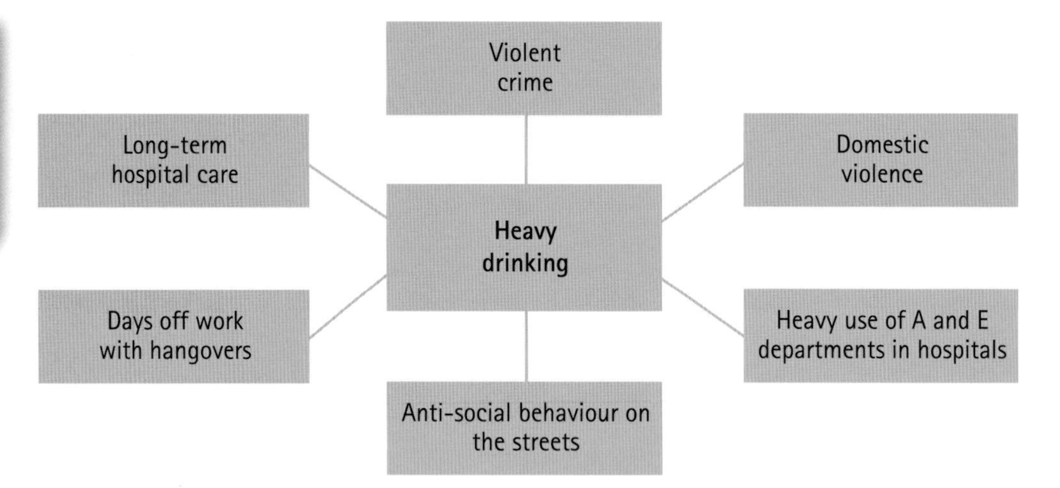

A health plan would need to point out the short- and long-term physical, emotional, social and intellectual health risks attached to high levels of alcohol consumption. In particular, the message would need to get across to young men and women:

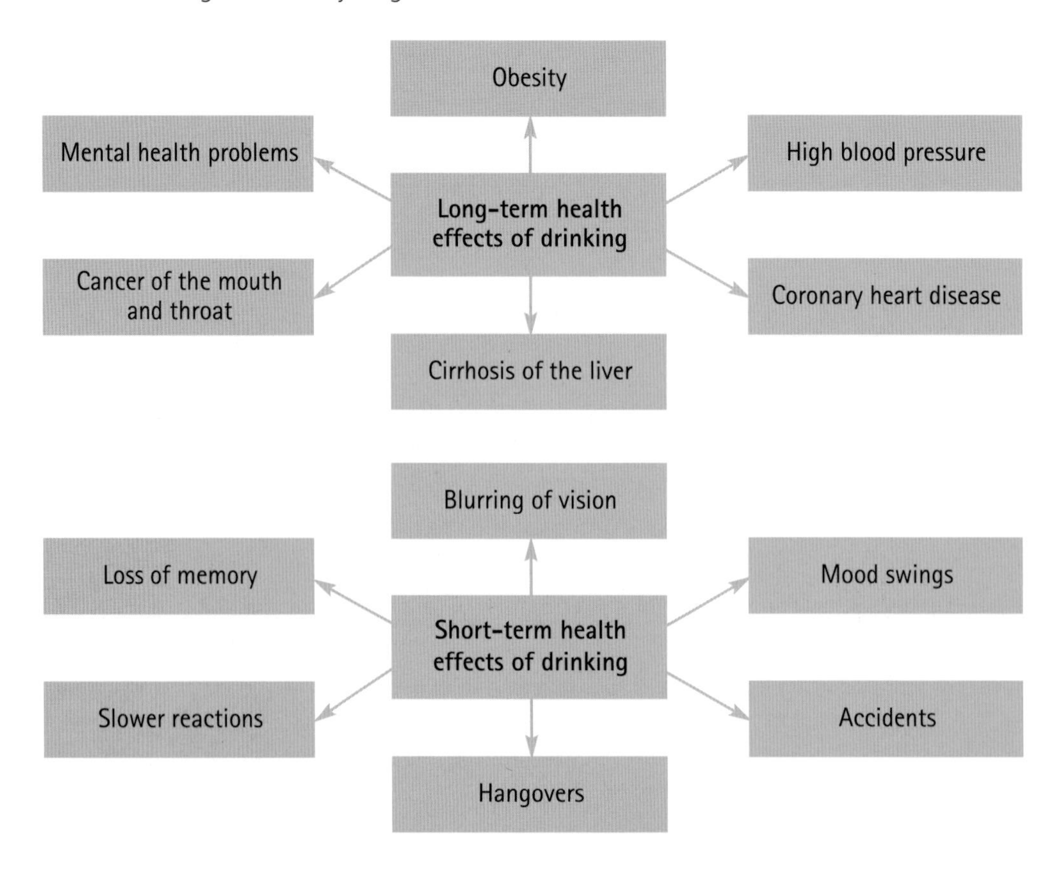

Prescription drugs

Drugs prescribed by doctors and those bought over the counter at chemists and supermarkets are obviously used to solve a short-term illness. The risk is that some individuals become dependent upon them and cannot live without them. An example of the risk was the admission to rehab hospital in 2007 of the singer Robbie Williams for his dependency upon prescription drugs.

What finally killed the actor Heath Ledger was not heroin or cocaine. Despite his alleged addiction in the past to illegal drugs, the drugs found in his apartment where he died had all been legally prescribed. Of the six sedatives, painkillers and anti-anxiety drugs Ledger was taking, three had been prescribed by doctors in London.

Heath Ledger.

Illegal drugs

Solvents are substances used in the manufacture of glue, lighter fuel, petrol, paint, paint thinners and aerosols. Some people sniff or inhale them to get 'high' on the solvents they contain. A health plan for teenagers would need to point out the health effects of such behaviour.

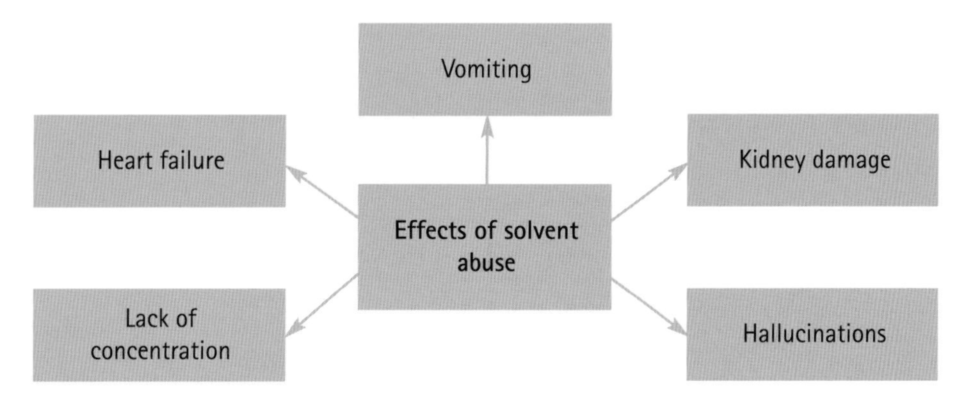

Potentially the greatest short- and long- term risk to health is the use of illegal drugs.

In a health plan, the advice given would have to be not just to moderate use, as with alcohol, but not to take such drugs at all, since in our culture it is against the law to do so and could result in a prison sentence. Illegal drugs are placed in three categories:

- Class A drugs, such as heroin and cocaine. These are regarded as the most dangerous and carry the heaviest punishments for use and possession.
- Class B drugs, such as amphetamines, which are regarded as slightly less dangerous.
- Class C drugs, such as tranquillizers, which can still carry a prison sentence.

It is important to look at the links between drug use and crime, as the statistics show that a great deal of property crime is committed in order to obtain money to feed a drug taker's habit. Large numbers of people in prison are there because they have committed crime due to the fact they are on drugs or they are drug dealers.

Group Activity

Find out by visiting www.homeoffice.gov.uk what the punishments are for possession and dealing in the different classes of drugs.

Try to arrange a visit to your school or college by a police officer and someone from an alcohol or drug advisory unit to discuss the risks involved in taking illegal drugs.

AN UNBALANCED, POOR QUALITY OR INADEQUATE DIET

What an individual eats is clearly a big factor in how healthy they are and what potential illnesses and diseases they might be at greater risk of suffering from. Not only does obesity affect individuals but it is very costly for society. It is estimated that in one average-sized city, Plymouth, the annual cost to the NHS of diseases related to obesity and being overweight was £68.5 million in 2007, rising to £76 million in 2015 unless something is done. Nationally, the cost of obesity to the health service was £4.2 billion in 2007.

According to Alan Johnson, the Health Secretary, the public health risk posed by obesity in the UK is a potential crisis on the scale of climate change.

A study by Safefood shows that poorer people facing financial worries, unemployment, crime and housing problems turn to junk food and comfort eating to ease stress. Dr Nolan, Safefood's Group Director of Human Health and Nutrition, said 'Many mothers and fathers turn to comfort food and treats for their kids'. Poor diets over many years increase the risk of:

- heart disease
- hypertension
- anxiety
- diabetes
- many cancers
- depression.

Too little sleep may explain increasing levels of obesity in children according to Dr Shahrad Taheri, a scientist from Bristol University. Computers, mobile phones, TVs and other gadgets should all be removed from children's bedrooms to enable them to get a good night's sleep, he argues.

It is estimated that 2.5 million cancer deaths worldwide could be prevented if people changed their diet and behaviour.

Source: *The Independent* 18.11.2005

CASE STUDY Chelsea

Chelsea is under stress both at home and at school. She has just started eating lots of junk food and chocolate as a comfort food. She is feeling tired and lethargic all the time. Her friends are worried and don't know how they can help.

1 What advice would you give to her friends so that they can try and help Chelsea improve her diet and lifestyle?

TOO MUCH STRESS

Many individuals suffer from stress for a number of reasons:

- financial worries
- pressure at work
- relationship problems
- unemployment.

It is well known that stress can cause immune system changes that make a person more prone to infections and other illnesses. There is now evidence that parents with stressful lives may be making their children, as well as themselves, vulnerable to illness. A University of Rochester study found sickness levels were higher in children of anxious or depressed parents. Long-term stress-related illnesses include:

- heart attacks
- ulcers
- depression
- stomach and bowel disorders.
- strokes
- anxiety
- high blood pressure

As well as causing the individual health problems, it is estimated that one in five workers suffers from stress at some time in their life and this costs industry an estimated £3.7 billion each year through stress-related absence from work (source: www.amian.co.uk).

If the individual in your health plan is in a stressful job then you will need to try and assess the level of stress and put forward recommendations for reducing this stress. This could include looking at the work–life balance, which will be considered later in this unit.

LACK OF PERSONAL HYGIENE

Poor personal hygiene is both unpleasant and can affect the health of the individual and those around them. Bacteria will grow on humans who are not careful about things such as washing their hands after going to the toilet or mishandling food. This is particularly important for people working in food outlets, and health and social care workers who work closely with individuals that are ill or weak and, therefore, vulnerable to the spread of infection.

Hospitals have recently had serious problems with the spread of superbugs such as MRSA and *C. diff*. These can be spread by not decontaminating mattresses and surgical instruments, not cleaning wards properly, and nurses continuing to wear their uniforms outside the hospital. All hospitals now insist that care practitioners and visitors arriving and leaving should use the alcohol-based disinfectant gel provided to try and reduce the risk of infection.

In assessing the personal hygiene of your chosen person and recommending improvements, you will need to be sensitive as it can be embarrassing talking about issues such as:

- washing hands after using the toilet
- using a deodorant
- keeping nails short and clean
- using tissues when you are sneezing
- cleaning teeth properly and regularly
- washing/showering after exercise.

▲ Using disinfectant gel reduces the risk of infection.

LACK OF REGULAR EXERCISE

According to a survey by Active People in 2006, more than half the population do no physical activity. Around 350,000 people aged over 16 were interviewed and the results showed the extent to which inactivity is contributing to the obesity epidemic. The survey found that 50.6 per cent of the population had not participated in 'moderate intensity sport or active recreation' for half an hour or more in the previous four weeks. If your health plan is for someone over 16 years of age, check to see if they are meeting the recommended target of 30 minutes of exercise at least five days a week. This target was only met by 21 per cent of the sample. It is easy to avoid exercise nowadays, as children are often driven to school by their parents and some parents think that, unlike in the past, it is not safe for their young children to play outside.

The level of exercise your chosen individual should do depends on their age, gender and how healthy they are. For example, moderate exercise can be undertaken by older and less mobile people, whilst young, fit people can take part in vigorous exercise. Many health experts hope that the 2012 Olympics in London will encourage more people to take up sport and exercise regularly. The fact is that exercise is necessary in order to reduce the risk of illnesses such as:

- osteoporosis
- strokes
- stiffening of the joints.
- obesity
- coronary heart disease

LACK OF SLEEP

Group Activity

Think about the possible reasons why adults and teenagers may not get enough sleep. Discuss these as a whole group.

The individual in your care plan may suffer potential health risks because of the lack of sleep. The recommended average night's sleep for an adult is 7–8 hours. A study in the USA found that teenagers should get 9 hours sleep a night but, on average, were sleeping for only 6.9 hours. The study found that about 25 per cent of teenagers were dozing off in lessons at least once a week!

According to research at the University of Warwick, lack of sleep can more than double the risk of death from cardiovascular disease. It is interesting that too much sleep can also more than double the risk of death. Shortage of sleep is also linked to:

- weight gain
- hypertension
- Type 2 diabetes.

UNPROTECTED SEX

There will be serious ethical issues if you build a discussion of sexual behaviour into your health plan. You need to discuss with your teacher the appropriateness of this for your chosen individual.

Despite the greater awareness of contraception and sexually transmitted diseases, many individuals still put themselves at risk by having unprotected sex. The main physical risk to health of unprotected sex is getting a sexually transmitted infection.

Health experts are very concerned about the rise in STIs, particularly among young people. The 16–24 age group accounted for about half of all newly diagnosed STIs in 2007. Figures from the Health Protection Agency showed a 6 per cent rise in STIs across all age groups between 2006 and 2007. Young women aged 16–19 accounted for the highest number of cases of chlamydia and genital warts in 2007.

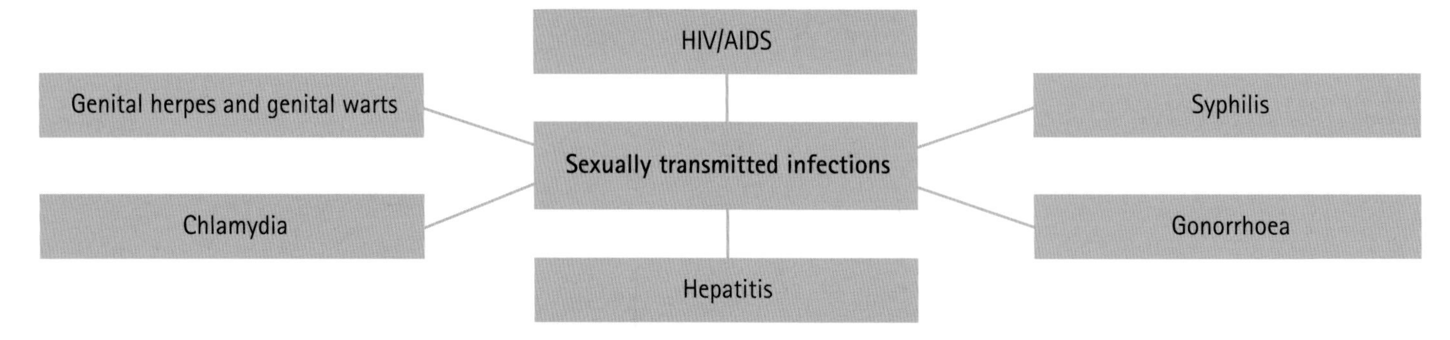

In addition to the damaging effect on the individual, the financial cost to society is growing rapidly for the treatment of people with an STI. According to the British Medical Association:

- It costs, on average, £14,000 a year to treat someone with HIV.
- It costs £400 million a year to treat all HIV patients.
- It costs £165 million a year to treat new cases of chlamydia, gonorrhoea, syphilis, herpes and genital warts.

Many genito-urinary clinics have not been able to keep pace with the massive increase in demand for their services, which has led to increased waiting times, some patients having to wait up to six weeks before they are seen. If individuals continue to have unprotected sex, whilst waiting for an appointment, it is likely that they will infect their partner(s).

Ask your teacher if you can arrange to have a talk from a health worker who deals with sexually transmitted infections. Find out which are the most common, how they can be treated and the long- and short-term risks to individuals.

CASE STUDY **Jimmy**

Jimmy, aged 18, has been showing off to his friends by telling them that he is having casual sex with a number of girls and often fails to use a condom because he feels it is the girl's responsibility to take the necessary precautions. Recently, Jimmy has seen signs of a rash around his penis and he experiences a burning feeling when going to the toilet. He also finds it painful when having sex. He thinks it will eventually clear up and is not worried.

What sexual health advice would you give to Jimmy if you were doing a health improvement plan for him? How could you try and support him with this advice?

SOCIAL ISOLATION

Social isolation can be measured by the number of social contacts a person has. Isolation is most commonly found amongst older and younger adults (for example, housebound or disabled due to a condition such as multiple sclerosis, or being a single mother with young children). Individuals who have sight or hearing disabilities find it very difficult to meet people and communicate with them. Loneliness can have very damaging effects on an individual.

More people tend to live in isolation today than in the past because of:

- the increase in divorce
- the break up of extended families
- more people choosing to live independently
- women living longer than men
- more people living in large cities than in small, close-knit communities.

▲ Being socially isolated can lead to health risks.

The health risks of social isolation include:

- emotional risks, such as depression
- physical risks, such as lack of sleep, poor diet, higher levels of alcohol consumption and general neglect of personal hygiene
- social risks, such as loneliness
- intellectual risks, such as not having anyone to talk to.

It is important that in your health plan you consider the social aspects of your case study. Are there particular difficulties facing the person in relation to their family and friends?

Health and social care workers who work with isolated individuals need to spend as much time talking to them about things in general that matter to them, as they do dealing with any specific health-related matters. The care worker may be the only person that the isolated client sees all day.

Many socially isolated people, particularly older adults, become very nervous and suffer from many fears, such as being the victim of crime, even if realistically they are unlikely to be such a victim.

CASE STUDY Mavis

Since her husband's death two years ago, Mavis has lived on her own in a ground-floor flat in a large council estate. For several days at a time she may not leave her flat or see anyone. Her main contact with the outside world is her television. Her mobility is beginning to worsen and she is worried about the future.

1. As a social worker you have been given Mavis as one of your clients. What would you try to do to reduce Mavis' worry about the future and her loneliness?

POVERTY

Poverty is a key factor affecting health and well-being. In Britain today, very few people suffer from absolute poverty, which is the condition found in many developing countries, where individuals are literally starving to death and are unable to meet the lowest level of Maslow's pyramid of needs. Poverty in this country is relative poverty, where an individual is unable to reach a level that is seen as acceptable for a relatively rich society. This could include not having three meals a day, not being able to afford one basic holiday a year or not being able to pay monthly heating bills.

A health plan would need to look at the financial situation of the individual and possibly suggest ways that would help overcome any debt and all that it leads to. A weekly budget plan would be one possible suggestion to identify where the individual is spending their money, if this was a problem.

The economic cost to society increases if poverty grows, as more people will be claiming welfare benefits and, therefore, more taxes will be required to cover the money paid out. The possible impact upon crime levels is that they are also likely to rise, as a lot of crime is linked to people who steal in order to try and survive.

According to a report published by End Child Poverty, an organization of children's charities and church groups, 'poverty is the UK's hidden child killer'. They show that:

- Children from poor families are at ten times the risk of sudden infant death than children from better-off homes.
- Babies from disadvantaged families are more likely to be born underweight.
- Poorer children are two and a half times more likely to suffer chronic illness when toddlers, and twice as likely to have cerebral palsy.

'From the day they are born, children's health and very survival are threatened by family poverty', according to Donald Hirsch, co-author of the report.

Group Activity

Look up this report and find out how poverty is still a problem affecting growing numbers of children in the UK (www.endchildpoverty.org.uk).

Fact: According to the Department of Work and Pensions, 2.9 million children were living in poverty in the UK in 2008.

INADEQUATE HOUSING

Inadequate housing is a good example of how the risk factors are closely linked together. Individuals who live in poverty are almost certainly living in housing that is unhealthy, badly heated, too small for their needs and possibly unsafe.

The charity Shelter tries to campaign to improve the living conditions for millions of people in the UK. They have found that children who live in overcrowded and damp housing are:

- at higher risk of viral or bacterial infections, including meningitis
- at greater risk of tuberculosis and respiratory problems, including wheezing and asthma
- more likely to suffer mental health problems.

The British Medical Association, which represents doctors, found that children who live in temporary housing, such as bed and breakfast accommodation, have an increased risk of:

- behavioural problems
- stress
- poor sleep
- infections
- gastric (stomach) problems.

Poor housing can have long-term health effects according to Shelter.

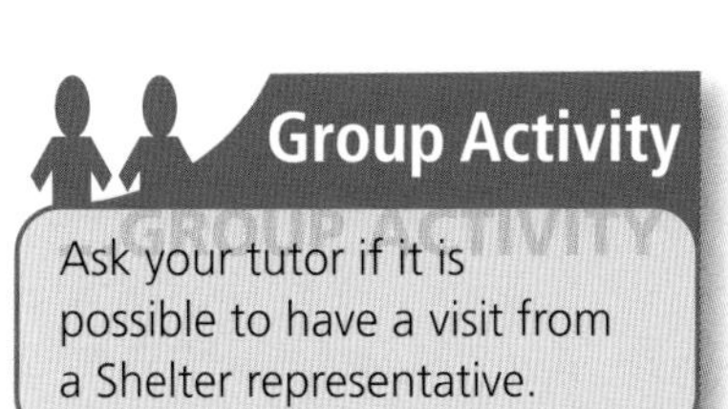

Group Activity

Ask your tutor if it is possible to have a visit from a Shelter representative.

CASE STUDY — Real life case study from Shelter: 'Amanda's story'

'When I was 16, I found that my mother's alcoholism was too unbearable to be around. She was constantly asking me to leave the house, slapping me and getting rid of my belongings. Eventually she threw me out for good and I went to stay on my friend's bedroom floor for 11 months. My friend lived there with her three siblings and her parents, so eventually I had to move to a local homeless youth hostel. It was a dangerous place to live and I found it quite hard to manage my college work. Eventually my college raised funds to help me move into a small bedsit. It was quite a dangerous area and after being a victim of violent crime, I had to move out and stay with another friend's family. Eventually a Connexions personal advisor helped me to get a job and to move to a different area.'

1. Discuss with other members of your group the risks to Amanda's physical, intellectual, social and emotional development caused by having no permanent safe accommodation.

UNEMPLOYMENT

Group Activity

GROUP ACTIVITY

Work in small groups to discuss how, in a health plan, if the individual is unemployed it is important that they should try and keep themselves busy. In what ways would you encourage them to keep occupied?

Share your ideas as a group.

For an adult, not having a job usually leads to serious risks to their health. The Samaritans believe that unemployment triples the risk of suicide. They believe that this is partly linked to social isolation, which was discussed earlier. Possible emotional sources of support for an unemployed person, such as work colleagues, are no longer there. A person's self-esteem is also badly damaged through losing their job.

According to Professor Aylward, of the Wales Centre for Health, the damage to a person's health of being unemployed for more than six months is the same as smoking 200 cigarettes a day! Unemployment causes:

- depression
- social exclusion
- loss of self-respect
- loss of identity.

All of these have a big impact upon a person's physical health and well-being. In some parts of the UK, several generations of the same family have not worked because of the lack of jobs in those areas. More and more doctors are seeing clients with health problems brought about by loss of jobs and all the worries that go with that.

POOR WORK–LIFE BALANCE

Many individuals find it hard to balance their work with the rest of their life. They may feel pressured to work longer and longer hours in order to earn enough money to provide for their family's needs. The Mental Health Foundation carried out a national survey on work–life balance and found that workers frequently sacrificed activities that are vital to their overall health in order to work longer hours. The activities most frequently neglected were:

- exercise (48 per cent)
- quality time with partner (45 per cent)
- time with friends and social activities (42 per cent)
- hobbies and entertainment (41 per cent).

These are all factors that promote good mental and physical health. The impact upon the individual's family can be devastating with the possibility of children being neglected and partners feeling ignored. This can all lead to serious relationship problems.

CASE STUDY Jasmine

CASE STUDY

Jasmine is a single mother with two small children who attend a local playgroup. She works in a local estate agent's office. Her employer has asked her to increase her hours to include weekend working. Jasmine needs the extra money to buy Christmas presents for her children but she also feels guilty for not spending enough time with them. Her mother is willing to help out but she is finding it increasingly tiring getting the children's tea after school. Jasmine's employer has made it clear that he expects her to start working weekends and Jasmine feels that if she refuses she will be overlooked for promotion in the future. Jasmine's health is beginning to be affected but she is afraid to take any time off work.

1. In a health plan for Jasmine, what advice would you give her about her work–life balance? What practical things could she do to maintain a good balance between work and the rest of her life?

ENVIRONMENTAL POLLUTION

According to The Royal Commission on Environmental Pollution, tens of thousands of people are dying early because of where they live. The report says that these problems are worse in towns and cities, where 80 per cent of the population now lives. Air pollution is estimated to be responsible for 24,000 premature deaths a year. Pollution in central London increases death due to heart and lung disease by about 3 per cent compared with rural areas of the country. The main examples of pollution are:

- air pollution, such as carbon monoxide from car exhaust systems
- water pollution, such as waste dumped in rivers from factories and farms
- noise pollution, such as living near a main road or motorway.

The impact of noise pollution upon an individual can be very stressful. Not being able to sleep because of constant noise can cause stress and damage relationships. If the individual in your health plan is exposed to constant noise, they may also suffer hearing impairments such as a constant buzzing in the ear known as tinnitus.

Air pollution will have long-term effects upon respiratory diseases, such as lung cancer, heart disease, and even damage to the brain, nerves and liver.

Water pollution is linked to a range of diseases, such as cholera, dysentery and typhoid. In this country we do not suffer from such problems very often but an example of the potential damage caused by water pollution occurred in Camelford, a town in Cornwall, in 1988.

The impact of pollution upon the environment is potentially huge. One of the more recent examples is fly tipping, where people dump rubbish, including old cars, on the streets because it is cheaper and quicker than taking them to a proper waste disposal site.

▲ Trying to sleep becomes impossible.

Fact: In 1988 thousands of homes were affected when a lorry driver accidentally dumped 20 tonnes of aluminium sulphate into a tank at the Camelford treatment works. A total of 20,000 homes were affected and local people complained of a wide range of health problems ranging from mouth ulcers to vomiting and rashes. Two years later, about 400 people were suffering from symptoms including loss of short-term memory and a study in 1999 suggested that the chemical did cause considerable damage to the brain functions of at least 55 people.

ASSESSMENT PRACTICE: PREPARATION

The Jackson family live in the centre of a large, busy city in the north of England, next to a motorway junction. The father, Joe, used to work in the local engineering factory but the credit crunch caused it to close, resulting in over 500 redundancies. There is very little work available and his two sons, having just left school, are unable to find a job in the area. They are spending a lot of their time on the streets with very little to do. Judy, the boys' mother, has a small part-time job as a cleaner at the local school but the money she earns is not enough to pay the rent and buy the essentials, such as food. Joe is getting frustrated and this is causing relationship difficulties with both his wife and his children. He is beginning to spend more time out of the house and his redundancy money is gradually being spent at his local public house. The boys are mixing with local lads who are known to be involved in petty crime and illegal drug use.

1. Identify the potential risks to the health and well-being of each member of the Jackson family.
2. What impact might their situation have on the health and social care workers in their area?
3. What money and financial problems might occur in the town where the Jacksons live?
4. Explain how the risks to the health of the family are linked, making them very difficult to escape from.
5. What possible health advice could you give to this family to try and improve their health and well-being?

Health promotion and improvement methods

How can individuals be motivated and supported to improve their health?

Getting started

You will:

- know why physical health assessment and target setting should happen before a health improvement plan is produced for an individual
- learn how realistic health improvement targets are established for others
- understand how different health behaviours can help people achieve their targets
- know about the different types of health promotion materials that are used to inform, motivate and support people to improve their health and well-being.

HOW CAN INDIVIDUALS BE MOTIVATED AND SUPPORTED TO IMPROVE THEIR HEALTH?

Group Activity

Work in a small group to look at published health promotion materials.

Which would help you to maintain your own health and well-being?

Why is the material suitable for you? Think about presentation, vocabulary and information given when making your decisions.

In this section you will learn about the need for realistic assessment, advice and targets in health planning. You will also see how people's behaviour affects their level of target achievement.

When trying to make a positive change, it is important to compare the individual's needs with what is considered to be good health and well-being. For example, when formulating diet plans, it is important to use physical measures of health such as height and weight ratios and food tables. Organizations such as The National Advisory Committee on Nutrition and Education (NACNE) produce a comprehensive range of information that can assist in the management of improvements to people's health.

When creating the plan, it is important that it is in a form that is useable by the person for whom it is intended. It is also important to be aware of the health risks that different groups of people are influenced by and how promotional material can be used to support them. During the planning, attention should be paid to the current publications and legislation that help support and guide those wishing to improve their health. This is because they can provide a good foundation for the understanding of how health and well-being can be supported.

Existing materials should be used to support the person chosen, as they are readily available in a variety of forms. This makes them a useful tool, as they are available from a variety of sources.

In this section you will learn about the government health improvement targets for improving health and well-being and link these to individual plans for health.

There will also be a need to:

- know why physical health assessment and target setting should happen before a health improvement plan is produced for an individual
- understand the benefits of accurate advice and support
- look at methods of assessment and motivation
- understand why planning is important
- show how we can set achievable targets
- understand the need for health promotion and information.

HEALTH IMPROVEMENT TARGETS

Many people believe that too many people suffer from poor health. Too many people are ill for much of their lives. Too many people die too young from illnesses that are preventable. At the same time, many people realize the value of better health and already take exercise, eat properly and don't smoke.

The government believes that by working together with us it can tackle poor health. This way it will achieve the aim of better health for everyone, especially the least fortunate. To do this, the government is trying to combat the key killers in this country, which are:

- cancer
- heart disease
- strokes
- accidents
- mental illness.

One of the main ways the government is trying to support individuals is to encourage them to take action for themselves and their families. Communities are now working together and can offer real help. This means that the government can continue addressing the bigger issues that affect health, such as housing, jobs and education, whilst at the same time supporting the key health issues that have already been mentioned.

In 1992 the government published a White Paper called '*The Health of the Nation*' which was the first attempt by the government to provide a targeted approach to improving the health of the population. From 1992–1997 '*The Health of the Nation*' was the basis of health policy in England and was used in planning health care throughout the country.

The areas below were targeted by the government in the hope that they would achieve:

Main killer of under 75s	Reduce death rate by year 2010	Actual number saved
Cancer	20%	100,000
Coronary heart disease and strokes	40%	200,000
Accidents	20%	12,000
Mental health	20%	4000

During 1999, the Labour government published '*Saving Lives: Our Healthier Nation*'. This was an action plan to:

- improve the health of everyone
- improve the health of those socially less fortunate.

▲ The Department of Health.

This meant that the government could target the main killers.

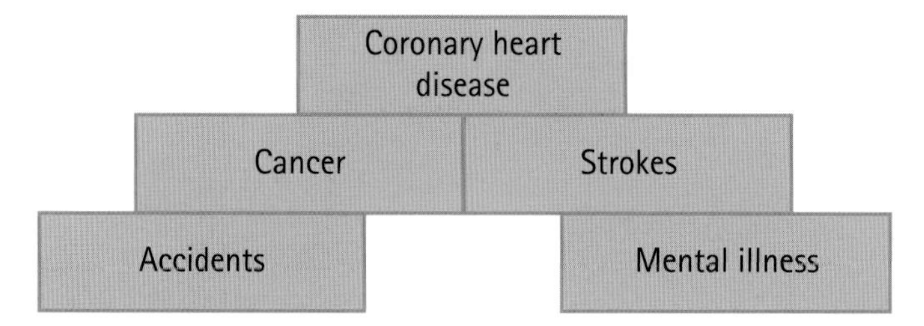

In order to achieve better health for everyone, especially those who were disadvantaged, the government decided to:

- put an extra £21 billion in the NHS to help secure a healthier population
- tackle smoking as the biggest preventable cause of ill health
- integrate government and local government, working to improve health
- stress health improvement as a key role for the NHS
- press for high health standards for everyone.

The race was now on!

Choosing Health: Making Healthier Choices Easier

...WORD CHECK

inequalities – not equal or not fair.

agenda – list of intended actions.

priorities – the most important aspects of something.

conjunction – along with or by the side of.

In 2004 the Department of Health produced its first ever White Paper on Public Health – '*Choosing Health: Making Healthier Choices Easier*'. '*Choosing Health*' set out a wide range of proposed actions to address major public health problems, placing population health and health **inequalities** at the centre of the government's health policy **agenda**.

'*Choosing Health*' identified the following priorities for action:

- reducing smoking rates
- reducing obesity and improving diet and nutrition
- increasing exercise
- encouraging and supporting sensible drinking
- improving sexual health
- improving mental health.

National targets

The **priorities** need to be considered in **conjunction** with a number of national targets that have been set over the past few years. In 1999, '*Saving Lives: Our Healthier Nation*' identified targets aimed at reducing deaths from the four main killers: cancer, coronary heart disease and strokes, accidents and mental illness. Targets for life expectancy, infant mortality and health inequalities were added in February 2001.

ACTIVITY The Health Promotion Team

With your tutor's permission, contact the local Health Promotion Team to find out:

1. What their local health improvement priorities are.
2. How their choice of health promotion campaigns match the government health improvement targets.
3. Who is the main audience targeted in your area and why?

In July 2004 the following targets were all confirmed in the '*National Standards, Local Action*' document produced by the government. The core of the plan was to:

- Improve the health of the population. By 2010, increase life expectancy at birth in England to 78.6 years for men and 82.5 years for women.
- Substantially reduce mortality rates by 2010 (from the '*Our Healthier Nation*' baseline, 1995–97).
- Reduce coronary heart disease, strokes and related diseases by at least 40 per cent in people under 75.
- Reduce cancer by at least 20 per cent in people under 75.
- Reduce suicide and undetermined injury by at least 20 per cent.
- Reduce health inequalities by 2010 by 10 per cent as measured by infant mortality and life expectancy at birth (from a 1995–97 baseline), with reduction in the inequalities gap in areas worst hit by deprivation in the population as a whole.

▲ Rt. Hon. Alan Johnson MP, Secretary of State for Health, talks to patients at St Mary's Hospital in London.

The government also decided to tackle important causes of ill health and health inequalities by:

- Reducing adult smoking rates (from 26 per cent in 2002) to 21 per cent or less by 2010, with a reduction in prevalence among routine and manual groups (from 31 per cent in 2002) to 26 per cent or less.
- Halting the year-on-year rise in obesity among children under 11 by 2010 (from the 2002–04 baseline) in the context of a broader strategy to tackle obesity in the population as a whole.
- Reducing the under-18 conception rate by 50 per cent by 2010 (from the 1998 baseline), as part of a broader strategy to improve sexual health.

This paper supported the benefits of agencies working together to improve public health. It also highlighted the government's intention to tackle social inequality. From this, three core principles emerged to help support the new plan and they were:

1. Informed choice – in that people needed and wanted to make their own decisions but needed reliable and accurate information to enable them to make the right choices.
2. Personalization – for health inequalities to be improved, the support had to fit the individual's needs with services and support personalized in a flexible and sensitive way.
3. Working together – there had to be a partnership across all communities that included:
    - local government
    - the NHS
    - business
    - advertisers
    - retailers
    - the voluntary sector
    - communities
    - the media
    - faith organizations and others.

Only then would the actions help make the desired improvements.

Other activities

Along with the major schemes set up by the government, a number of smaller campaigns were started. These were focused on various activities that could either support health or could be reduced to support health. These campaigns have been **extensively** advertised and the areas covered included:

- Five-a-day programme – a scheme that aims to improve people's access to, and awareness of, fruit and vegetables.
- Local exercise action pilots – designed to identify and test the best ways of getting people more active.
- Teenage pregnancy – a national strategy designed to halve the under-18 conception rate and increase the participation of teenage mothers in education, training or work.
- Providing coordinated and **comprehensive** regional approaches to tobacco control to reduce smoking rates and the associated burden of tobacco-related illness.

'*Healthy Weight, Healthy Lives*' illuminated the effects of doing nothing, with a predicted 60 per cent of the population being obese by 2050 and potential costs of £45.5 billion to the NHS and wider society.

...WORD CHECK

extensively – wide ranging.

comprehensive – complete and containing a high level of information.

assess – to make decisions about what is required.

indulge – to have or to take part in.

ACTIVITY Legislation and policy

Legislation and policy are very important in supporting good health.

1. Why is it important that the country has legislation that supports good health?
2. How do the government's policies help individuals to improve their lifestyle and health?
3. Identify two pieces of legislation and outline their purpose in supporting good health.
4. For one client, identify and explain how a government target could assist them to improve their health.

THE NEED FOR INITIAL PHYSICAL HEALTH ASSESSMENT

It is important to **assess** the person before the plan is designed. This is done to maintain the person's personal safety. There are a number of areas that need to be assessed, which include the activities that they already **indulge** in. Ask them if you can measure their health. With their agreement obtain the following measurements:

- height
- weight
- pulse rate
- body mass index
- respiration rate
- diet habits (what they eat and drink)
- how often they exercise
- type of exercise they do.

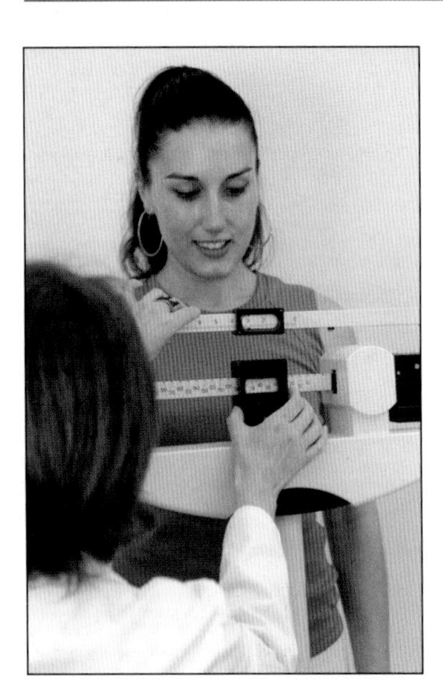

A physical health assessment.

These measurements and the information gathered earlier in this unit will help to show how fit they are and what activities (such as exercise and diet) they will be able to cope with.

There will also be other **considerations** to be made about the person before they start any plan. These will be done so that risk is kept to an absolute minimum. Before they take on any new sports or exercise, it is important to find out if they have a problem or past injury. It is also important to find out if they:

- have been previously inactive
- are significantly overweight
- have a history of heart problems
- have a chronic medical condition, such as diabetes
- are over 40 years of age.

By considering the above, **accessible** activities can be created that are achievable. This will have the added bonus of not **demotivating** the person. They will then be one step closer to achieving their goal.

...WORD CHECK

considerations – thoughtful or sympathetic regard or notice.

accessible – easy to access or approach; approachable.

demotivating – something that stops people having the interest to do something.

motivation – encouragement to continue with an action or event.

targets – goals; points that must be achieved.

unrealistic – something that is not possible to do or sensible to undertake.

review – to look at an event in detail again.

Planning

Providing people with a good plan to improve their health is very important. When planning, it should always be remembered that the plan should be:

- drawn up with the person – so that they feel in control
- ***accessible*** – they should be able to do the activities included
- ***achievable*** – the goals that are set should match the goals of the person and the plan should include short- and long-term targets
- ***accurate*** – if you say something or plan something, it must be correct
- the goals must be clear – what is the aim?

If there is failure in any of these areas, then the plan may fail to work. The biggest **motivation** for a person is to see results. Even the smallest change for the better can be motivating. This means we should aim for small goals to start with and bigger ones to follow, making it *accessible*, *achievable* and *accurate*.

...WORD CHECK

accurate – precise, exact or careful conformity to truth.

modify – to make changes to an object or event.

Setting targets

Setting **targets** is important. These must be achievable for the person for whom the plan is intended. **Unrealistic** targets are the biggest reason why health improvement plans fail. The target that is set can reach the goal in step-by-step stages. It does not have to be achieved all at once. Targets should not be so large that they are dangerous. Often, a little at a time is best. If the targets are not working, **review** them. They may not have been correct in the first place!

By keeping **accurate** records during the health plan, it is possible to monitor what is happening. If a plan begins to fail, there has to be a reason. Investigate the reason and see if the problem can be repaired; you may need to **modify** the plan. This will help the person to get back on track and to succeed.

Group Activity

Work with another person in the group and select two targets that you could each work towards to maintain or improve your own health and well-being.

What actions could you take to meet these targets?

20 What three A's should be considered when drawing up a plan?

Presenting the plan

When presenting a plan to help improve a person's health, it must be in a form that they can use. For example, if the plan is for a child, it should have more pictures than words; if the plan is for an older person, it may need to be in larger print.

For some people, this will mean preparing a plan so that it can be placed on a wall where it can be accessed easily. Other people would prefer to have the plan in a booklet. Whichever way it is used, the plan needs to look attractive to the user.

ACTIVITY Producing a plan

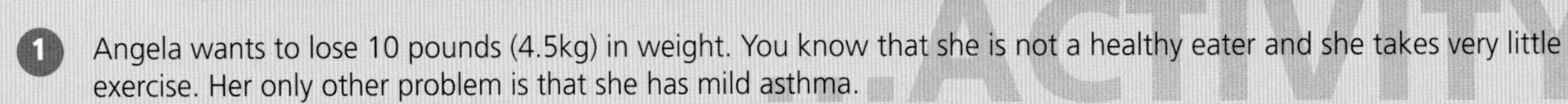

1. Angela wants to lose 10 pounds (4.5kg) in weight. You know that she is not a healthy eater and she takes very little exercise. Her only other problem is that she has mild asthma.
   - Design a two-day plan for diet and exercise to help Angela.
   - Explain how you will make sure that the plan does not affect her asthmatic condition.
2. How do you think a person will feel physically, intellectually, emotionally and socially if they succeed in achieving their plan?

Before any progress can be made, there has to be an overall picture of what is going to happen. All planning should be carried out with the following approaches in mind. It is important that all objectives are:

SMART

This means that the plan must be:

Specific	all aspects of the plan must be clear
Measurable	there must be a measurable outcome
Achievable	all targets must be achievable and realistic
Relevant	activities must be suitable and help the person to achieve the final outcome
Timed	everything must happen in a realistic time frame.

The diagram below gives an overview of how all of the main events could occur in improving a person's health and well-being. This seven-point plan gives a framework to base all of the activities around. The main idea is to create an overall plan that is SMART and achievable.

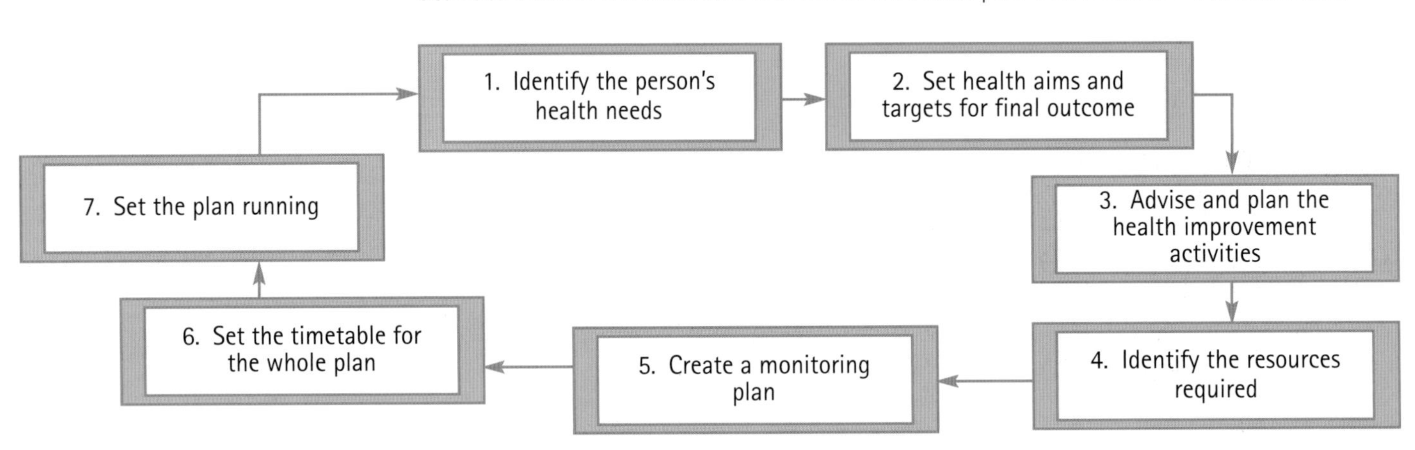

If all of the activities are planned and well explained, then the targets will be reached and the final outcome will be achieved.

Assessment and measurement

Identifying the person's needs

When assessing an individual, everyone's needs are different. Many different factors will affect a person's ability to take part in a health improvement plan. The factors that should be taken into account are:

- Age, diet and activity have to be appropriate for each other. Asking someone who is 70 to start cross-country running is neither safe nor suitable.
- Gender – many women do not have the physical strength that men have but they could easily have more **agility**.
- Physical condition – if an individual has not exercised for a long time, it will be necessary to start off safely. Gentle exercise to start with, building up as the individual gets fitter.
- Health condition – care must be taken not to ask an individual to take part in health plans that might make their condition worse. If someone is recovering from illness, they may need their doctor's advice before starting on a health improvement plan.
- Social position – many people may not have the time or money to go to a gymnasium. The exercise part of a health plan need only take up a maximum of 30 minutes a day. Special equipment does not need to be purchased to get fit. A set of stairs may be enough. People often have to put their family commitments first. They should not be put under pressure to make unacceptable commitments.
- Motivation – this means that the individual for whom the plan is intended really wants to improve their health. A genuine reason will need to be found to motivate them; for example, being able to get into a size 12 dress rather than one that is size 14!

▲ Keeping fit does not have to cost money.

Assessment needs to look at the whole person. This is known as an **holistic** approach. It has to take into account the person's physical, intellectual, emotional and social situations (P.I.E.S.). This way a better picture of the person is often achieved. If their lifestyle can be understood, the assessment is more likely to be successful.

...WORD CHECK

agility – the quality of being agile; the power of moving the limbs quickly and easily; nimbleness.

holistic – looking at the whole (person).

Advice

The advice that is given must always be based on the assessment. If this is not so, the advice could be wrong or prove dangerous. Always remember the person producing a plan may not know all of the answers and so they should always be prepared to ask for advice. It is not a failing to ask; health care professionals do this all the time. When advising an individual, it is important to make sure that:

- they understand the plan
- it is written down (as a plan or description)
- it is suitable (to their age, gender and condition)
- it is accurate
- it is not dangerous and is within their ability to do.

Being able to motivate and support is a vital part of producing the plan:

- To motivate – help the individual to find a good reason 'why' they want to improve their health.
- To support – decide with the individual who could provide help to achieve the plan, for example, a friend or an organization such as Weight Watchers.

21 Why does assessment and advice have to be accurate?

22 What factors affect the assessment and advice that is given to people?

THE EFFECTS OF BEHAVIOUR ON ACHIEVEMENT

Motivation is essential for any plan to improve our condition. The less motivated we are, the more we have to rely on willpower. Good willpower may work for a little while but it does not always last. It is unlikely to result in long-term successful results. To succeed, we must have good motivation. This applies to anyone we are trying to help and especially to ourselves. We must really want to achieve the targets set.

So what is motivation?

'If I swim three times each week, in a month I will start to look slimmer.'

Basically, motivation is what makes an individual succeed. Everyone has to have a really good reason; it needs to be a genuine reason. People who are only doing something because they have been told to do it are less likely to succeed, unless it has a big impact. The reasons for improving health could include:

- My doctor told me to stop smoking; he does not understand.
- My girlfriend said she would leave me if I did not lose weight.

Good motivation is taking action because people want to. They have a positive reason and it is something they really, really want to do:

- I want to look good, for me.
- Being fit will be great and improve my social life.
- My health will improve and I will be able to do so much more with my family.

It is important to keep in mind that keeping a positive attitude is essential to success.

When motivating and supporting someone else, we have to keep reminding them:

- how well they are doing
- how good they will feel and look when they reach their target
- how much more active they will be.

And in the case of giving up smoking:

- how much money they will have saved for that holiday.

Although some people like to exercise alone, others prefer to be in groups. For these, group activity may be the incentive they need to succeed. Community-based fitness groups often provide the positive support and company that is needed. A little competition from others in the same position can also sometimes help.

Whatever people are trying to do, motivation and support are essential. Being positive can make a major difference to achieving goals.

23 Describe three different ways of motivating a person to succeed with a health plan.

24 Describe three different ways of providing support for an individual who is using a health plan.

THE BENEFITS OF HEALTH PROMOTION MATERIAL

Health promotion materials are important because they motivate people to act positively in order to reach their goal of improved levels of health.

Everyone can play a key role in helping to **maximize** their potential for good health. It is important to help people understand the value of health and freedom from disease, and to understand the known causes of disease, both physical and psychological. With this knowledge, individuals can reduce the risk of certain diseases and develop a healthy lifestyle – health is a shared responsibility involving prevention as well as treatment when things go wrong. Activities that promote health can be either passive or active. With passive strategies, individuals obtain benefit through the **intervention** of others. Normally this is through government intervention, for example, the provision of services such as:

- monitoring of food and food outlets
- air quality
- infection control in primary health care settings
- vaccination programmes and advice on parenting
- advice on diet
- advice on alcohol consumption
- advice on smoking
- advice on safe sex.

In contrast, active strategies are those that individuals actively seek out and adopt for themselves, for example, regular exercise and keep-fit activities (either alone or as a group member), **cessation** of smoking, weight watching, stress reduction, and of course keeping the mind active.

Health promotion material is available in a variety of different **formats**. This is to appeal to as many people in as many different ways as possible. As individuals' likes and dislikes can be **incorporated**, this means that the more methods used to pass on information then the greater the success will be.

The importance of having good health has lead to health promotion becoming a very active area. It is a good way of providing accurate and helpful information to large numbers of people. It has shown that health promotion can make a real difference to people's health and well-being.

We have probably all seen information from health promotion **campaigns**. These will have been on TV and radio, and in newspapers, magazines and pamphlets. These campaigns will have covered many topics from alcohol and smoking to exercise and obesity. Advertising on the ways to achieve good health is all around us. It is found in health centres, leisure centres, schools, colleges and supermarkets.

Advertising is targeted at different groups of individuals, for example:

- smokers
- young people
- the homeless
- drinkers
- pregnant mothers
- older people.

There are other campaigns aimed at every age group. All campaigns are designed to appeal to the audience and be eye catching. It often takes a great deal of money, expertise and effort to make them work.

...WORD CHECK

maximize – to make best use of or to make bigger.

intervention – an extra activity that helps a situation, an activity that is added in to something that is already happening.

cessation – to stop or to end.

formats – different types or versions or methods of producing or doing.

incorporated – included in.

campaigns – political operations, often preceding an election.

There are many different methods of providing information to people. Some of these are shown below:

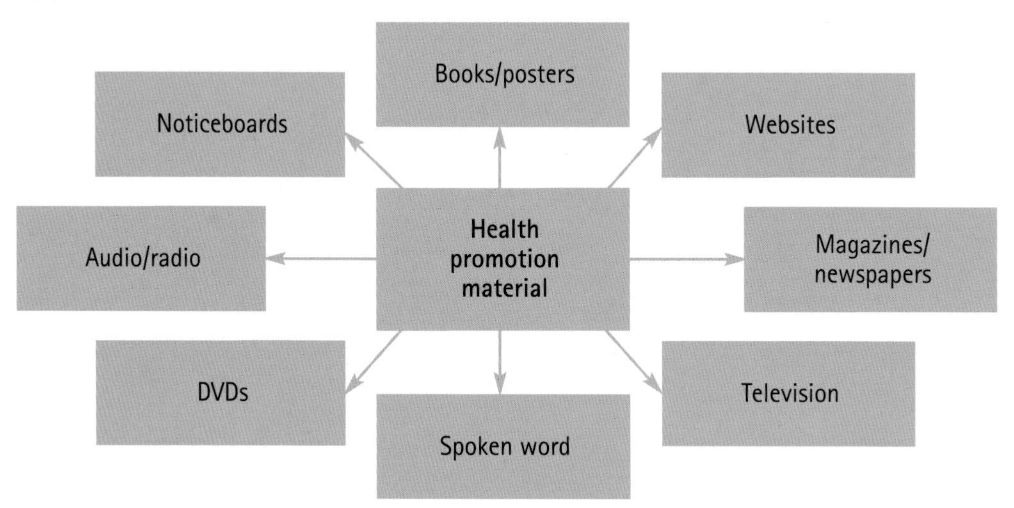

...WORD CHECK

appeal – to find favour.

anonymous – to keep one's identity a secret.

impersonal – formal and not linked with a particular person.

dismissed – not included or cast aside.

impact – the effect or action on an event or person.

The diagram above shows the main methods used to convey information. All of these are used to great effect because they allow many people to see or hear the information. They can be targeted at different groups of people, in different languages, anywhere in the country. They are very effective methods of reaching large numbers of people. They can also be designed to reach different areas of the community by delivering in ways that **appeal** and are appropriate to specific groups.

They can, however, be **anonymous** and **impersonal** in that they do not always convey feeling or emotional warmth. This often means that, although people will have seen or heard the information, it may be easily **dismissed**. If its **impact** is not strong enough, then people often take no notice. This is why information delivered in this way has to be dramatic, colourful and have that 'Wow' factor.

The diagram also shows us the wide range of availability of information. Many of these methods can be used to reach people in their homes. This means that they will receive the information without stepping outside of their front door.

Personal delivery

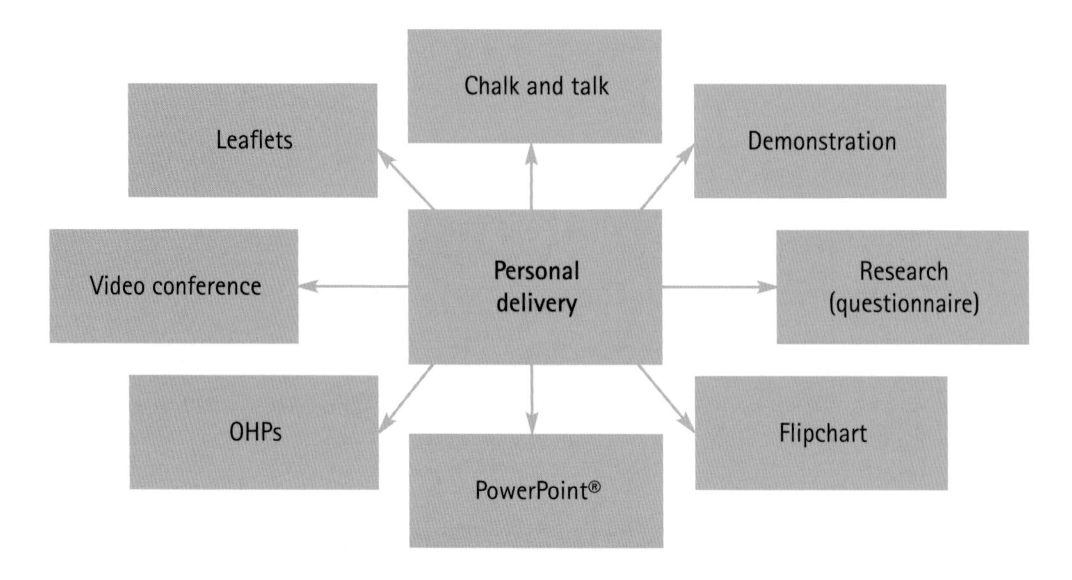

ACTIVITY Health promotion materials

1. Look at a selection of **four** health promotion materials. These can be leaflets, advertisements or any other form of information. Briefly explain the aim of each item.
2. List the audiences that each campaign is targeting.
3. Explain why you think the best ones are effective. What catches your eye? Are they easy to read? Is there a balance between the number of illustrations and the number of words used?
4. Select one piece of health promotion material. In no more than 50 words, explain how it would provide support for a person who is trying to improve their health.

Availability

Health promotion resources can be obtained from a variety of places that are accessible to the public. Leaflets and publications giving advice will be found in many locations that include:

- GP surgeries
- clinics
- dental practices
- schools
- hospitals
- libraries.

Health promotion resource centres provide health promotion, public health materials and resources to keep and to loan. They are usually free of charge to anyone with a role in health promotion. This service is also available to anyone who works or lives within the boundaries of the area that they serve. All new users complete a registration form and they can then use the services. So there is no reason why people should not access these resources. However, they may not always know exactly where to go to find them.

ACTIVITY Success or failure?

Think of an example of health promotion material that made an impact on you.

1. Why do you think it was successful?

Now think of a material that did not impress you.

2. Why was this?
3. What would have made it more successful?

Informing

In this modern technological age there are a variety of ways of getting the message across to the public. Health information does not only come in written form. Everywhere you look there are pieces of information designed to make individuals notice them.

Television is the strongest **medium** available because virtually everyone watches TV. This makes it a **primary** force for providing health messages in the form of adverts and public information films.

Radio is a less popular medium as fewer people listen to radio than in previous years. As it has no visual component, it tends not to have the impact that TV has, but may appeal to older adults. Whatever format the information is presented in, it will be creatively designed to have the maximum impact, the idea being to make individuals notice and remember the message.

...WORD CHECK

medium – a method or way that information is delivered.

primary – the first or most important.

Motivation within health promotion materials

▲ Providing support and motivation.

Health promotion resources must also motivate, as they will not be successful if they don't! This can be done in two main ways:

1. Fear – by vividly describing the damaging effects an activity like smoking will have, people automatically take notice. Those who are keen to either give up or extend their life will be affected most and benefit from the message.

The positive message can be given by demonstrating how much better an individual's lifestyle could become. This can be done by **emphasizing** improvements to the person and also how this could have a beneficial effect on friends, family and loved ones. A good example of this is the work that has been done to show smokers how they can have a **detrimental** effect on those around them. The fear of harming a loved one by causing them to become a passive smoker is often enough to make them give up.

2. Support – often the information provided in health promotion resources will have an element of support. This can include help lines where a person can ring up and obtain advice. The materials can explain where to go to get help and the type of help that is available. It can also provide information about like-minded individuals who have got together to help each other. These are known as self-help groups and are one of the most effective ways of reducing negative activities like drinking and smoking. So health promotion resources can be a powerful weapon in helping to improve individuals' health and lifestyle.

...WORD CHECK

emphasizing – to highlight or draw attention to.

detrimental – causing detriment; injurious; hurtful.

CASE STUDY Bill

Bill is 47 years old and believes he is 22 pounds (10kg) overweight. He smokes 20 cigarettes a day and drinks five bottles of red wine a week.

He has discovered that light physical exercise now makes him out of breath; this has worried him. He has turned to you to help him get back to a normal size and weight. He also wants to become fitter.

He is 70 inches tall and weighs 14 stone (he does not use metric measurements).

1. Produce a plan to help Bill stop smoking.
2. Why is it important to assess his capabilities before he starts any plan?
3. Design and present the plan for Bill.
4. Describe ways that you can use to motivate him.
5. What health promotion materials can you use to help him?
6. What levels of support will he require? How can these be achieved?

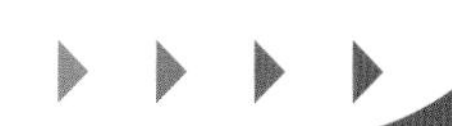

ASSESSMENT PRACTICE: PREPARATION

Now that you have obtained the information from the chosen individual about their health and well-being you need to:

- Explain the features of the individual's lifestyle that have affected their physical health.
- Identify **two** physical needs to focus on within the health plan and explain why these needs have been selected.
- Identify **two** targets for the individual (you can include short- and long-term targets).
- Draw up a plan for the individual, explaining why the plan is relevant to them.
- Explain **two** ways the individual could be motivated to succeed.
- Explain **two** ways in which the individual could be supported through the plan.
- Analyse the difficulties that the individual may have in following the plan.
- Describe the possible impact of the plan on the health and well-being of the individual, including P.I.E.S. (physical, intellectual, emotional and social well-being), drawing conclusions.
- Explain how the targets meet the individual's needs.

Remember to include the bibliography and to present the information in an appropriate format, using appropriate technical terminology.

4 Safeguarding and Protecting Individuals

Contents

About this unit

At the end of this unit you will need to be sure that you have learnt all the facts as the external assessment (test) will decide the mark you receive for this unit. You will need to learn about:

- what is meant by ill-treatment, who requires protection and the consequences of ill-treatment
- the name of Acts/regulations that help to protect individuals and their purpose
- the key features of Acts and regulations that help to protect and safeguard individuals
- how the Acts/regulations are applied in care settings so that clients are protected and safeguarded
- how to prevent the spread of infection in order to protect individuals and groups
- how to use basic first-aid practices and procedures to deal with minor emergencies
- how to recognize potential risks to service users' safety and how to reduce risks in a setting.

Introducing this unit

Individuals in care settings can feel at risk or vulnerable because they have to rely on others. They may feel that they are not in control of their lives, and so could become quite distressed and upset. This can happen in the home situation as well as in care settings. When this happens, wherever it occurs, individuals will need support from those who are caring for them.

With another person, think about what could cause the following people to be really upset in a care setting:

- a child
- an older adult
- a person with a disability.

How could each be protected in the situations you have identified?

Exchange ideas with another pair and compare your answers.

In this unit you will find out about the different types of ill-treatment that people can experience and how they can be protected. You will also need to think about the effects ill-treatment could have on individuals. How will ill-treatment cause them to behave? How will people react to ill-treatment? How will ill-treatment affect their development?

Acts (legislation) are in place so that some protection can be provided for individuals and groups. Legislation is put in place by the government and has to be implemented in care settings. The government has recognized that ill-treatment not only affects the individual but can also have an effect on the wider society. Have a whole-group discussion about:

- who is the wider society?
- how can the ill-treatment of an individual affect the wider society?

Have you ever had an illness or condition that has been infectious? How were you prevented from spreading the infection to others? Most of us will have had chickenpox or flu. Those caring for us will have probably kept us away from others so that the illness could not spread. It is important that all who work in a care setting should know how to protect themselves and others from the spread of infection and the methods that could be used to clean and sterilize the environment.

About this unit

Work with another person to complete one of these tasks:

- draw or cut out a picture of a care worker and glue it to a large piece of paper. Show what personal hygiene methods could be used to prevent the spread of infection. Explain to others how these would protect self and others from the spread of infection

OR

- cut out or draw some items of personal protective clothing. Explain to others how these would protect self and others from the spread of infection.

Have you ever carried out any first aid? When carrying out first-aid procedures, care must be taken not only to prevent the spread of infection but also to prevent further harming of the individual who is receiving first aid. If the injury received is more serious, you may have to call the emergency services. It is important to know which service is needed and what information to give. To give inaccurate information could waste time and cause the casualty further pain and discomfort.

With another person, write down five situations where first aid would be needed. How could you make sure the person was protected from:

- danger
- infection?

Share your thoughts with others.

When working in a care setting it is important to make sure that individual clients are safe and that hazards do not exist. In this unit you will need to be able to identify potential risks in care settings and which safety equipment could be used to make sure that the risks are reduced.

Work with another person and make a list of all the possible risks that could occur in:

- a community room
- a kitchen.

Discuss your findings as a whole group.

Safeguarding individuals

Who requires safeguarding and what are the consequences of a lack of safeguarding?

Getting started

Clients often feel distressed because they do not feel in control of the situation they find themselves in. They need protection from harm. In this unit you will learn about who is in need of protection because they are vulnerable. This might include:

- children
- children in care
- older people
- people with disabilities
- people with learning difficulties
- people with mental illness
- people who reside in care settings.

We look at examples of a variety of situations where clients may need protection from:

- being emotionally ill-treated by being deprived of love or physical contact
- verbal abuse
- having to witness violent scenes
- having parents who are unable to put the child's needs before their own
- being physically neglected
- being left to look after themselves without adult protection
- bullying
- a carer who psychologically ill-treats a person by swearing, humiliating or harassing them
- being physically abused
- forcible isolation, where a carer denies a person access to the outside world or to a particular service
- sexual abuse
- financial ill-treatment or exploitation.

The effects of ill-treatment or abuse can cause clients to blame themselves for what is happening. It can also result in:

- lack of confidence
- withdrawal
- demonstrating abusive behaviour towards others
- low self-esteem/self-concept
- difficulty in communicating with others
- a change in personality.

There is legislation and guidance in place that contributes to protection, such as:

- The Children Act 2004
- Mental Health Act 2007
- Disabled Persons Act 2005
- Disability Discrimination Act 2005
- NHS and Community Care Act 1990
- *'Every Child Matters'*
- CRB checks.

We look at how ill-treatment and abuse can affect both the individual and wider society.

WHO IS IN NEED OF PROTECTION?

Positive and negative emotions

Most people want to be happy. One of the main **characteristics** of happiness is having a feeling of 'joy'. To be happy is to:

- have a satisfaction about life
- have a feeling of joy about what we do
- have the absence of fear
- feel secure and protected.

Positive emotions contribute to being happy. Sometimes people are happy for long periods of time. On other occasions, an individual will feel happy or **exhilarated** for a short period, for example, if they win a race or achieve a good examination result. On the other hand, people can also experience **negative** moods, such as anger, anxiety or depression.

Throughout life, individuals will have times when they feel positive or happy, and other occasions when they feel negative. This will depend on what is happening in their lives at particular times. If individuals are ill-treated they are likely to become distressed and will feel **vulnerable**. This could be because they do not feel in control of the situation they are in, particularly if they are dependent on others. Emotions control our feelings. The table below shows some of the positive and negative emotions that an individual can experience:

...WORD CHECK

characteristics – features of or contributors to (being happy).

positive – on the plus side; good things about being.

exhilarated – being happy; overjoyed.

negative – not very good; not making a positive contribution.

vulnerable – not able to cope by themselves; needing support.

Positive emotions	Negative emotions
excitement	tension
delight	anger
satisfaction	depression
pleasure	distress
gladness	annoyance
interest	alarm
contentment	misery

CASE STUDY Carla

Carla is one year old. She is left in her cot on her own for most of the evening, while her mother goes to the local pub with her boyfriend. There is no heating in the flat and she is only wearing a vest and a nappy. She is left with a bottle of milk but Carla soon finishes this and is hungry. Her nappy gets very wet and needs changing. She does not like being left in the dark.

Work in pairs if possible.

1. Use some of the negative emotions given in the table above and state why Carla would experience these.
2. Write a four/five line scenario to show how a one year old could show positive emotions.
3. Why would the one year old in your scenario feel positive?
4. Share your scenario with others in the group and ask them to say why they think the infant would feel positive.

People from all the different life stages could require protection from the **consequences** of ill-treatment. Look at the life stages given below.

1 Who do you think are the most vulnerable? Why?

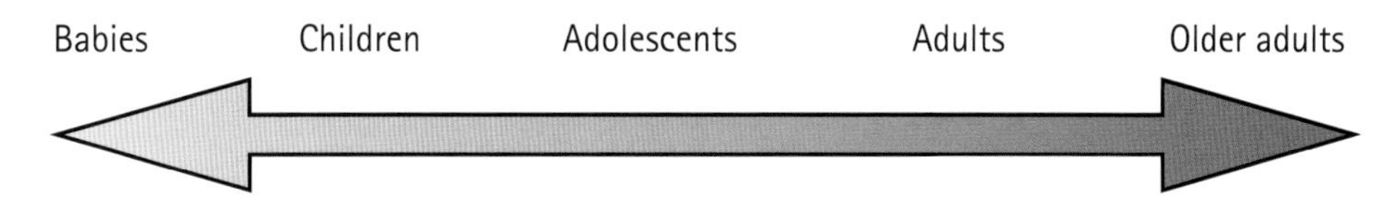

2 Can you think of any other individuals or groups who could feel vulnerable? Why?

Ill-treatment or **abuse** can be **spontaneous**, that is a single act that ill-treats an individual, or can happen repeatedly, that is over and over again. Abuse can be **active**, that is, for example, physical; or **passive**, which means needs are neglected. Most ill-treatment or abuse occurs in a relationship where there is an **expectation** of trust, in other words the person causing the harm is well known to the individual who is being ill-treated. This could be a professional care worker or a family member. A person who does ill-treat or abuse another person is often known as the '**perpetrator**'.

The General Social Care Council emphasizes in its Code of Practice for professional care workers that all individuals must be treated as an individual, their views and opinions must be treated with respect and that the individual must be given dignity. Other care settings, such as hospitals, nursery schools and playgroups also have Codes of Practice that clearly set out how the care provided for clients must include effective communication, active listening and empathy. This will play a major part in achieving a relationship of trust and a supportive atmosphere.

The table below gives some examples of vulnerable people:

Vulnerable people	Some examples of ill-treatment
Infants, children and young people	Physical, sexual, emotional, verbal, bullying, witnessing violent scenes at home
Older adults	**Isolation**, financial, physical, sexual, verbal, left without protection
People with disabilities/ learning disabilities	Verbal, neglect, being left to look after themselves
People with mental illness	**Neglect**, financial, psychological, emotional
People who reside in care settings	Isolation, bullying, sexual abuse, psychological, neglect, financial

3 Which clients are likely to reside in care settings?

Understanding the views of individuals is an important feature of a relationship.

...WORD CHECK

consequences – the results or effect of an action.

abuse – hurting a person and causing distress or pain.

spontaneous – a natural response; automatic.

active – marked by action.

passive – not doing something when it is obvious that it is needed; not acting upon.

expectation – the prospect of future good.

perpetrator – a person who abuses another or takes advantage of another.

isolation – being separated from others.

neglect – failing to care for someone.

How can infants and children be ill-treated or abused?

▲ 'Keep away from me, you don't need a cuddle.'

...WORD CHECK

nutritionally – having the correct content or nutrients, for example, protein, vitamins.

protection – keeping someone or something safe or free from harm.

psychological – of the mind, for example, fear.

thriving – doing well; achieving success.

An infant or child can be physically ill-treated or abused by:

- being physically injured by a parent or carer, for example, slapping, punching, kicking – this includes not preventing an injury from occurring
- being given a poisonous substance, such as drugs, alcohol or cleaning fluids
- being drowned
- being neglected, that is not being kept clean or fed **nutritionally** balanced meals
- being left without adult **protection**
- being bullied at school or by other children who live in their community
- being parented by people who are unable to put their children's needs before their own
- deliberate force-feeding or starvation
- leaving a child in a wet bed or soiled clothing.

These types of physical abuse can be applied to clients in all life stages, regardless of their age or needs.

Most adults, however much they love their child, will get angry with them from time to time. Some parents often have trouble with controlling their anger and they punish their children too severely. This can take the form of hitting the child or emotional abuse, which can make the child very frightened. Many children who are abused are afraid of talking about it, as, often, the perpetrators are those who look after them.

4 Work with others to answer this question:
Someone in your group is covered with lots of bruises that they obviously didn't get from playing with others or playing sports. When you ask them about it, they break down and tell you their mum has done it. What would you do?

Other forms of ill-treatment or abuse of infants and children are:

Other forms of abuse to infants and children	How ill-treatment takes place
Emotional neglect	Failing to show affection and love to the child, for example, refusing to show them physical affection. This is a form of **psychological** abuse.
Verbal	Shouting at, bullying or threatening the child.
Sexual	Forcing the child to take part in sexual activities, which causes a child a great deal of unhappiness and could prevent them from **thriving**.
Violent scenes at home	Parents may get involved in arguments about home life, being short of money or about having an affair with another person. They may be always shouting or injuring one another and do not have the interest or energy to look after the child properly. This could cause the child to become frightened and withdrawn.

ACTIVITY Can you find the answers?

...ACTIVITY

1. Dan's parents are shouting at one another and throwing vases and photographs around the room. Dan is hiding behind a chair. What type of ill-treatment is this?
2. Abigail is locked in her room most nights while her mother goes out clubbing. What type of ill-treatment is this?
3. Amir's mother never cuddles him. What type of ill-treatment is this?

Protecting older adults from ill-treatment and abuse

An older person may be handled roughly while receiving care, and develop bruises, or they may be pulled or pushed while they are being moved from one position to another. These are forms of active physical abuse. Older adults can be very demanding, particularly if they are dependent on others, and could be slapped or kicked as the person caring for them becomes angry and cannot control their feelings. Any such behaviour is unacceptable and that is why all care settings that care for older adults must have procedures in place to **detect** abuse quickly.

Passive abuse is when an older adult's needs are neglected. For example, an older adult may wish to ring the bell because they are in need of attention but the bell could be dropped just outside of their reach. Another example is that a client in a hospital may need help with eating and drinking, but because staff are very busy, they ignore these needs and the meal is taken away exactly as it was brought in. The older person is hungry and becomes dehydrated. Such neglect will affect the person both physically and emotionally.

▲ 'Joan, take this – it will help you to calm down.'

Often, **sedatives** are prescribed for older people when they are found wandering around a care setting upsetting other clients. Staff need to find out the reason 'why' they are wandering. For example, they could be looking for a book, searching for a handbag or looking for a relative. Sedation solves nothing! It is a form of **medical** abuse.

Sexual abuse occurs when an older adult is involved in sexual activities to which they have not consented. This is forcing an older person to take part in any form of sexual activity. It includes touching, fondling, kissing, oral contact, genital contact, rape, or being forced to watch or read pornographic material. Older people can be sexually abused by a professional care worker, a relative, a visitor or a complete stranger, but the last is not common.

...WORD CHECK

detect – to find out about.

sedatives – a drug or something to calm someone down.

medical – relating to health.

prejudiced – being biased; making up one's mind about someone or something before really knowing what they are like.

Protecting people with disabilities

People with disabilities need protection from ill-treatment. Some people consider individuals with disabilities to have less worth than themselves. This can be shown by an individual ignoring a person who is sitting in a wheelchair and talking to the person who is pushing the wheelchair, as though the person with disabilities is not present.

Other people in the community may believe that people with disabilities are not capable of working. This is a **prejudiced** view.

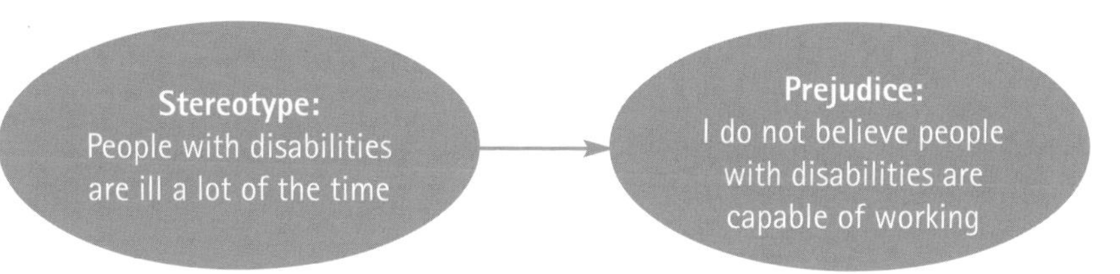

▲ 'How is Margaret today?'

5 What is the difference between stereotyping and prejudice?

▲ 'How can I access the GP?'

Discrimination can be defined as the 'unfair treatment and denial of rights to one group because of their identity'. This does not necessarily relate to how they would identify themselves but how others see them. A person with asthma wishes to enter a marathon, knowing the condition is under control and she is capable of running the distance. Her entry may be refused, as the organizers believe a person with asthma cannot safely run that distance. She is being discriminated against because of their perceived views.

The way other people 'see' you can affect your self-image/concept. It can produce a 'looking glass' effect (Cooley, 1902). This means what is mirrored or reflected back to us, from others, can become part of what we believe about ourselves. Have there been occasions when you have felt ok until someone said: 'You do look pale'? From that moment on you feel unwell!

Discrimination can be direct or indirect. Direct discrimination tends to be obvious, intentional and visible. Indirect discrimination tends to be less obvious, but is just as effective in terms of denying access to goods and services and basic civil rights. It may be unintentional or done mistakenly in the person's 'best interest'. A shop offers a service to all, but a wheelchair user finds the only entrance is via a flight of steps; a disabled person is not invited on a night out to save them from the embarrassment of being stared at, and a companion of a person with impaired vision is asked what the individual would like to drink, when they are able to answer for themselves.

6 What do you think is meant by the term, 'looking glass effect'? How could this affect you?

...WORD CHECK

diffuse – spread widely.

generic – broadly; not to be specific.

unpredictable – not to know what they might do next.

Protecting people with learning difficulties

Group Activity

Discuss with others:
How would you feel if you were known by any of these terms:

- idiot
- imbecile?

What effect would it have on your self-concept and self-esteem?
How would you feel if you had a learning disability and heard these terms being used in name-calling between others?

The term 'learning disabilities' refers to a range of conditions that affect the way or the ability of an individual to learn, when compared to others. This could be as a result of being born with Down's syndrome, developing autism or suffering from a brain injury. The degree of severity and the effects on the individual vary greatly. Using the term 'people with learning disabilities' is as broad as using the term 'people with physical disabilities' or 'the elderly'. It covers such a wide and **diffuse** group of people as to only indicate, in **generic** terms, people with a certain type of disability.

People with learning disabilities have been treated in different ways, at different times in our history. For example, they have been thought to be:

- 'sub-human', having primitive and **unpredictable** behaviour
- childlike, with no rights but needing care
- an 'object of pity', of whom there are little or no expectations
- a 'sick person', who needs medical care and control.

It is only in more recent times that disabled people have been seen to have the same rights as other citizens, and as individuals who are entitled to the same respect and dignity as others.

Clients with learning disabilities need protection from:

- Being isolated
- Verbal abuse
- Being left without protection
- Being humiliated (made to feel small and unworthy) and from being harassed when they cannot protect themselves
- Being physically neglected
- Financial abuse
- Emotional abuse

An individual who has learning difficulties can be from any life stage and will have different needs depending on their age and circumstances. They may live with their family, with an adoptive family or in residential care. Wherever they live, they must be treated with respect, given dignity and protected from ill-treatment or abuse.

CASE STUDY Brendan and Joel

Brendan is 14 years old. Before he was 13 years old, he attended a school where all the students had learning difficulties. He liked it at the school and had a lot of friends.

When he was 13 he was moved to the local comprehensive school for three days each week, as there was a larger range of subjects available for him. He is very unhappy at the school because no one talks to him at break times and some boys follow him around the playground calling him names and making gestures. They laugh at him a lot.

Brendan has decided that he will not go to the comprehensive school any more; he will pretend he is going, but not turn up.

Joel is 50 and has been living in a long-stay hospital for 30 years. He was born with cerebral palsy and his single parent was unable to look after him and the rest of the family. He has spasticity (tight muscles) in one arm that reduces his ability to control his arm movement. He also has poor speech and learning disabilities.

Joel is now living in a supported house, run by a voluntary agency, with two other patients. He has very limited practical skills because he never had to learn them (all hospital meals were provided, clothes were washed in the communal laundry and cleaners were employed to keep the ward clean and tidy).

He likes reading very simple books with lots of pictures and doing large wooden jigsaws. He is able to get out into the community and has tried saying 'Hello' to some people but they have ignored him. When he went out one evening, a group of youths threw stones and bricks at him. They then surrounded and threatened him. He is too frightened to go out any more. Joel would like some paid employment but it shouldn't be too demanding, as he did not work whilst in hospital.

1. Think about Brendan's situation. What types of ill-treatment and abuse is he experiencing?
2. What are Brendan's needs?
3. How could the following help Brendan to cope with this situation:
   - other students
   - adults at home and at school?
4. Think about Joel's situation. What types of ill-treatment and abuse is he experiencing?
5. What are Joel's needs?
6. How could the main carer at Joel's new home improve the situation for Joel?
7. Compare the two clients, considering similarities and differences. What could be done to help both feel more fulfilled and satisfied (see Level 5 of Maslow's pyramid of needs on page 5)?

Protecting people with a mental illness

...WORD CHECK

detach – separate themselves from others; to stand alone.

stigma – something that does not present a good image of the person.

traumatic experiences – events that cause shock or upset.

abnormal – different from others of the same age or type.

exploitation – to take advantage of.

ECT – electroconvulsive therapy is a form of treatment that was widely used to attempt to cure psychiatric disorders by giving the patient electric shocks.

bio-feedback – chemically based mechanisms within the body that allow the brain to receive information from various organs and body systems. For example, the sensory cells in our carotid arteries that tell the brain the level of oxygen in the blood.

The term 'mental illness' is often frowned upon in today's society. Many people who suffer from mental illnesses are ashamed to admit it and suffer in silence in order to **detach** themselves from the **stigma** that comes with being mentally ill. A broken leg or physical disability is easily identified and it can be seen that someone is in pain. However, the illnesses that are possibly more difficult to identify are those without physical effects, and they are, therefore, often ignored. Years ago, to have a mental illness, such as depression or obsessive compulsive disorder, meant that the best treatment was to be thrown into an institution. Nowadays, the health and social care service is very advanced in care for patients with mental health conditions but, often, they are still unacceptable to the rest of society.

There are many different types of mental health issues, all affecting people's lives in different ways. Some people are born with mental health conditions such as autistic spectrum disorder, and it is usually in the early stages of development that problems are identified. This is often around the age of three. Other mental health issues, such as obsessive compulsive disorder or depression, are brought on through **traumatic experiences** during life.

Why are clients with mental disorders at risk? Often such clients will behave in a way that is not common with other people. For example, they may demonstrate **abnormal** behaviour, they may not speak and be isolated, they may not look after themselves or manage personal hygiene or finances, they may have mood disorders or they may have eating disorders.

What type of 'traumatic experience' could cause an individual to develop a mental illness or condition?

Whatever the reason, people experiencing mental ill health are often vulnerable and require safeguarding. The diagram below shows some of the ways that individuals with a mental illness or condition could be helped to overcome their difficulties.

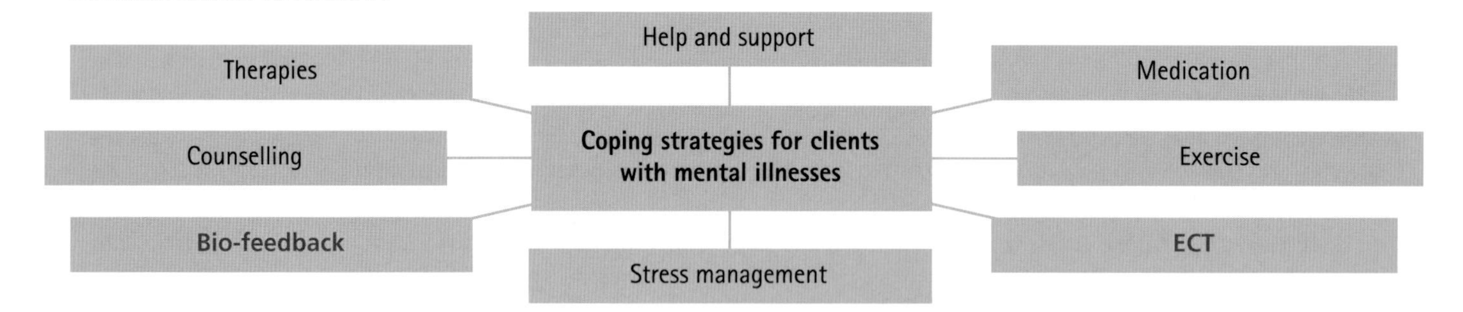

Clients could find that while they have mental ill health they are unable to:

- manage their financial affairs
- look after their children
- cook meals or eat well-balanced meals
- look after their personal hygiene
- maintain relationships with others
- claim the benefits to which they are entitled.

While a client is experiencing mental ill health, professional and informal carers will need to make sure that they are protected from **exploitation**. That is that they are not cheated out of money or benefits, they are not physically, emotionally or psychologically abused and that they are not physically neglected.

Protecting individuals who reside in residential care

Effective communication is essential when responding to the needs of individuals who reside in care settings, whether they are children and young people, adults or older adults. The way in which professional care workers communicate with clients will need to take individual needs into account. Some individuals will be physically frail but mentally alert. Some may be mentally confused but physically able, and others will be both physically and mentally frail. Making time to get to know an individual and to talk to them will be an important aspect of a professional care worker's role. Sometimes a client will relate better to some care workers than others and this will need to be taken into account.

In some health and social care settings 'key workers' have been introduced. This means the individual is looked after by a small number of people, with one of the group being identified as taking responsibility for a particular number of individuals. Key workers help to make the care provided 'personal', which improves the quality of care provided and prevents individuals who live in residential care from becoming vulnerable. They could be at risk of:

How are clients at risk?

- Being exploited by professional care staff and taken advantage of when they cannot protect themselves
- Being sexually abused by professional care staff
- Being kept in isolation because a care worker denies them access to a facility or service
- Being humiliated or harassed by those who care for them
- Being bullied by the people they live with, go to school with, or go out with
- Being verbally abused by being regularly shouted at or being sworn at
- Never being praised for their attempts to do something
- Not being given the right food or having their personal hygiene needs attended to

Abuse in residential homes can happen because there are too few staff to meet the clients' needs. It also occurs where the setting is poorly managed. Residential homes have to provide care for people with a wide variety of needs, and staff sometimes find that they have not been trained to deal with particular situations. It is in situations such as this that abuse can take place, even though regular checks are made when employing staff. A residential home may also unwittingly admit a client who has been regularly abused by a relative or a friend. If staff do not detect the problem, the abuse could continue.

ASSESSMENT PRACTICE

1. Name **two** types of individuals who could feel unprotected if they were left without anyone to look after them. [2]
2. Explain what is meant by a client who has a 'learning difficulty'. [2]
3. List **two** ways that clients who have a mental illness could be at risk. [2]
4. Explain why some clients are vulnerable. [5]
5. Explain how positive and negative emotions could affect a client. [10]

FORMS OF ILL-TREATMENT

Bullying

▲ Bullying can take many forms.

...WORD CHECK
racial – relating to the race.

Bullying is a form of emotional abuse. Individuals can be bullied physically, psychologically and financially. Bullying can also be **racial**. Bullying means to wear down another person with fear. It can happen:

- at school
- in the community where a person lives
- in the workplace
- during leisure activities
- in health and care settings.

Bullying is unfortunately becoming more common in schools. Whether at work or at school, those who are being bullied may:

- be frequently absent from work or school
- be distressed
- become withdrawn
- be aggressive
- cry a lot
- attempt to self-harm, for example, cut themselves
- stop eating
- be frightened to walk to and from a place
- do not achieve well at work or at school.

8 Why do individuals or groups bully a person?

There are a variety of reasons why a person may be bullied. These can include:

Looking different from other people in the group, for example, wearing different clothing, looking scruffy, or being very well dressed.

They may be from a different race from the main group of people who live in an area and have different coloured skin

They may look as though they are frightened of those around them and may prefer their own company, not wanting to mix with others.

They could have a different religion or different lifestyles from the main group. Others could feel threatened by this.

The person being bullied could have a disability or a learning difficulty. They may look different because of their disability and may be considered to be a 'good laugh' when bullied.

A person being bullied in a residential home may not have any relatives or friends who visit, so the person doing the bullying may think they are less likely to be found out.

The person who is being bullied may be afraid of speaking up for themselves or may be incapable of defending themselves.

They or their parents may have a good job, which is better than most other people. This could be considered to be unfair.

They may appear to live in a better/worse area or have more/less of certain personal belongings, such as cars or boats, than the main group of people who live in the locality.

Bullying is a form of **discrimination** and those who experience it have the right to be protected. It is no good telling a person who is being bullied, 'you need to stand up for yourself' because they are unable to do so without help.

CASE STUDY Marcus

Marcus is the eldest child of five in the family and is cared for by his mother. His father does not live with them. Marcus is eight years old and has to look after his brothers and sisters quite a lot, as his mother has a mental illness and cannot cope.

His mother is often in a very bad mood and regularly shouts and swears at Marcus because the younger children have started to argue and quarrel. She never praises him or thanks him for helping, she just seems to expect him to do it. His mother often takes the side of the two younger children and cuddles them quite a lot. She never cuddles Marcus or his brother Tom.

When Marcus goes to school he is often too tired to pay attention to his lessons and, because he looks scruffy and unclean, no one wants to play with him. He can't go out and play with anyone after school because he has the younger children to look after.

After school, Marcus has to get all the children something to eat because his mother cannot be bothered to do it. There is very little money for food and they are often hungry. Marcus is becoming angry when things at school get on his nerves.

Marcus is having to take responsibility for his brothers and sisters, which is too much for him at the age of eight. His mother is unable to cope as she has a mental illness and so relies on Marcus to do some of the 'coping' or 'looking after' the children for her. There is no other person in the house to help with daily living tasks and so Marcus does the best he can.

He is never shown any love by his mother but the younger children are given cuddles and affection. While Marcus does not show any **resentment** or bad feeling to his **siblings**, his anger and resentment are being shown through his anger to his **peers** when they annoy him at school.

Marcus is not experiencing any social relationships. He is not mixing with his peers at playtime because he looks unkempt and dirty, and they do not want to know him. He is too tired and is unable to go out to play in the evenings because of his responsibilities to his brothers and sisters.

Marcus and the other children are not being fed food that will enable them to **thrive**, so they are likely to be **prone** to illness, and lack energy and interest in what is going on around them. Also, they are not following good hygiene routines so they could easily become ill from infection.

Being shouted at regularly means that Marcus is being verbally abused, which will add to the anger he is already feeling because of the lack of love demonstrated towards him by his mother.

...WORD CHECK

discrimination – to show a bias or intolerance.

resentment – anger; irritability; feeling bitter.

siblings – brothers and sisters.

peers – people who are the same age.

thrive – to do well; to achieve success.

prone – likely to get or have (an illness).

The table below sets out the different types of ill-treatment experienced by Marcus in his daily living:

Type of ill-treatment/abuse	Examples of how it is displayed
Emotionally ill-treated	lack of cuddles, lack of love being shown
Verbal abuse	being shouted at regularly
Having a parent who is unable to put their child's needs before their own	mother not taking responsibility for the family
Physical neglect	mother not showing an interest in buying food or cooking food; not making sure the children are clean and presentable
Humiliation	mother swearing at Marcus and making him feel he is unworthy

Marcus and his siblings are not having a very good experience of life and this is likely to affect them as they grow up into adulthood and throughout their lives.

CASE STUDY Nadia and Jay

Nadia

Night after night, Nadia, who is seven years old, wakes up to the sound of shouting from the room below. She listens and hears her mother and father arguing. The voices are raised and then comes the sound of things being thrown across the room. Even when she puts her head under the duvet she can still hear it.

Her mother starts to cry and she hears her father hitting her mother, who starts screaming. The front door bangs loudly and she looks out of the window and sees her father going off down the road. All is quiet for a while so she goes downstairs. Her mother is sitting in a chair crying. There is blood dripping from her nose and lip.

Her mother suddenly realizes that Nadia is in the room. She jumps up and runs out of the back door.

Two hours later, neither Nadia's mother nor father has returned home. This has happened several times during the past week.

Jay

Jay is in his early fifties. He is not working because he has Alzheimer's disease and can remember very little.

His wife, Rosemary, is looking after him but she is very house proud and worries what the neighbours will think if they find out that Jay cannot feed himself and often urinates on the floor.

Rosemary tells her neighbours that Jay is working overseas for at least a year. She thinks this will stop them asking awkward questions.

She moves Jay into the back bedroom, which is not overlooked by anyone. She keeps the door locked and only goes upstairs to give him food, which she has to feed to him. She only cleans him up every two days because it seems pointless to do it more often as he gets just as dirty again quite quickly.

Jay spends his time watching the TV or sleeping. He is very bored. He keeps telling Rosemary that he needs to see the dentist as he has toothache but Rosemary does nothing about this.

Work with someone else in the group if possible. Read both case studies carefully and then answer the questions:

1. Complete a table showing:
   - three types of ill-treatment or abuse experienced by Nadia
   - for each, give examples from the case study to explain how each type of abuse is occurring.
2. Complete a table showing:
   - three types of ill-treatment or abuse experienced by Jay
   - for each, give examples from the case study to explain how each type of abuse is occurring.
3. As a pair, write a short scenario to show bullying. Draw up a table to show the types of ill-treatment or abuse, giving examples of where they occur in the scenario.
4. Exchange your scenario with another pair in the group (not the answers). After listing all the types of abuse and giving examples for each, exchange your work back with the same pair and mark their answers.
5. Give and receive verbal feedback to/from the pair (peer-assessment).

Sexual abuse

When sexual abuse occurs, whether it is abuse of infants, children and young people, adults or older adults, it involves taking advantage of a position of power. This could mean a family member taking advantage of an individual or a professional carer forcing someone to perform acts unwillingly. Sexual activity is abusive when **informed consent** is not freely given. Infants and children can never give 'informed consent' to any sexual activity of any description.

Sexual abuse can include one client abusing another, particularly if the person being abused is weaker than the other. Sexual abuse horrifies us all so much that we would rather not think about it. It is important that it is identified as quickly as possible and stopped. Occasionally an extreme case of sexual abuse is reported, after **detection** by newspapers. The headline below gives an example of this:

...WORD CHECK

informed consent – having the knowledge to make a decision about something.

detection – the act of detecting; the laying open what was concealed or hidden; discovery.

limited – restricted; within a small boundary.

THE MORNING NEWS

The nation's best-selling daily newspaper

Austrian man held his own daughter captive for 24 years

Persistent abuse inflicts misery!

Signs of sexual abuse can include:

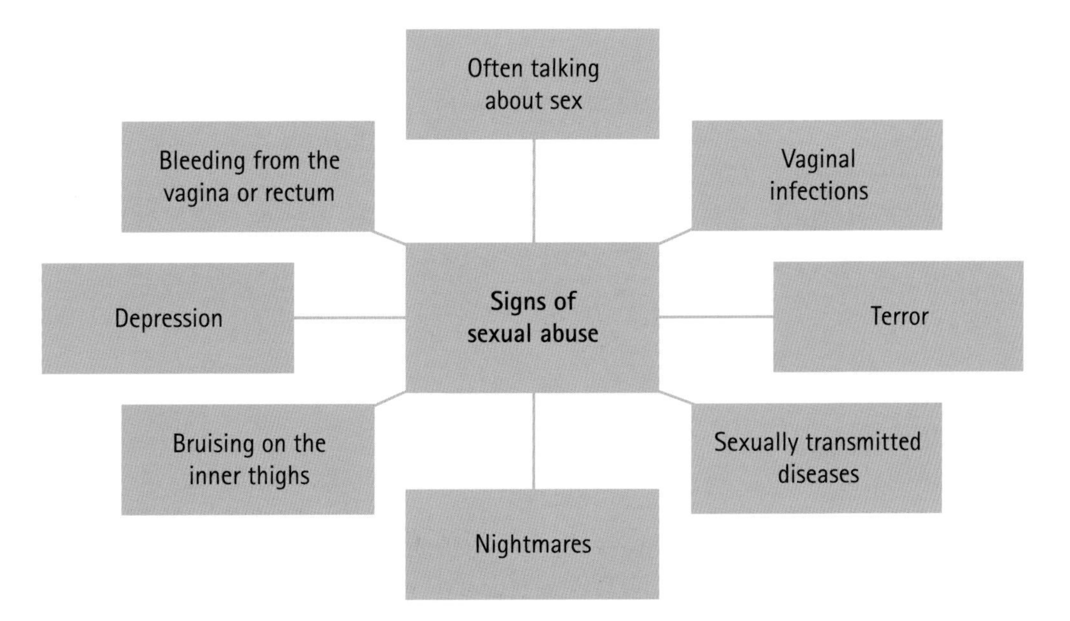

Sexual abuse is totally unacceptable. For many adults, informed consent can never be given because the adult has very **limited** understanding of the issues.

Financial abuse

...WORD CHECK

informal carers – those who look after individuals but who do not hold the qualifications to do so, for example, parents, spouses, partners, family.

professional carers – a person who is trained to carry out the caring role.

account – to keep a record of.

infringing – preventing someone from achieving their rights.

empowering – to give control to a person or group.

Individuals using services should, if they have the ability, be allowed to control their own financial affairs. Those people who are older adults or in residential or nursing care should be able to decide for themselves how they spend or save their money. Just because they are being 'looked after' by **informal carers** or **professional carers**, does not mean that they give up their right to manage their own financial affairs.

Theft of money from an individual client should be taken very seriously and is a crime. Theft could involve a professional care worker or another client deliberately taking money from an individual for whom they care. In other words, trying to cheat a person of what is rightfully theirs. It could also be a relative or another resident doing some shopping on behalf of a client and not giving the right amount of change or any change. When carrying out any financial transactions on behalf of an individual, it is important to **account** for how the money has been spent. To not do so is **infringing** on the person's rights and can lead to poor relationships with the individual.

CASE STUDY Brad

Brad, who is 90 years old, is a resident in Happy Days Residential Home. His sister collects his pension each week and pays most of it into an account to pay for his residential care. The remaining £15 is given to Brad to buy newspapers and personal items he might need. Each week, a care assistant does some shopping for Brad. She buys writing paper, stamps, sweets, birthday presents for friends and so on. Brad hands over all of his money. The care assistant does the shopping but never hands over any change. After a few months, Brad complains about this to his sister when she visits.

1. Discuss how the care worker is infringing Brad's rights.
2. Explain what the care worker should do when she has purchased the items for Brad.
3. Explain what the likely effects might be on Brad as a result of the care assistant's actions.
4. With another person, plan a role play showing a different way that a client could be cheated of their money. One person should take the client's role, while the other should be a professional or informal care worker.
5. Present the role play to others. How was the person being abused? What do you think the effect of being abused would be on the person?

Not providing information about the benefits that could be obtained is another way in which some care workers and relatives prevent clients from having what is legally their right. The client should be given sufficient information so that they can claim any benefits to which they are entitled. The attitude of a care worker or relative could be 'They've got plenty of money anyway, they don't need any more'. This is a method of trying to control the client's money and the individual themselves. It is exerting power, not **empowering** the client.

ASSESSMENT PRACTICE

1. List **two** possible signs of sexual abuse. [2]
2. Give **two** reasons why sexual abuse may take place in a residential home. [2]
3. **Explain** why witnessing violent scenes at home is abusive. [4]
4. Eric is 75 years old and has Alzheimer's disease. He is kept in total isolation. **Explain** why this is a form of abuse. [5]
5. Bullying can occur at school. **Explain** what happens when a person is bullied. Why does this happen? [10]
6. What is physical abuse? **Explain** why this could happen. [10]

THE EFFECTS OF ABUSE

The effects of ill-treatment or abuse can cause people who have been abused to turn their anger against themselves and to blame themselves for everything that has happened. When this results in someone causing injuries to themself, this is known as self-harm. When a person self-harms they are showing deep distress. Often the person doing the self-harming does not know why they are doing it, but afterwards they feel that they can cope again for a little while.

A person who self-harms may scratch themselves, cut themselves, drink substances that will harm them, swallow harmful medication or other tablets, or develop eating disorders, such as anorexia or bulimia. The individual does this because their anger, rage, sadness, grief, fear, guilt or loneliness threatens to overwhelm them. People who do self-harm often self-punish in order to get some control over their life because they have gone through very difficult times.

Women are more likely to self-harm than men, but the numbers among males are rising quite quickly. Research also shows that ten per cent of 15–16 year olds have self-harmed. They harm themselves because:

▲ 'What is happening to me is my fault'.

- they may have been neglected
- they may have been involved in physical violence
- they may have experienced emotional or psychological abuse
- they may have been made homeless
- they may have been bullied
- they may have been separated from someone they loved.

These are just a few examples of why a person may inflict an injury upon themselves.

The effects of self-harm, or any form of ill-treatment or abuse, can have an enormous **impact** on an individual. For example:

Lacking confidence – the person feels that they cannot do anything correctly and that they are not valued by themselves or anyone else.

Becoming withdrawn – not wanting to mix with others and being by themselves because they fear that others will find out what has happened. They also think they are not as good as anyone else.

Demonstrating abusive behaviour to others – harming others by physically slapping or taking money from them can help the individual feel they are repaying what has been done to them.

Having a low self-esteem or self-concept – feeling not valued or worthless and so the person does not attempt to achieve anything because they think they are not good enough.

Communicating with others could become a problem – the person may not want to speak to anyone as they feel guilty, as though it was their own fault that the ill-treatment happened.

Personality could change – from being a happy, well-balanced individual to an angry person.

Eating could become a major crisis – eating lots of food and then making themselves sick or eating very little.

Neglecting self – not taking care of personal hygiene or appearance because of having a low self-opinion.

Taking no interest in life – living in a world of their own and not looking to achieve good examination results or a job.

...WORD CHECK

impact – the effect or action on an event or person.

All people should be treated with respect and dignity if they are to develop, whatever their life stage, into well-balanced human beings. They should experience the positive emotions discussed at the beginning of this chapter, so that they can feel safe and secure. Anyone working in health, social care or early years settings should make sure that they know about policies and procedures that are in place for that setting, to ensure protection of all who are cared for and all those who work in the setting.

ASSESSMENT PRACTICE

Sue is in the reception class at infant school. She has only been attending for half a term but her teacher is quite concerned about her. While she is talking to her teacher during the lunch break, Sue confides that she does not like it when her uncle looks after her on Saturday evening as he does things to her when he is getting her ready for bed. He also likes to look at her and makes her lie on the bed with nothing on.

Sue's teacher notices that Sue has become very withdrawn and does not mix very well with the other children. She sometimes gets into a rage when she is doing something with the others in the group and throws her books across the room.

The teacher decides she must report this to the named person at the school responsible for child abuse.

1. Give **two** reasons why Sue's teacher is concerned. [2]
2. List **two** other signs that sexual abuse could be happening. [2]
3. **Explain** why Sue may throw her books across the room and isolate herself from other children. [6]
4. Explain the effect on Sue that child abuse is likely to have as she develops. [10]

LEGISLATION AND GUIDANCE THAT CONTRIBUTE TO PROTECTION

The Children Act 1989

Local authority social services departments are required by the Children Act 1989 to act together to provide services and support for children, young people and their families, including disabled children. The Act covers children and young people under 18. The main focus of this legislation is:

- to protect children who are at risk – the paramouncy principle
- children have the right to be heard
- children's wishes have to be taken into consideration
- support to be provided to keep families together where this is at all possible.

The physical, emotional and educational needs of the child must be considered when a child protection case is being discussed. Decisions have to be reached as to whether the parents have the ability to meet these needs when caring for the child. The panel of professionals who have responsibility for the child or children have to take into account any harm that the child is caused and the risks that are associated with this. They also consider whether any circumstances have changed for the child and whether such changes could have a positive or negative effect on the child.

The services provided under The Children Act can include:

- help with housing and support
- equipment and adaptations
- occupational therapists or other specialists
- an advocate or representative for individuals or families
- short-term breaks.
- social work
- benefits advice
- counselling
- interpreters

The main purpose of child protection is to keep a child safe and secure, protecting them from harm. Children now have to be kept informed about what is likely to happen to them and their opinions should be taken into account, particularly if decisions are to be made that will affect their future.

The local authorities have a statutory duty to investigate any reported cases of child abuse in order to protect a child from harm. Abuse could be in the form of verbal, sexual, physical or emotional abuse. When the child protection conference is set up, a decision may be made to place the child being discussed on the **child protection register**. Both the children and their parents are then supported by social services to try and avoid any future difficulties. An approved social worker is often provided to help with such responsibilities.

...WORD CHECK

child protection register – a list of children who live in a particular area who need to be closely monitored because they are vulnerable.

There are several ways in which help can be provided in emergency situations. These can include:

How help can be provided	What is involved?
Emergency Protection orders	This is a crisis situation where a child needs immediate help. Social services will make an application to the court for an order which will allow them to act.
Care orders	Under this type of order, the child is usually removed from the parents and placed in a foster home as a temporary measure. Often this action is taken when an emergency order has been served. A Care order can only be made when it is considered that a child is likely to be harmed either physically or emotionally. Children who are taken into care are known as 'looked after children'.
Education Supervision orders	The aim is to make parents more responsible when their child is failing to attend school. The order places the child under the supervision of the local education authority.

As a result of the Children Act, the County Court has the ability to protect a child by making them a ward of court, placing them under the protection of the court and the official solicitor. The court also has the ability to make orders that can remove a child to safety or other protective action.

The Children (Scotland) Act 1995 and the Children (Northern Ireland) Order 1995 have similar provisions for children's services in Scotland and Northern Ireland.

 How does the Children Act help a child who is being physically abused?

ACTIVITY Child protection

Invite a child protection officer to your centre (with your teacher's permission) to find out about:

- how a child protection register is set up and organized
- how a family can benefit from being on a child protection register
- how a child can benefit from being on a child protection register.

Discuss the findings from the talk. Write a report using the points above as a guide.

The Children Act 2004

▾ Victoria Climbie.

This Act was prompted by the failure of social services and other organizations who were involved in the care of Victoria Climbie to protect her. They had not shared information across the different services, for example, health, education and social services. The '*Victoria Climbie Report*' (2003) and the green paper, '*Every Child Matters*' (2003) proposed changes to legislation and policies in England, in order to minimize risks to all children. The Act is intended to force different services who are involved in the care of children to work much more closely together in an attempt to prevent other deaths.

The Act requires local authorities in England to have in place a 'Director of Children's Services', who will be accountable for children's services. These services will be inspected and departments will have their performance levels 'rated' so that the accountability set out as a requirement under the Act can be clearly seen. Also, an 'information database' will be established. This will make it easier for professional care workers to network and share information about children for whom they are concerned.

Local authorities will be required to produce plans for children that take their specific needs into consideration and that make children aware of the forward planning that is intended. This will be linked to the appointment of a 'Children's Commissioner', whose task will be to:

- initiate enquiries on behalf of children
- find out about the needs of children and young people
- investigate, specifically, the needs and interests of children and young people.

10 How could this Act have affected the life of Victoria Climbie, if it had been in place before her death?

CASE STUDY Megan

A neighbour has reported to social services that she has noticed the child living next door being left alone for several nights each week. She has been woken up by the child's cries during the night. She also reports that the child, Megan, is very thin and has bruises on her arms and legs.

1. **Explain** how the Children Act of 1989 would help Megan.
2. What are the differences between the Children Acts of 1989 and 2004?
3. Explain what would happen through social services once the neighbour had reported that Megan had been left alone.
4. The government introduced some amendments to the Children Act in 2004. Explain the main amendments that were made. How would these changes affect Megan's case?

Other legislation that can help to protect individuals

Other pieces of legislation have some direct influence on the protection of clients. These are:

Legislation	How it protects
Mental Health Act 1983 and 2007	Mental health problems can affect people at different times in their lives and can do so in a variety of different ways. A person who has mental ill health can experience anxiety, depression, schizophrenia or dementia. They may also self-harm. The Mental Health Act clearly sets out the way in which a person who has a mental disorder can be treated without their consent. It also sets out the safeguards that the person with the disorder is entitled to. The 2007 Act introduced a new 'medical treatment test', which means that patients cannot be detained for long periods of time unless they need appropriate medical treatment. It also gives patients the right to make an application to the county court to displace their nearest relative and to choose someone that they feel is more appropriate. Civil partners are amongst those who can be selected as a relative.
Chronically Sick and Disabled Persons Act 1986 and 2005	This Act should reduce discrimination against disabled people. It ensures local authorities provide services for disabled people by recommending what should be available and makes it a legal requirement for all new public buildings to have suitable access for disabled people.
The Disability Discrimination Act 1995 and 2005	The 1995 Act is concerned with preventing discrimination against people with disabilities. It covers housing, transport, employment, access to education and obtaining goods and services. This Act is constantly in the process of being reviewed and improved, especially in the area of public transportation.
NHS and Community Care Act 1990	The Act is wide ranging; one of its aims is to allow vulnerable people to lead an independent life within their own home or community. Local authorities must: • publish their plans for organizing community care • invite any other organization (health authority, housing department) that would be useful to a client to attend assessment meetings • publish details of their complaints procedure • make sure clients get the services they are offered. Only part of this Act applies in Scotland. In Northern Ireland it is the Health and Personal Services (Northern Ireland) Orders 1991 and 1994.

CASE STUDY Fiona

Fiona has been living alone since her husband died four years ago. She seldom goes out and does not bother to cook any meals. She forgets to pay her bills and refuses to answer the door when anyone calls to try and help her. Her neighbour hears strange animal-like noises through the wall but she knows that Fiona does not have any pets. The neighbour telephones Fiona's cousin and asks her to visit as she is worried about Fiona.

Research the Mental Health Acts of 1983 and 2007 (some information is given on page 267).

1. How could Fiona's cousin obtain a compulsory admission order for Fiona under the Mental Health Act?
2. What were the main changes in the Mental Health Act of 2007?
3. How would these changes affect Fiona's situation?
4. With another person, find out what the term 'advocacy' means. Under what circumstances would advocacy be used?
5. Carry out research to find out how the Mental Health Acts would **impact** on the ways in which a care setting would deal with a client who had a severe mental illness. Report your findings to others in the group.

ACTIVITY Research and reporting

1. Work in small groups to find out about **one** piece of legislation given below. You should find out about:
   - the main purpose of the legislation
   - how it helps to protect individuals.

   The legislation for your research should be selected from **one** of the following:
   - The Mental Health Act 1983
   - The Mental Health Act 2007
   - The Disability Discrimination Act 1995
   - The Disability Discrimination Act 2005.
2. When you have carried out your research, give a presentation to the whole group about the purpose of the legislation and how it helps to protect individuals.
3. Write a case study/short scenario about an individual who has been affected by a condition that the legislation you researched would affect.
4. Write three questions that could be used to test others to see if they have the knowledge from the case study short scenario to answer the questions. (Look at the previous two case studies to help you.)
5. Work out the answers to the questions.
6. Exchange the case study/scenario with another group and try to answer their questions.
7. Mark the answers to the questions for the case study/scenario that you developed and give oral feedback.

Every Child Matters

...WORD CHECK

impact – have an effect on; influence.

welfare – well being.

minimized – reducing the risk; to make as small as possible.

partnership – working with other organizations/people.

Making sure that children are safe and promoting their **welfare** is the responsibility of everyone. In 2004, the government identified, through *'Every Child Matters'*, two aspects to promote the welfare of children. These were:

- to take all reasonable measures to ensure that risks of harm to children's welfare are **minimized**
- to take all appropriate action to address concerns about the welfare of a child, working to agreed local policies and procedures, and through working in **partnership** with local agencies.

Safeguarding children covers such things as:

- health and safety
- bullying
- medical needs
- medical conditions
- providing first aid
- school security
- safeguarding against drugs and substance misuse.

The child must be kept safe from **maltreatment**, neglect, violence and sexual exploitation. They must also be protected from accidental injury, death, discrimination, crime and anti-social behaviour.

Regulation through '*Every Child Matters*' tried to make sure that children have security both in and outside of school, and have **stability** through being cared for by reliable parents or carers. Peer mediation should be introduced in schools as a strategy for reducing incidence of bullying and discrimination amongst students.

Consulting with children about decisions that will affect their lives is an important aspect of '*Every Child Matters*', as is listening to what the child says. This helps children to feel valued and helps them to make important decisions later on in life.

...WORD CHECK

maltreatment – not treating properly; abusing another.

stability – steadiness.

CRB checks

The CRB is the Criminal Records Bureau. The CRB is an Executive Agency of the Home Office set up to help organizations make safer recruitment decisions. The CRB provides access to criminal record information through its 'Disclosure' service. Checks are made, on behalf of organizations, to detect criminal convictions before a person is employed in an organization, particularly if they are going to be employed to work with children or vulnerable adults. Checks are also made through the Bureau on those who wish to work with organizations for whom security and safety are essential aspects of their work. The CRB can provide clarity and remove doubt about the suitability of an employee. This means providing in-depth criminal history to help the employer decide on the applicant's suitability for any given position.

ASSESSMENT PRACTICE

1. Give **two** ways that the government's green paper '*Every Child Matters*' could help to protect children. [2]
2. What do the letters 'CRB' represent? [1]
3. Give **two** ways that the CRB helps to protect individuals. [2]
4. **Explain** how The Children Act protects and safeguards the rights of children. [5]
5. **Explain** how the Mental Health Act could help to protect an individual who has a mental health condition. [10]
6. Dominic has a disability and is confined to a wheelchair. He lives in a residential home and is cared for by the staff. Using the information provided on page 267 and research that you have carried out yourself, **explain** how the Disability Discrimination Act of 1995 protects Dominic from being exploited. [10]

HOW THE CONSEQUENCES OF ILL-TREATMENT CAN AFFECT BOTH THE INDIVIDUAL AND WIDER SOCIETY

Ill-treatment can take many forms. It could involve:

- physical abuse, in the form of hitting
- verbal abuse, by shouting or swearing at an individual
- sexual abuse, which is taking advantage of a person by interfering with their sexual organs or having sexual intercourse without their permission
- emotional abuse, through not showing any affection for an individual
- psychological abuse, for example, creating fear.

Some examples of the results of abuse are shown in the diagram below:

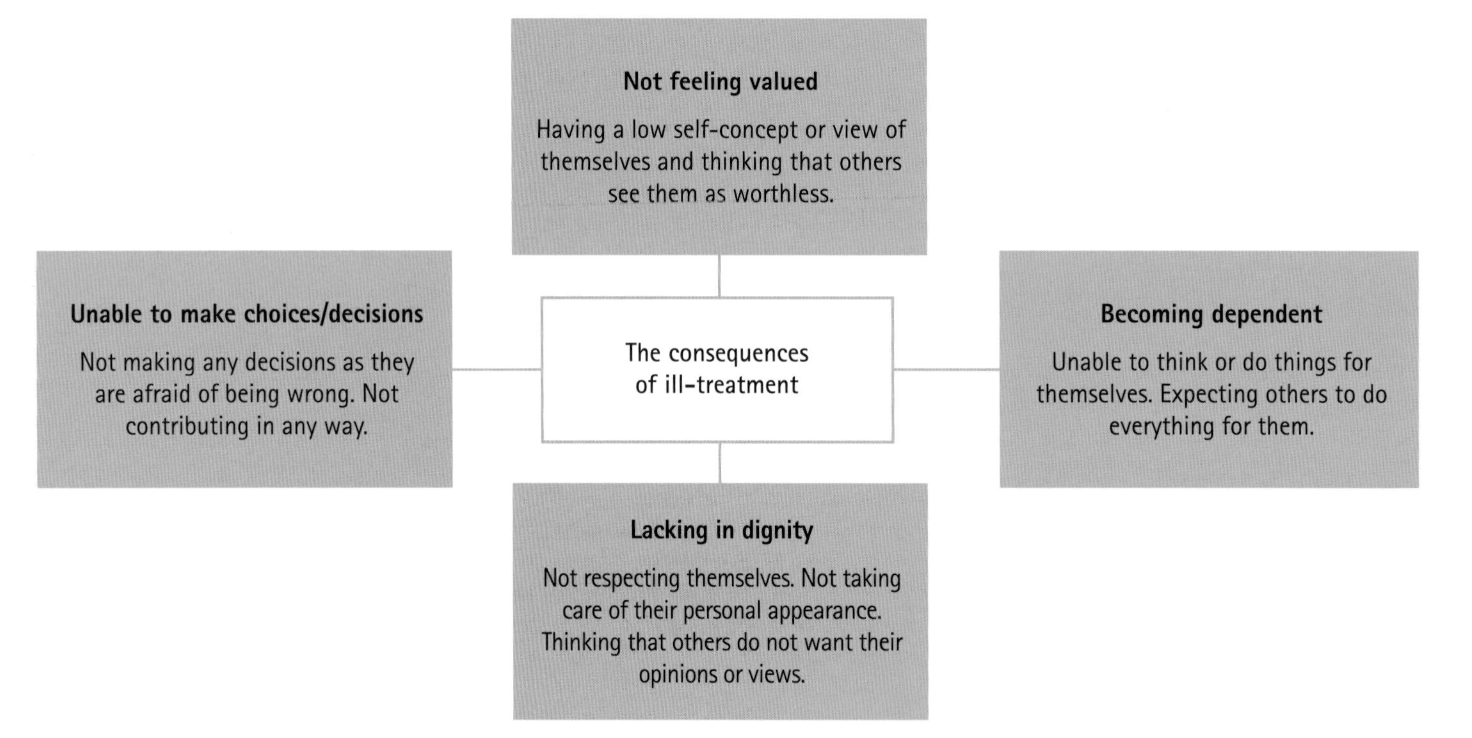

Protecting an individual includes empowering them or allowing the client to have as much control over their lives as possible. It involves helping them to participate in decision making and activities, respecting their opinions and providing choice.

If an individual is ill-treated, the whole of society can be affected because more individuals will become dependent on others and there will be fewer people to take responsibility. This could result in more people not wanting to work and fewer people being prepared to take responsibility in the community. In the long term this could lead to increased crime and lower standards of achievement in schools. It could lead to abuse of alcohol and drugs with individuals losing all self-respect and feeling worthless, which in turn would lead them to inactivity and poverty. This type of outcome would affect us all. Protecting and safeguarding individuals means promoting a positive attitude within each person, besides making sure that they are physically safe.

The diagram below gives an outline of how this can best be achieved:

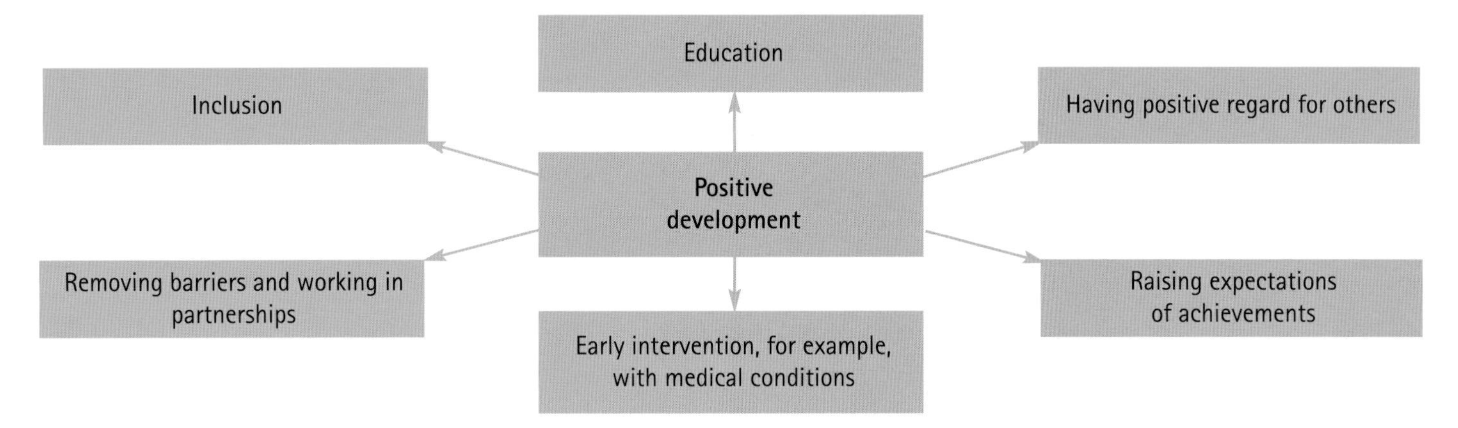

ASSESSMENT PRACTICE

Melstock Nursery admits children from the age of six months to four and a half years. It has good facilities for each age group and has well-qualified and caring staff. Parents can take their children from 7:00am until 7:00pm.

1. Give **one** type of client who could feel vulnerable at the nursery. [1]
2. Give **two** reasons why the individual might feel vulnerable. [2]
3. Ronaldo is four years old and attends the nursery. It is noticed by the staff that on two separate occasions he is bruised on his stomach and back.
   - **a** List the type of ill-treatment that Ronaldo may be experiencing. [1]
   - **b** Describe **three** effects this could have on Ronaldo. [6]
4. The staff report the suspected ill-treatment of Ronaldo to social services, who make enquiries about the situation. They carefully follow the Children Act.
   Explain how the Children Act could influence the actions they take. [5]
5. Ronaldo's older sister, Hermionie, is at secondary school. The school are following the government's green paper, '*Every Child Matters*'.
   Explain how the school could make sure that they were protecting and safeguarding the individuals in their care. [10]
6. If individuals are ill-treated this could have consequences for the society in which we live.
   Explain the consequences ill-treatment could have on society. [10]

Infection control

Preventing the spread of infection

Getting started

Preventing the spread of infection means you will need to know about:

- good personal hygiene – dress, hair care, footwear and oral hygiene
- wearing personal protective clothing
- following standard precautions
- washing hands correctly.

When working in care settings it is important to understand ways to clean and sterilize an environment, to include:

- general cleaning
- disinfecting
- sterilizing
- dealing with spillages
- disposal of hazardous waste
- disposal of medication.

You will need to understand conditions that need reporting, to include:

- diseases – malaria, tetanus, typhoid, typhus
- illnesses – measles, salmonella
- conditions – overflowing drains, chemicals, gases.

You also need to know how vaccination and immunization can help to prevent the spread of infection.

When preparing food such as snacks and meals you will need to know about good hygiene practices, for example:

- food preparation areas, for example, surfaces
- equipment used for food preparation, for example, chopping boards
- cooking food
- storing food
- 'sell by' dates.

You will need to understand the purpose of legislation that underpins the prevention of the spread of infection, to include:

- Health and Safety at Work Act 1974
- The Reporting of Injuries, Diseases and Dangerous Occurrences Regulations Act 1995 (RIDDOR)
- Food Safety Act 1990
- General Food Hygiene Regulations 1995.

PREVENTING THE SPREAD OF INFECTION

Infection is the spread of illness through **micro-organisms**. These micro-organisms could be:

- bacteria
- viruses
- fungi.

They cannot be seen by the human eye but only by examining them under a microscope. Many micro-organisms are harmless and are called **non-pathogenic** but those that can cause disease and illness are known as **pathogens**.

ACTIVITY Finding out about micro-organisms

1. Carry out research in pairs to find out more about:
   - bacteria
   - viruses
   - fungi.

   What do they look like?
   How are they spread?
   What illnesses and diseases do they spread?
2. Cut some white card into oblong shapes that you can use to write facts on. Have about 12 pieces of card to make a 'pack of cards'. For **three** micro-organisms write out some facts, for example, 'They need warmth to grow'.

   Write the names of the three micro-organisms on three more pieces of card.
   Jumble up the pack of cards.
3. Use the cards with another pair in the group asking them to match the facts to the correct micro-organisms.
4. Now, use their 'pack of cards' with them to see if you can match the facts to the micro-organisms.

Preventing the spread of infection is one way of protecting clients, so it is very important that health, social care and early years settings follow measures that help to reduce the risk of the spread of infection. Infections can cause suffering and, in vulnerable people, those who are ill or older adults, it can cause death. The prevention and control of infection is an issue of very great importance for every health care professional and for every setting. To prevent and to help reduce the risks of infection, it is important to follow certain basic procedures of cleanliness.

Personal hygiene

Organisms such as bacteria, viruses and fungi that cause disease can live in and on the body and can cause infection if high standards of personal hygiene are not maintained. Paying attention to personal hygiene is therefore important, and should include regular washing and wearing clean clothes to help protect other people against infection. Those who are caring for or protecting others should make personal hygiene a priority. Wounds such as cuts, grazes, scratches and boils can easily become infected and the infection can be easily passed to others. The best way to stop this happening is to keep wounds properly covered with a suitable waterproof dressing. In this way, both the carer and the individual are protected from infection.

...WORD CHECK

micro-organisms – structures that are only visible through a microscope.

non-pathogenic – an organism that does not produce disease.

pathogens – an organism that produces disease.

Personal hygiene means:

...WORD CHECK

appropriate – suitable.

tabard – an apron worn over the back and front of the upper part of the body.

Dress and footwear

Wearing clothing that is **appropriate** for the work that is to be carried out is very important in a care setting. For example, it would not be appropriate to wear high-heeled shoes if you were required to move and handle individuals. Neither would long scarves or flowing garments be suitable. In health, social care and early years settings, employees are often asked to wear a uniform. For example, nurses have a specific uniform, and nursery nurses and care assistants are often asked to wear a **tabard**.

Besides providing protection from the spread of infection, a uniform will make care workers easily recognizable. Work clothing should not be worn outside of the work environment as this helps stop the spread of any infection from one environment to another. The same applies to wearing daily casual clothing in the client environment.

A uniform protects both the professional carer and the individual who is receiving care.

It is important that a professional care worker wears clothing that is suitable for the tasks that they have to carry out. For example:

Examples of suitable clothing

- Trousers rather than a skirt if moving equipment, moving and handling individuals or working with children.
- Clothes that are not too tight so the professional care worker can move easily without putting a strain on the clothing. Also, for females, skirts that are not too short, as these can cause embarrassment.
- Flat shoes rather than heeled shoes if a lot of walking or going up and down stairs is involved, to prevent tripping or back injury. Shoes without laces are preferable, as, often, the laces can come undone and could cause a fall.
- Short-sleeved tops that do not need to be constantly rolled up to prevent the edges of sleeves becoming wet when attending to clients or washing hands.

Whatever clothing is worn, both personal clothing and/or uniform, it must be clean.

Rings and bracelets should not be worn while working in care environments. The skin area under the jewellery can warm up and encourage the growth of infectious organisms, and increase the risk of infections that can be passed on. Watches, too, can encourage the growth of bacteria.

Hair care

Disease-causing organisms can live in hair and on the scalp. Unwashed hair can carry bacteria that can easily fall onto individual clients, onto their food or into a wound, if hair is not correctly managed.

Long hair should always be kept tied back and not left loose. If a care worker keeps touching their hair, then there is a risk of transferring bacteria to the client.

Good practice for hair care includes:

- shampoo hair frequently
- keep hair tied back or covered if necessary
- avoid touching hair
- never comb hair in the presence of others, especially clients
- do not comb hair in the food preparation and cooking area.

Hair that is left hanging and not tied back could also become caught up in equipment and cause injury.

Oral hygiene

Bacteria live in the nose, mouth, throat and ears. By repeatedly touching these areas, bacteria can be **transferred** to work surfaces, equipment and the people for whom we are caring. It should be remembered that if a person sneezes or coughs, they should always cover their nose and mouth, preferably with a tissue. Droplet infection from a sneeze can travel up to four metres in certain environments.

...WORD CHECK

transferred – moved to another place.

Sneezing and coughing without covering the mouth is a way of spreading infection.

Always:

- avoid coughing and sneezing directly onto people and equipment
- avoid touching your face and head – particularly the mouth, nose and ears.

Professional care workers spend a great deal of time in close **proximity** to individuals who are receiving care; therefore, good oral hygiene is essential as 'bad breath' is likely to cause an individual not to have contact with the carer, or to try and avoid being too near the care worker. Brushing teeth morning and evening, as well as after eating meals, will not only help to promote teeth and gum health but will also mean that neither the care worker nor the client are trying to avoid contact due to poor oral hygiene.

...WORD CHECK

proximity – close/nearby.

cross-infection – infection that spreads from one item or from one person to another.

soiled – dirtied.

Protective clothing

In addition to wearing a uniform, care workers may also be supplied with other forms of protective clothing. These are there to help protect the care worker, as well as the clients. Protective clothing can include:

Masks – paper masks help to prevent the spread of infection through breathing in micro-organisms. This is known as infection through the respiratory route.

Aprons – made from latex, aprons protect both the wearer and the client from infection, as they can be disposed of after each use.

Gloves – can be disposed of after each use and provide excellent barriers to infection. Gloves should be disposed of before dealing with the next client.

Overshoes – can prevent the spread of infection from one room or area to another. They fit over normal footwear and can be disposed of easily.

Theatre hoods/caps – used to contain hair when in the operating theatre, to prevent the spread of micro-organisms from the professionals who are caring for the clients.

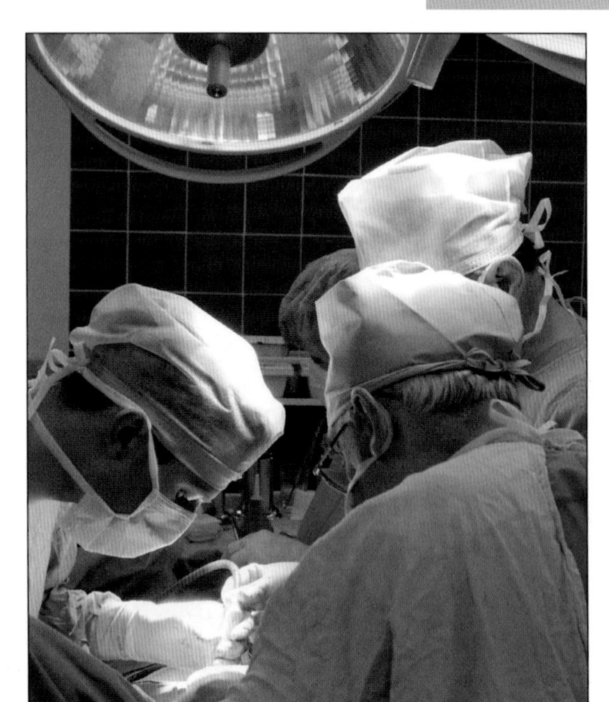

It should be remembered that all protective clothing should be changed when beginning care for another individual. This greatly reduces the risk of **cross-infection**. Care workers may often find that they have to change their apron or gloves part-way through a task. It is important that this is done, especially if an article of clothing has become heavily **soiled**, as a matter of safety and good practice.

11 Why should professional care workers wear protective clothing?

◂ Protective clothing helps to prevent the spread of infection.

Following standard precautions

Standard **precautions** are also known as universal precautions and must be used by all health, early years and social care workers to prevent the spread of micro-organisms that could cause infection. Standard precautions should be used, whether an infection is known to be present or not, when dealing with:

...WORD CHECK
precautions – safety measures.

- blood
- excretions (for example, urine, faeces, vomit – not sweat)
- secretions (for example, saliva, sputum).

The main purpose of following standard precautions is to protect:

- the carer
- other professionals
- the individual receiving care
- visitors, relatives and friends.

There are nine main standard precautions that can help the prevention and control of infection. Standard precautions are also known as Standard Infection Control Precautions (SICPs).

	Summary of standard precautions	
	Standard precaution	**Reason**
1	Maintain hand hygiene • when necessary, for example, before and after contact with client, or before or after wearing gloves. This could be by hand washing or by using alcohol products or gels.	This is an important precaution as it protects against cross-infection.
2	Using personal protective equipment (PPE) • gloves, aprons, gowns and footwear • eye and face protection.	To protect skin, face, eyes, mouth and clothing from soiling, splashing and potentially harmful micro-organisms.
3	Prevent infection through the workplace • protect all breaks in skin by covering wounds • avoid sharps injuries • prevent splashes with blood or body fluids • report anything that is a risk of infection.	To protect professional workers and others from exposure to micro-organisms that cause infection, for example, MRSA, HIV, and so on.
4	Prevent infection through blood and body fluid spillages • immediately after it has happened, follow the stated policy for the setting.	Protects those in surrounding area from risk of infection by micro-organisms, for example, in spillages that could cause harm.
5	Care for equipment correctly • prevent the re-use of disposable items • make sure re-usable equipment is sterilized/cleaned between uses • prevent any environmental contamination • make sure contaminated items are handled safely.	To make sure equipment does not contribute to the spread of infection.
6	Maintain safety of the environment • make sure cleaning and maintenance schedules are clear.	To make sure fittings and fixtures in care setting are kept free from contamination and maintained to prevent cross-infection taking place.
7	Safely dispose of waste – including sharps • make sure professionals know the procedure for safe disposal of clinical waste.	To prevent harm to professionals and others from infection through careless disposal of waste, including sharp instruments.
8	Safely care for linen • make sure linen is stored, handled and transported correctly.	To prevent exposure to micro-organisms that could harm professional workers and others.
9	Provide care in the most appropriate place • if there is concern, always seek advice from the Infection Control Team.	To prevent spread of infection through not transporting clients, equipment or materials correctly.

Hand washing

Did you know:

- One germ can multiply to more than 2 million in just four hours.
- Germs can stay alive on hands for up to three hours.
- Damp hands spread more germs than dry ones.

Large numbers of germs are carried on people's hands every day. A few of these can cause illnesses such as diarrhoea, colds and other, more serious and sometimes even life-threatening diseases. When people forget to wash their hands, or don't wash their hands correctly, they can spread these germs to others.

Hand washing, when done correctly, can help everyone stay healthy and avoid spreading and receiving germs. Hands should be washed:

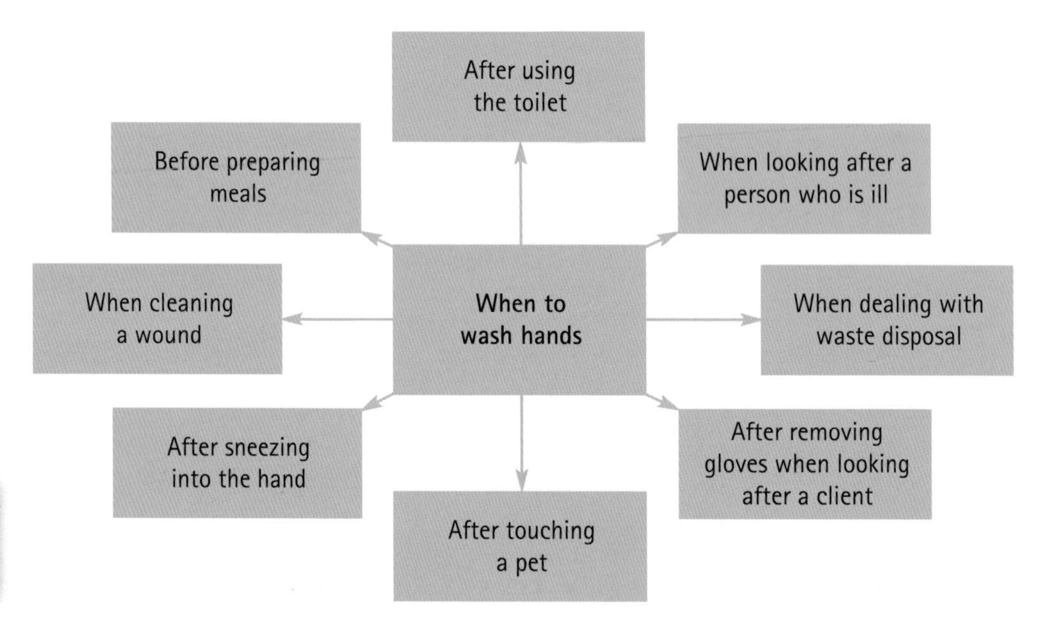

...WORD CHECK

massage – to rub gently.

rotate – to turn round and round.

Hands must be washed properly. To do this correctly, wet hands and apply soap. Then:

1. **massage** palm to palm
2. rub right palm over back of left hand and vice versa
3. rub palm to palm with fingers interlaced
4. massage backs of fingers in the right palm and vice versa
5. **rotate** right thumb clasped in left palm and vice versa
6. rotate fingers of right hand in left palm and vice versa

Finally, rinse hands with water.

The hand-washing process should not take any longer than 30 seconds.

◂ Hand washing.

CASE STUDY Babs

Babs works in a playgroup as a care assistant looking after infants and children between the ages of six months and four years. In her job she has to help the children with hygiene routines, such as changing nappies, getting children dressed to play outside, helping with toileting and feeding, as well as lifting children onto the large equipment in the play area outside.

Babs wears a tight, short skirt to work and high-heeled shoes. She also has a lot of jewellery, including rings, earrings and necklaces. Babs' supervisor is not very pleased with her, as her clothes are not always clean when she has worn them out the previous evening.

1. How is Babs' appearance putting individual clients at risk from the spread of infection?
2. List **three** disease-causing agents that could be present in the playgroup.
3. List **three** ways that an infection can be spread.
4. Prepare a handout or a leaflet to provide advice for care workers like Babs about cleanliness and its importance.
5. Explain how protective clothing can protect both the children and other care workers from the risk of infection. Give examples of the types of protective clothing Babs could use in her work, stating when she would use them.
6. If Babs was working in a hospital, explain other types of protective clothing that she would need to wear. How would these help to prevent the spread of infection?

Group Activity

Preparation: Write **five** questions each that you could ask a member of your group on the 'spread of infection'.

Then:
Stand in a large circle (outside if possible), with a large ball. One person stands in the centre of the circle. The ball is thrown to a person in the circle and they have to answer a question on the spread of infection that the teacher has prepared. If the person who catches the ball cannot answer the question, they have to sit down. The person who answers the question correctly asks the next question. The last one to remain standing is the winner!

ASSESSMENT PRACTICE

Amir works in the local hospital as a care assistant. His main work is with older adults in the geriatric ward, caring for individuals who are ill or recovering from surgery.

1. List **four** ways that Amir could make sure his appearance meets personal hygiene standards. [4]
2. Describe why it is important for Amir to have good oral hygiene. [2]
3. Identify **two** items of personal protective clothing that Amir could wear while working on the hospital ward. Explain how each would help to prevent the spread of infection. [6]
4. Identify **three** stages in the hand-washing process. Explain why it is important that Amir washes his hands correctly. [5]
5. Identify **three** different micro-organisms that cause the spread of infection. Explain how infection can be spread by each type of micro-organism. [10]

CLEANING AND STERILIZING ENVIRONMENTS

General cleaning

...WORD CHECK

environment – to do with the surroundings.

It is important that those who work in care settings understand ways to clean and sterilize an environment so that infection is prevented from spreading and also so that the **environment** is pleasant to be in.

When cleaning a client's room, use of a detergent and then drying will usually be sufficient for most areas that have plastic or ceramic surfaces. Wooden surfaces can be polished. A regular programme of cleaning should be planned, with clients' rooms being cleaned on a regular basis. Carpets should be vacuumed daily but if floor covering is of linoleum or tiles then they should be cleaned daily with a detergent solution, then rinsed and dried. This will help to prevent the spread of any infection that might be present.

Disinfecting

Disinfectants should not be used for general cleaning. When cleaning rooms, the following points should be remembered:

Item to be cleaned	Promoting safe working practice
Baths/showers/sinks	Clean with a detergent solution
Waste bins	Make sure bins do not overflow – they should be emptied daily and cleaned with a detergent solution
Toilets	Clean daily with a detergent solution
Bed pans	Should be washed in hot detergent solution, dried thoroughly and wiped with hypochlorite solution
Table tops	Should be sanitized before use

Promoting a safe working environment when considering clients' rooms means making sure that all cleaning materials are correctly put away. Many cleaning materials are highly toxic and can cause injury if drunk.

CASE STUDY Maria

Maria lives in her own home with professional staff calling to get her up, put her to bed and provide her with a cooked meal. She also has a cleaner, who she pays for herself, who comes twice a week to help keep the house clean. Maria has rheumatism and is very forgetful.

One day, she goes into the kitchen and finds that the cleaner has left the toilet cleaner on the side as she had forgotten to throw it away. There was a little left in the container. Maria thinks it is an orange drink, picks up the toilet cleaner and drinks what is left in the container.

Maria is found several hours later by the health care assistant who has come to get her ready for bed, but by this time it is too late. Maria has died.

This is an example of how easy it is to cause accidental injury or even death.

Sterilization

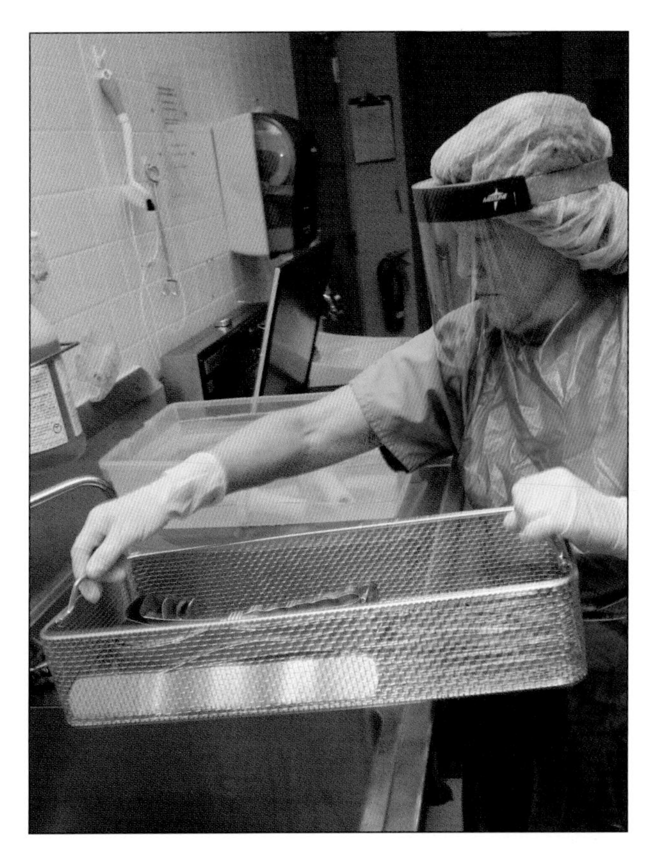

Sterilization means making an object free from all micro-organisms. There are many methods available for sterilization. Sterilization may use:

- exposure to heat
- radiation
- chemicals.

Equipment that is used to penetrate the skin or to enter the body must be sterilized, for example, instruments used during operations. Such instruments can be reused many times, as long as they have been through the sterilization process after each use.

Plastic pieces of equipment cannot be sterilized because the temperature will cause them to melt. Such items can be sterilized by the use of gas or chemicals.

◂ Sterilizing pieces of equipment must be done with care.

Dealing with spillages

All spillages of body fluids (urine, vomit or faeces) should be dealt with immediately. Gloves (disposable) should be worn and as much of the spillage as possible should be mopped up with absorbent toilet tissue or paper towels. These can be disposed of in a plastic waste sack or flushed down the toilet if there are only small amounts. For spillages indoors, clean the area with a detergent, for example, washing-up liquid and hot water, rinse and dry. For spillages outside, the area should be sluiced with water. Gloves should be disposed of and hands washed after taking off the gloves.

When dealing with blood spillages:

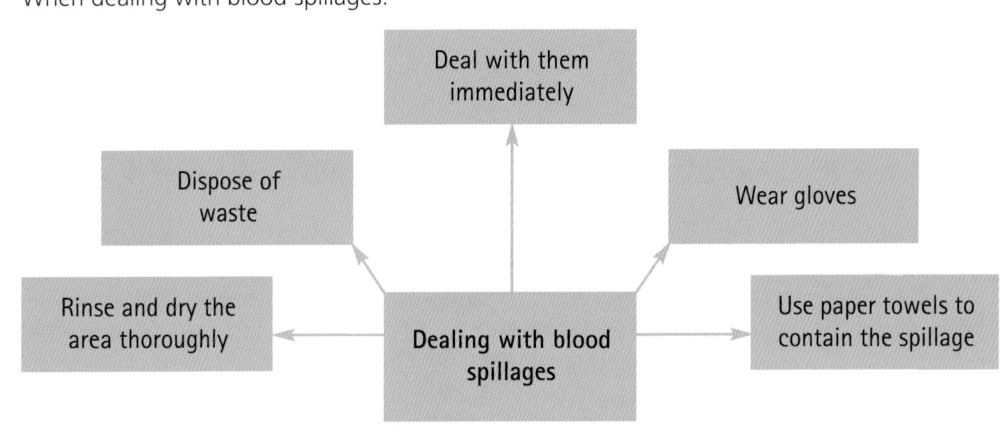

Disposal of hazardous waste

Hazardous waste must be dealt with in a particular type of way. Waste can be a source of infection, so it is very important to follow the procedures for disposing of such waste very carefully.

Hazardous waste can include:

Used dressings – clinical waste
Method of disposal:
Yellow bags that are clearly labelled with contents and location. This waste is incinerated.

Needles – syringes, cannulas (sharps)
Method of disposal:
Yellow sharps box. Never put sharps into any other type of container. The sharps box is firmly sealed and is incinerated.

Body fluids waste – urine, vomit, blood, sputum, faeces
Method of disposal:
Flushed down sluice drain. The area will need to be cleaned and disinfected.

Soiled linen – bed linen, dressings, clothing
Method of disposal:
Red bags sent directly to the laundry. The bags will disintegrate in the wash. If handled, gloves must be worn.

Recyclable instruments and equipment – operating equipment
Method of disposal:
Blue bags, to be returned to the Central Sterilization Services Department (CSSD) to be recycled and sterilized.

Blood-borne viruses are most frequently transmitted in health and social care settings when a sharp instrument, which contains contaminated blood of an infected person, penetrates the skin. Conditions that run a high risk of being transmitted in this way are:

- hepatitis B
- hepatitis C
- HIV.

An effective policy must, therefore, be in place within all care settings to prevent injury through sharp pieces of equipment.

Disposal of medication

...WORD CHECK
pharmacist – a person who prepares medicines.

Medication that is out of date or no longer required should be returned to the **pharmacist**. In this way it can be disposed of safely. Medication should never be thrown into a dustbin in case it falls into the wrong hands. Liquid medication can be washed down a drain with the aid of running water. Tablets could be disposed of by flushing them down the toilet. For both disposal methods it is important to be sure that there will be no damaging effect on the environment.

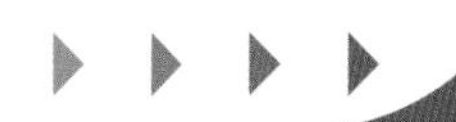

ASSESSMENT PRACTICE

Norman works in a nursing home where he cares for adults who have had amputations or who have other medical conditions that require care. Most of the clients are unable to look after themselves.

Norman is responsible for the work of other professionals and must make sure that they follow all the policies and procedures relating to health and safety.

1. List **two** points that should be remembered when carrying out a general clean of a client's bedroom at the nursing home. [2]
2. Explain the difference between disinfecting and sterilizing. [4]
3. Norman is teaching a new care assistant how to deal with a spillage of blood. What advice should Norman give to the new worker? [5]
4. Norman has to dispose of the following. Explain how each should be correctly disposed of: [6]
   - blood-covered dressings
   - urine-soiled linen
   - sharps.
5. Explain how having an environment that is clean and free from infection could improve the quality of life for individual clients and staff at the nursing home. [10]

CONDITIONS THAT NEED REPORTING

Professionals who work in care settings need to be aware that some illnesses, diseases and conditions must be reported because they are very infectious or dangerous.

WORD CHECK

density – closeness/depth.

Hospitals and other residential health care settings could have specific problems relating to infection control, for example:

- They have a high **density** of people who are vulnerable to infections because of illness.
- They have many sources of infection because people with severe infection are often hospitalized.
- There is a high level of close interpersonal contact between care professionals and individuals or groups of clients.

Disease

Care environments have a need to be constantly aware of the effects of disease. A number of diseases known as 'notifiable' under the Infectious Disease Regulations 1981, and revised in 1988, include:

- malaria
- rabies
- smallpox
- tuberculosis
- measles
- rubella
- tetanus
- typhus.
- plague
- sexually transmitted diseases
- typhoid and paratyphoid

These are just some examples of the many notifiable diseases that are considered to place the public at risk. Under the Infectious Diseases Regulations 1981, medical practitioners are **obliged**, as soon as they become aware that a patient is suffering from or is a carrier of a notifiable disease, to notify the local medical officer in writing. However, immediate notification is **obligatory** in the case of certain infectious diseases, such as cholera, or where a serious outbreak of infectious disease is suspected.

Illness

Whether the illness is that of the client or the care worker, the correct people need to be informed. If the client develops a new illness then their medical practitioner will need to know. This is always done in the best interests of the client and in confidence. If a care worker develops an illness then it is their personal responsibility to notify the appropriate people. This is because they have a duty to their clients and others. Salmonella is an example of an illness that must be reported.

Conditions

Various environmental conditions need to be reported in the interest of public safety. Overflowing drains and sewers should always be reported as soon as possible in order to limit the spread of infection. **Unsanitary** conditions should always be reported to the Environmental Health Department of the local council. The environmental health officers have far-reaching powers that allow them to shut down environments where they see there is a serious danger to public health.

...WORD CHECK

obliged – to have to do something.

obligatory – to agree to do something.

unsanitary – not clean.

ASSESSMENT PRACTICE

diseases measles contagious interpersonal illnesses reported

1. Place one word in each of the spaces provided. Use each word only once.
.... and .... that are highly .... must be .... immediately. An example is .... , which young children could catch from .... activities, such as playing together at playgroup. [10]
2. Give two reasons why hospitals could have a high level of notifiable diseases and illnesses. [4]
3. Describe how cleaning materials should be stored. Explain why this is necessary. [5]
4. Explain how to dispose of medication should it no longer be needed. [4]
5. Explain where disinfectant should be used and why. [5]
6. Identify and explain three different ways to prevent infection from spreading in a kitchen or bedroom (choose one). [10]

VACCINATION AND IMMUNIZATION

Vaccination, also called immunization, is responsible for a reduction in the number of deaths from fatal infectious diseases. Examples of the success of vaccinations are diphtheria and tuberculosis.

When given, a vaccine will stimulate the immune system to produce **antibodies** that will fight against the disease. This is known as 'active immunity'.

A different approach is when the body is given the antibodies rather than having to produce them for itself. This happens in new babies when antibodies pass through the mother's placenta to the unborn child. This is known as 'passive immunity'. In this way, a baby can be protected from mumps, measles and rubella for up to a year after birth. MMR is not given to an infant until after their first birthday.

Vaccines are made by using pathogens, which are organisms that produce the disease. The pathogen has to be altered so that it does not cause the disease.

...WORD CHECK

antibodies – proteins produced by blood cells to help the body fight against disease.

ACTIVITY Finding out about immunization and vaccination

1. Collect newspaper articles about the debate relating to immunization/vaccination. Some people support their use while others oppose them. Discuss the advantages and disadvantages of vaccinations.
2. In small groups, go to the NHS website: www.immunisation.nhs.uk and click on 'About immunisation' and then 'Science'. Find out all you can about immunization.
   What would you do if you had to make the choice about your child being vaccinated/immunized?

ASSESSMENT PRACTICE

1. List **two** diseases that can be prevented through the use of vaccinations. [2]
2. Explain the difference between 'active' and 'passive' immunization. [4]
3. Explain why being vaccinated is a way of promoting good health. [5]

PREVENTING THE SPREAD OF INFECTION THROUGH FOOD

Food poisoning is an unpleasant illness, which usually occurs within one to thirty-six hours of eating contaminated food, and is caused by bacteria and their poisons, viruses and chemicals, for example, weed killer, poisonous plants and metals. The most common forms of food poisoning bacteria are:

- *Salmonella*
- *Clostridium perfringens*
- *Staphylococcus aureus.*

▲ Food poisoning chain.

Other bacterial illnesses that can be transmitted through food include typhoid, paratyphoid, tuberculosis and dysentery.

Professional care workers may from time-to-time be required to prepare a snack for clients. It is, therefore, important that they know of good hygiene practices required by the setting and also have knowledge about legislation that affects the preparation of food.

Food poisoning affects many people each year, with many cases being unreported. The exact number of cases of food-related illness that occur each year is unknown because many people do not seek the help of their doctor when they develop **symptoms**. Food poisoning and other related conditions that result from poor hygiene when preparing and cooking food can be extremely dangerous, especially for the very young or older clients, who are particularly vulnerable. To prevent contamination of food it is necessary to follow recognized hygiene procedures to make sure that risks are kept to a **minimum**.

Food poisoning bacteria multiply over a period of time and people eating such food will become ill. There is a 'food poisoning chain' that will cause this to happen.

ACTIVITY The Environmental Health Officer

1. Invite an Environmental Health Officer to your centre (with the tutor's permission). The purpose of the visit is to find out about:
   - What causes contamination of food?
   - What is the result of eating contaminated food?
   - How to prevent food becoming contaminated.
2. After the visit, have a whole-class discussion to see how much you can remember from the talk.
3. In pairs, draw a picture or use cut out shapes from magazines to show what is wrong with a kitchen in a care setting. Try to include at least eight things that illustrate very poor practice.
   Show your picture to others in the whole group to see if they can see what is incorrect as far as good hygiene practice is concerned.

   For each incorrect hygiene practice, they must tell you how to put the situation right.

Surfaces

...WORD CHECK

symptoms – a recognized sign.
minimum – the least amount.
aerosol – a spray.
excess – too much.

All surfaces used for food preparation and serving food must be kept clean. Usually this is achieved by adding chemicals to water to make a cleaning solution.

Substances used for cleaning food-preparation areas fall into three groups:

- Detergents – these dissolve grease and assist in the removal of stains and dirt, but it must be remembered that detergents do not kill bacteria.
- Disinfectants – are chemicals that destroy bacteria. They will reduce the bacteria to a safe level. Disinfectants are not effective for removing grease. They can have a strong smell and can affect the taste of food if used to **excess**. The need to use them should be limited.
- Sanitizers – are chemicals that combine the roles of detergent and disinfectant. They are designed to remove dirt and grease, and disinfect all in one action.

The combination of chemicals and very hot water provides an effective way of keeping surfaces clean. Any work surface that is used for food preparation must be:

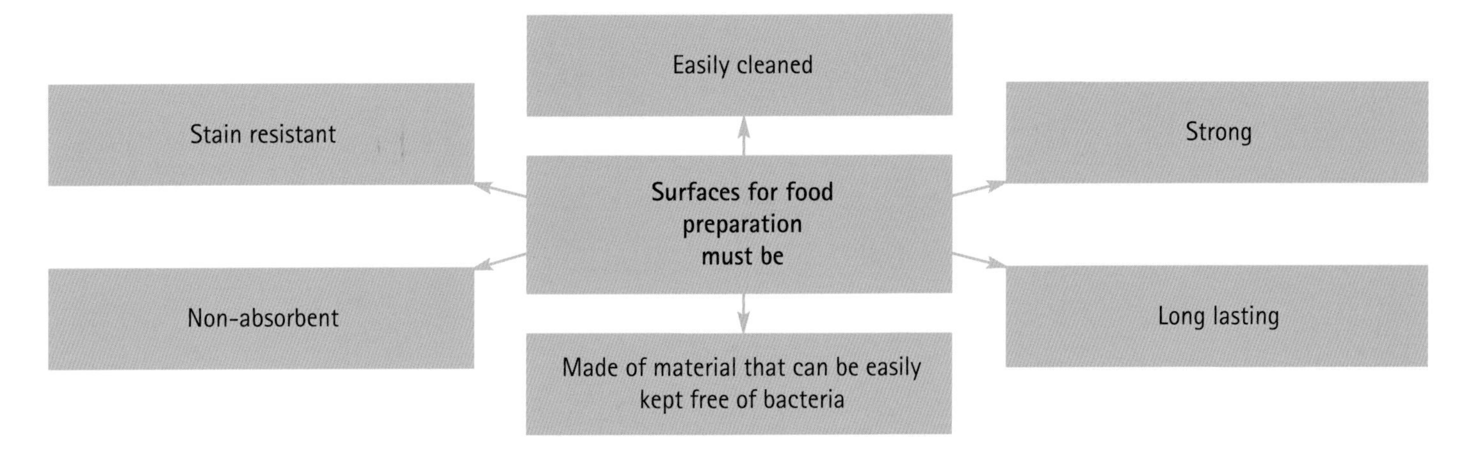

In professional food areas, stainless steel tables are used for food-preparation activities. They are usually on wheels that have brakes so that they can be moved easily, which also allows for ease of cleaning.

It is vital that work surfaces are kept clean and bacteria free. To keep work surfaces clean, the 'clean as you go' approach should be used. This means that all equipment and surfaces are cleaned as soon as they have been used. Any spills are also mopped up immediately. Work surfaces should be left clean and clear when work has finished.

The stages of cleaning are:

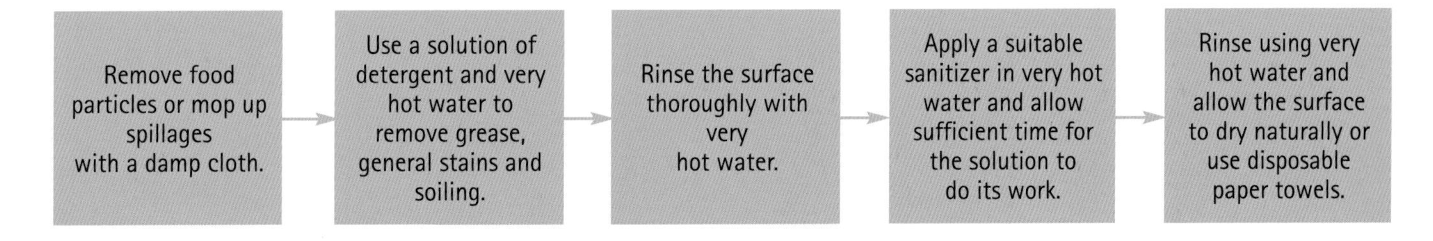

Equipment

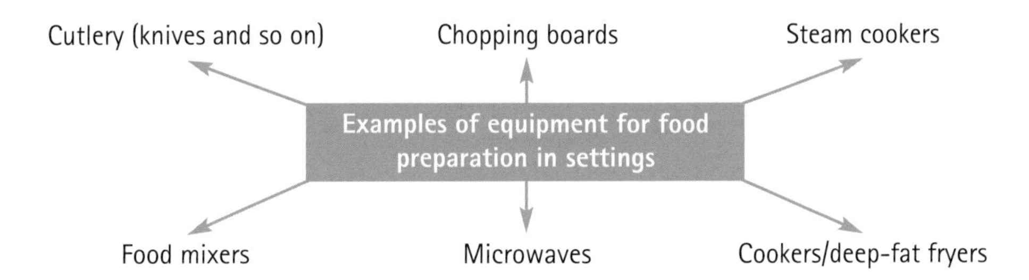

Never attempt to clean equipment unless you have been trained to do so. This is especially important where the equipment has sharp cutting surfaces and or moving parts that are run by electricity. Care should also be taken with equipment that is hot or produces a lot of heat, for example, cookers and deep-fat fryers.

When cleaning equipment, the steps shown below should be followed:

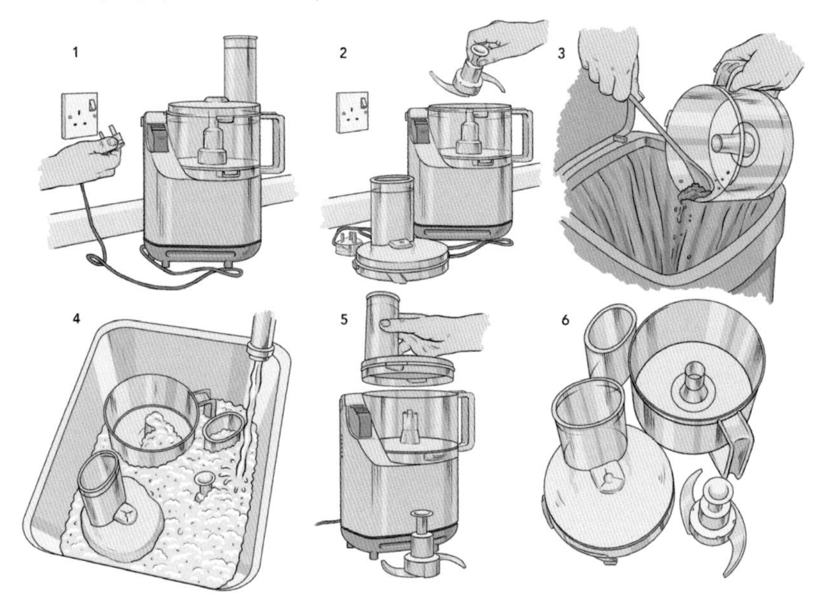

▸ Steps for carefully cleaning cooking equipment.

...WORD CHECK

cross-contamination – infection that spreads from one item or from one person to another.

Chopping boards

Different coloured chopping boards (colour coded), for the preparation of different types of food, help to avoid **cross-contamination**.

Colours used are:

Green	fruit and vegetables	Red	raw meat
Yellow	cooked meat	Blue	raw fish.

Chopping boards must be cleaned thoroughly with detergent and a sanitizer, and be thoroughly rinsed before reusing, or micro-organisms will be spread from one chopping board to another.

This is called cross-contamination or cross-infection. Cross-infection means passing infection from one person to another and occurs when microbes are passed in different ways, for example:

- not washing hands properly between tasks
- using equipment that has been used for the preparation of other foods without correctly cleaning it
- storing foods incorrectly
- touching the mouth or nose, or using the toilet without washing hands
- not washing hands between handling cooked and raw meat.

ACTIVITY Visiting a kitchen in a care setting

...ACTIVITY

Arrange a visit to a setting where food is prepared for clients (this must be done with the tutor's permission). Alternatively, this could be completed while on work experience.

1. Before the visit, work in groups to prepare some questions to ask about kitchen hygiene. Look at all the topics in this section about food preparation and hygiene to help you with these.
2. Prepare a questionnaire to help you collect the information you require.
3. After the visit, discuss, as a group, how the setting maintained good hygiene practice for:
   - surfaces
   - equipment.

Cooking food

Before cooking, it is important to prepare food correctly. This can be done by remembering to:

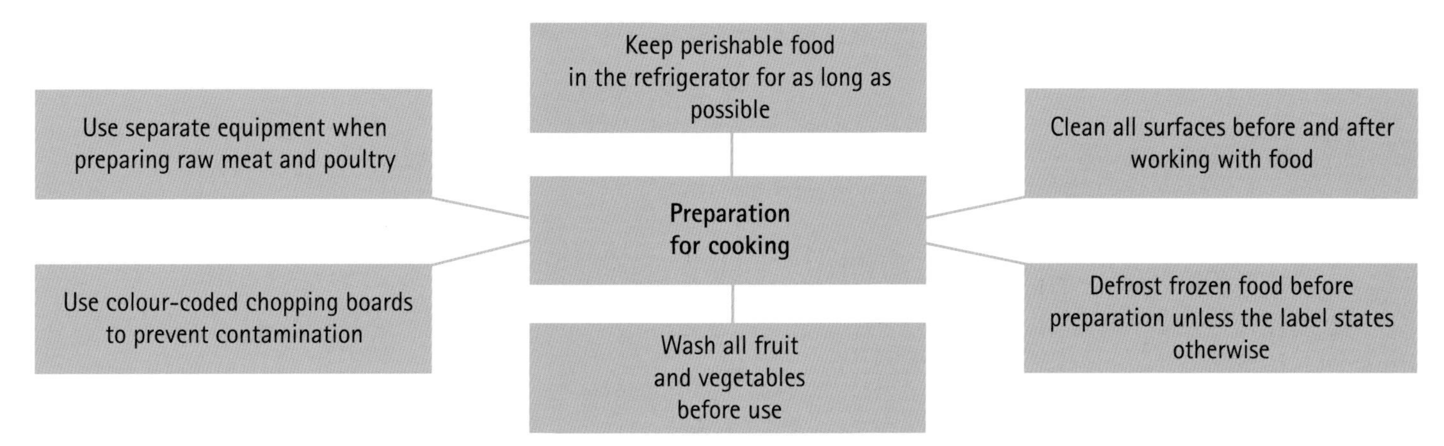

It is important that certain precautions are taken when providing food for clients. The table below shows what should and should not be done, giving the reasons why.

What should be done when preparing food?	Why should it be done?
Wash hands: • before entering the food area • after using the lavatory • between handling different types of food, for example, cooked and raw meat • before and after touching food • after coughing into the hands or using a handkerchief, or after touching the face and hair • after carrying out cleaning or handling rubbish	Many bacteria live on the surface of the skin. Many are harmless but some that are transferred can cause illness. Bacteria can be acquired from other sources and can contaminate food. Handling raw meat and poultry and then handling cooked meat is very dangerous unless hands are thoroughly washed between tasks.
• Avoid touching the food with your hands; where possible wear gloves	The less hands are in direct contact with the food, the less chance there is of contamination.
• Avoid touching dishes or cutlery that are to come into contact with food	This cuts down the transfer of bacteria.
• Keep hair covered with a net or hat and do not comb hair in the food area	Hair and scalp carry bacteria that can fall into the food.
• Do not smoke in the food area	Smoking is against the law and can contaminate the food.
• Keep cuts and grazes covered with a brightly coloured dressing • If you are ill do not handle food • Wear clean protective clothing	Wounds are infected with bacteria and if the dressing comes off, it can be easily located. A person who is ill could infect the food. There are fewer bacteria on clean cloths.

(Adapted from *OCR Nationals Level 2 Health and Social Care* by Fisher et al., Heinemann, 2005.)

Cooking

Most bacteria will not survive in food that has been cooked at a temperature of at least 70°C; this is why food must be cooked thoroughly. Meat and poultry, in particular, should be cooked thoroughly all the way through. The need for sufficiently high temperatures reaching the centre is very important. It is bad practice to mix previously cooked food with newly cooked food.

Re-heating food can increase the risk of food poisoning. Some food handlers often make the mistake of thinking that because the food has already been cooked, it will be free of bacteria.

CASE STUDY Jasbinder

While working as a care assistant at High View Residential Home, Jasbinder is asked to make an omelette and salad for a client who has missed lunch. Jasbinder immediately collects the ingredients and puts them on a plate. He sees an omelette pan on the side and wipes it round with a paper towel and then cooks the omelette. A small piece of cooked chicken is on the side so he cuts it up and puts it in the omelette. The omelette and salad are served to the client.

1. What should Jasbinder have done before preparing any food? Why?
2. Describe how Jasbinder should have prepared the salad ingredients. Why?
3. Jasbinder used a previously used omelette pan. Explain how equipment used for cooking should be prepared.
4. Explain why Jasbinder should not have used the piece of cooked chicken that had been left on the side.
5. Explain what is meant by the term 'food poisoning' and give **two** examples of illnesses that spread in this way.
6. There are several different types of chopping boards. Identify the coding used and describe the purpose of each. Explain how coded chopping boards help to prevent cross-contamination.

Storage of food

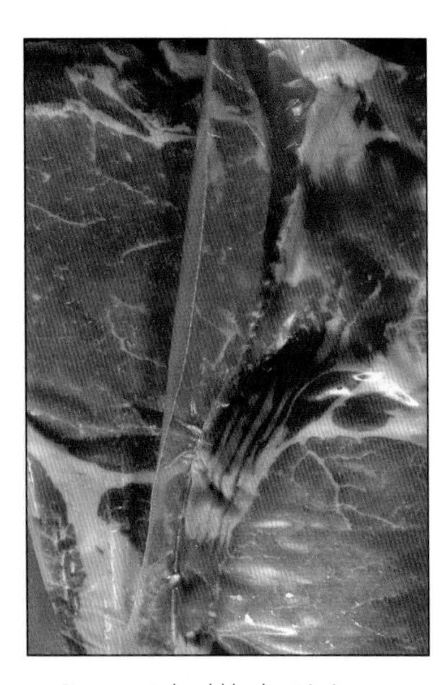

▲ Raw meat should be kept in its packaging and on the bottom shelf of the refrigerator in order to prevent cross-contamination.

Food should be stored correctly after it has been purchased. Also, this should be done soon after purchase in order to prevent contamination. Dry packaged food, for example, rice, flour and packets, should be stored safely in a non-damp place where there are no pests. Foods that should be kept at room temperature should also be covered but placed in a room that is well ventilated.

Food that is to be stored in the refrigerator must also be correctly placed. Bacteria multiply at a temperature of 37°C. Some foods are stored in a refrigerator because bacteria and viruses don't multiply below 6°C. The correct temperature for a refrigerator is between 0 and 5°C. It is important not to overcrowd the refrigerator as this raises the temperature. With cooked food, let steam evaporate first before covering and placing in the refrigerator. Always keep the refrigerator clean by washing the inside surfaces with warm, soapy water.

Keeping the refrigerator at the right temperature will help prevent bacteria from multiplying. To maintain a constant temperature, keep the door shut whenever possible. When storing food in the refrigerator:

- Don't allow the juices from raw meat, fish and poultry to spill or drip onto other foods. They can remain inside their store wrapping in the refrigerator for a day or two. If only part of the meat or poultry is to be used, store it in a secure container.
- Fruit and vegetable items should be placed in the salad drawer.
- Milk and fruit juices should be stored in the door rack.
- Dairy products, dressing, spreads, sauces, cream and convenience foods should be placed on the centre and top shelves.
- Raw meat, fish and poultry should be stored on the bottom shelf of the refrigerator. This prevents cross-contamination as the blood and other liquids from the meat and fish cannot drip down onto other foods.
- Cooked foods should be kept on the top shelves of the refrigerator.

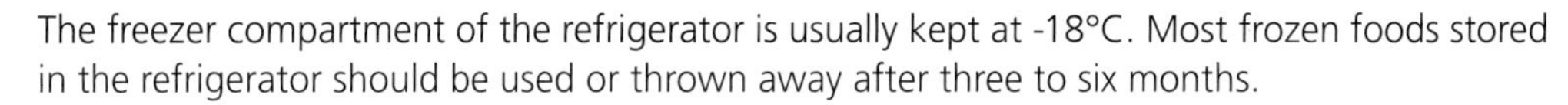

The freezer compartment of the refrigerator is usually kept at -18°C. Most frozen foods stored in the refrigerator should be used or thrown away after three to six months.

After a power cut, foods that have started to defrost should be thrown out. When the power comes back on, if there is any doubt about which foods have defrosted and refrozen, the food should be thrown away.

Sell by dates

Foods that are likely to go off quickly are known as **perishable**. They will normally have a 'sell by' date on them and a 'use by' date. It is an offence to sell food after the sell by date has passed. The food can be used up to and including the date shown. Most other foods carry a 'best before' date. This indicates the date up to which it will be in its best condition for eating.

Some foods are not required by law to carry a date mark. These include fresh fruit, vegetables and meat from the butcher.

...WORD CHECK

perishable – something that decays.

ASSESSMENT PRACTICE

Happy Days Nursery School provides for children between the ages of six months and four-and-a-half years. Some of the children will stay all day and need to be given meals and snacks.

The kitchen manager is having a training day with all those responsible for the preparation and cooking of food in the nursery school, to give them training about basic food hygiene required in the care setting.

1. List **three** ways that food poisoning could occur. [3]
2. Opposite is a photo of an empty refrigerator. Place the listed foods in the correct place in the refrigerator:
   - milk
   - cooked ham
   - salad
   - raw beef.

   Explain why each should be placed in the positions you have chosen. [10]

3. Michael is preparing a snack for Conor who is having lunch at the nursery. Conor's snack is:
   - jacket potato – cooked in a microwave
   - chicken
   - salad.

   Explain how Michael can make sure that Conor is not put at risk through eating the snack. Include information about:
   - the surfaces
   - the equipment used
   - the preparation of the food
   - the cooking of the food. [12]
4. Gemma has been asked to prepare information to help care workers understand:
   - what food poisoning is
   - examples of food poisoning
   - how not storing food correctly and not adhering to sell by dates could cause food poisoning.

   Write an explanation that would help Gemma to prepare the information she needs. [10]

LEGISLATION

Legislation helps to make sure that correct procedures are followed in care settings so that clients are protected and safeguarded. Legislation helps to prevent the spread of infection and to promote healthy living. The table below shows the legislation and regulations that apply to care settings, and their main purposes.

...WORD CHECK

employees – the people who are paid by somebody to do their work.

notifiable – must be reported, for example, certain diseases or illnesses.

asphyxia – a lack of oxygen in the blood.

Legislation and regulations	Main purpose
Health and Safety at Work Act 1974	EMPLOYERS must make sure they maintain the health and safety of their employees, and provide and maintain equipment and work systems that are safe. They must deal with substances such as chemicals safely. They must also provide a written health and safety policy statement when employing five or more people. Training to enable employees to carry out work safely must also be provided. They must also ensure that visitors, outside workers and members of the public are not put at unnecessary risk. **Employees** must take care of their own health and safety at work, and take care of health and safety of others. They must cooperate with their employer and should not misuse or interfere with anything provided for health and safety purposes. Residential care premises are workplaces as well as homes to vulnerable clients. Employers in residential settings must be careful to make sure that meeting the legal requirements does not override their duty to provide a pleasant home for the client.
The Reporting of Injuries, Diseases and Dangerous Occurrences Regulations 1995	There is a requirement to report major accidents and incidents that have happened in the workplace. **Notifiable** diseases, too, have to be reported. Reporting accidents, injuries, ill health and dangerous occurrences is a legal requirement, and these must be reported to the Incident Contact Centre (ICC). RIDDOR states that EMPLOYERS must report deaths, major injuries, accidents resulting in more than three days off work, diseases and any dangerous occurrences. Reportable major injuries cover a wide range, including amputations, loss of sight, fractures other than to fingers or toes, dislocation of shoulder, hip, spine or knee, unconsciousness caused by **asphyxia** or exposure to harmful substances.
Food Safety Act 1990	The Act is intended to reduce the number of cases of food-borne illnesses, such as food poisoning and contamination. It is an offence to sell any food that is harmful to health, or to falsely label or advertise food. Failure to comply with the regulations can result in fines.
General Food Hygiene Regulations 1995	These regulations lay down the standards for premises, equipment and personal hygiene to ensure the safety of food. They cover the preparation, processing, manufacturing, packaging, storing, transporting, distributing, handling and selling of food products. Areas included in the regulations are: hazard analysis, risk assessment and food hygiene training.

First-aid practice

How to use first aid to deal with minor emergencies

Getting started

For the external assessment you will need to know about the first-aid practices and procedures for health emergencies that could occur in settings. This will include:

- the principles of first aid
- the responsibilities of the first aider
- casualty management and how to prioritize needs
- information that should be given when calling the emergency services.

You should be able to recognize the key signs of common health emergencies and know how to carry out procedures for dealing with them. Health emergencies will include:

- burns and scalds
- wounds and bleeding
- fractures
- loss of consciousness
- breathing difficulties, for example, asthma, anaphylactic shock.

When carrying out first-aid procedures, you should be aware of the importance of preventing the spread of infection, for example, wearing gloves and making sure wounds are kept clean.

Relevant legislation that you need to know, understand the impact of and be able to apply is:

- The Health and Safety (First Aid) Regulations 1981.

This section does not qualify you to deal with any minor emergencies in the workplace.

FIRST-AID PRACTICE

Who is at risk and why?

Individuals in care settings may be vulnerable to many different types of health care emergency. This may be due to a variety of different factors, such as:

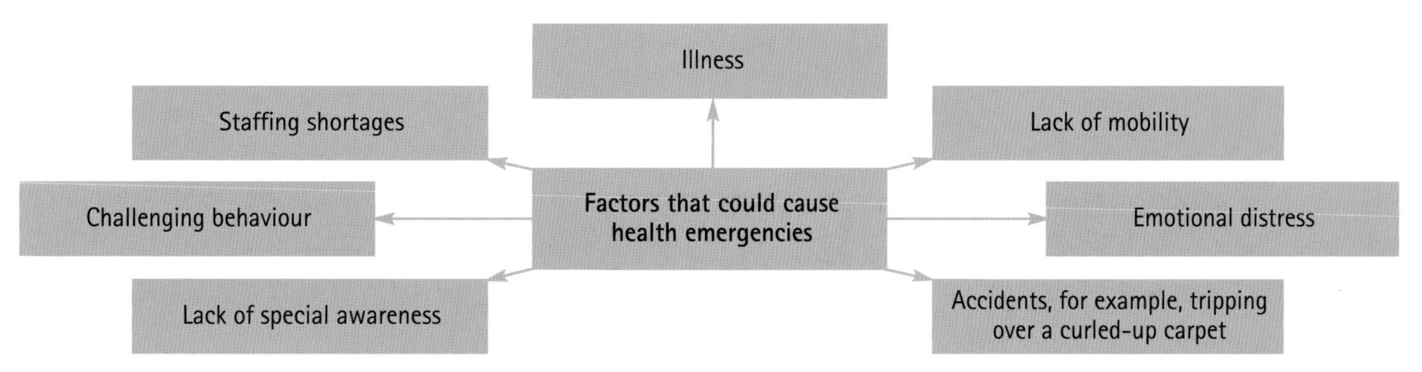

Minor emergencies may take the form of slips, trips and falls resulting in fractures, wounds, bleeding or loss of consciousness. These are often caused by hazards in settings, such as unprotected wires, faulty chairs, carpets that are frayed or poor lighting. It is, therefore, essential that staff caring for individuals make sure that they are trained in order to deal with any emergencies that might arise. They must make sure that they are trained in first-aid procedures and are within their **competence** for carrying out any necessary first aid.

...WORD CHECK

competence – to have ability/to do something well.

liable – to blame (for something).

indirect – not directly responsible/not obvious.

incidents – a happening/an event.

Who could deal with minor emergencies?

When working in settings, whether caring for individuals in need of health, social care or early years services, it is important to be trained in emergency first aid at work. This training may be a one- or two-day course for emergency first aid and up to five days for an appointed first-aid individual. The care worker must make sure that they never act outside of their own **competence** in emergencies. When dealing with emergencies at work it is important to make sure that the care worker seeks backup from other workers who may be more experienced in dealing with workplace health emergencies. This is not only to protect the casualty but also to protect the person dealing with the casualty. The worker could be **liable** under health and safety law if the casualty dies as a direct or **indirect** result of any first aid that they have carried out.

Group Activity

With another person, think about different minor emergencies that could happen in a care setting. List three health emergencies and to whom they could happen. For each, state why they could have occurred.

Think about how these health emergencies could have affected the individual.

Be prepared to share your answers with others in the group.

Examples of individuals who may need first-aid procedures are:

- older adults
- infants, children and young people
- adults.

It should be remembered that infants and children must receive first-aid care from those who are specially trained to provide it.

Minor emergencies are **incidents** that could take place in the care setting from time to time. Staff who look after individual clients should know how to deal with these if and when they take place.

Examples of minor emergencies are:

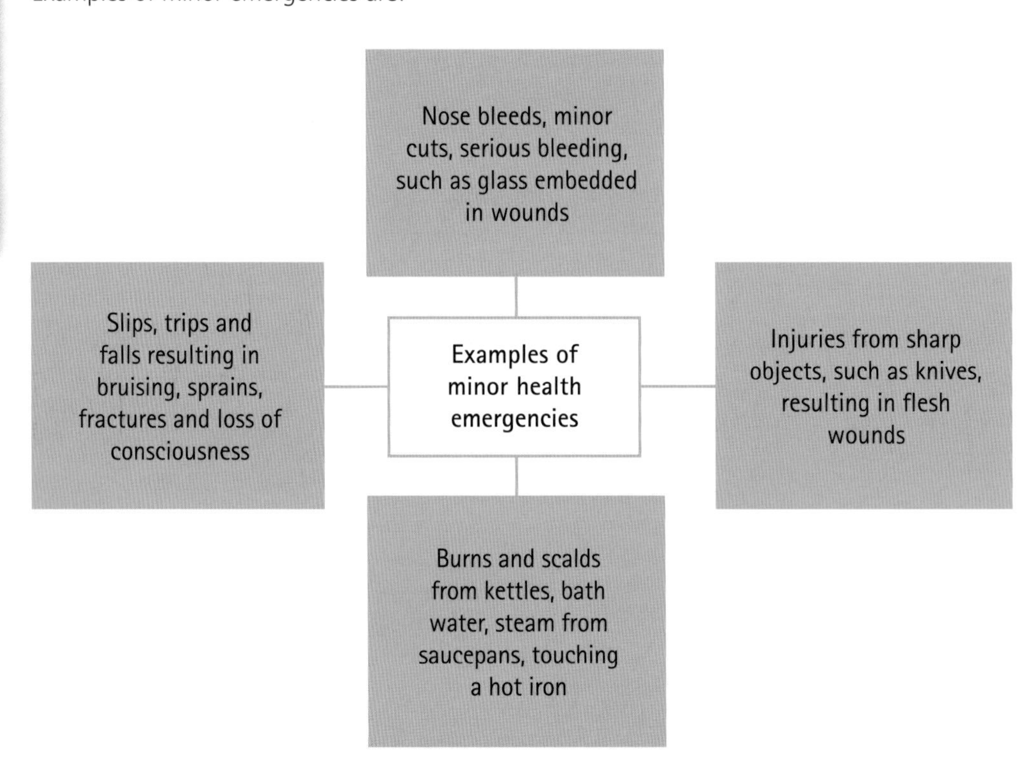

ACTIVITY Minor accidents

1. Invite a speaker from a health, social care or early years setting to your centre to talk about the different types of minor injuries that could occur in their setting. Find out:
   - Who has minor accidents?
   - What procedures are in place to deal with minor accidents?
   - Who is responsible for first aid in the setting?
   - What is their full responsibility?
2. Cut some white card into oblong shapes that you can use to write facts on. Have about eight pieces of card to make a 'pack of cards'. Write different types of health emergencies on three cards.

   Then, write **three** different ways that the emergencies could occur on different cards.
3. Use the cards with another pair in the group, asking them to match the health emergencies to the correct way they could occur.
4. Now you use their cards with them to see if you can match the health emergencies to the ways they could occur.
5. Why are some clients more vulnerable to accidents than others?

The principles of first aid

One of the main principles of providing first aid is to give care with confidence. Individuals who need first aid need to feel safe and secure with the person who is providing it. This will involve:

- speaking to the casualty in a friendly but clear way
- thinking **logically**
- being in charge of the situation
- answering questions truthfully
- talking to the casualty and reassuring them
- staying calm.

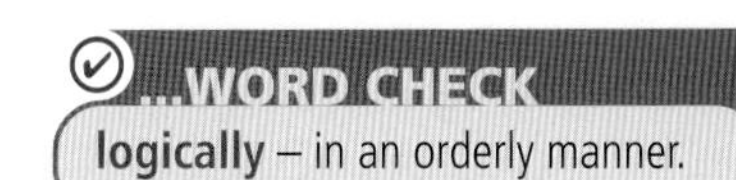

logically – in an orderly manner.

When providing basic first aid it is important to remember to always apply the principles of first aid. These include:

- Always check for any immediate danger to the casualty, including looking for anything or anyone that could cause possible harm to either the first aider or the casualty.
- Make a risk assessment of the situation for the first aider, the casualty, or others in the area who could be affected by the emergency. Always make sure that the area is safe before carrying out any first aid. The first aider should always put their safety considerations before those of any others in the area.

A first-aid risk assessment

When making a risk assessment of casualties it is important to:

- assess the immediate danger to oneself, as if someone sustains an injury they may be unable to administer first aid
- assess the immediate danger to others
- make sure that the area is safe enough to carry out any first-aid procedures
- use any people nearby to call the emergency services or to help by giving support, for example, talking with and reassuring casualties.

ACTIVITY Principles of first aid

1. Why is it important to remember the principles of first aid when carrying out a first-aid procedure?
2. Describe how a first aider could carry out a risk assessment if they found two cars and some pedestrians who had been involved in an accident.
3. What is the purpose of having 'principles of first aid'?

Responsibilities of the first aider

...WORD CHECK

assessed – making judgements about a person's needs.

unconscious – unaware of what is happening.

If at all possible, the first aider should make sure that they call appropriate assistance, for example, a trained first-aid professional and a senior member of staff.

Once the area has been **assessed** as safe, the worker should check the casualty. This should include speaking to the casualty, and asking them how they are feeling and if and where there is any pain. If the casualty is **unconscious** then the worker should gently shake the person without moving their head or neck, speaking to them and asking them if they can hear them or open their eyes.

When the worker has provided first aid this should be clearly reported to their line manager in both verbal and written form.

CASE STUDY Sally

Sally is a care assistant at Rising Sun Residential Home. One morning, Sally is summoned by the call alarm in the lounge of the residential home by one of the clients. The client is sitting in a chair and is quite distressed. She has pricked her finger in several places while sewing. The needle is deeply embedded in her finger.

1. How should Sally deal with the client?
2. Who should she call? Why?
3. What action should Sally take after the emergency first aid has been given? Why?

Sally is not the only member of staff on duty. Sally must remain calm at all times. She must conduct a risk assessment of the situation. She must also call for the help of a first-aid worker.

Casualty management and how to prioritize needs

The responsibilities of first aiders mean that 'casualty management' is a crucial part of their role, especially when there are multiple casualties. In an emergency situation a first aider should:

- check the quietest casualty first (if there is more than one) because they may have the most serious injuries
- if a casualty is conscious, call an ambulance
- treat conditions that are serious, for example, major bleeding
- treat for shock
- treat minor injuries.

It is important to hand over to the emergency services as soon as they arrive, explaining what help has been given.

Information that should be given to the emergency services

When summoning the emergency services, it is extremely important to make sure that the right kind of information is given on the telephone, so that the correct service and help is received. The table below gives examples of types of questions that the operator will ask and the reasons they may ask them.

▸ 'Which service would you like?'

Questions asked	Reasons for questions
Which service do you require?	So that the correct service is sent, for example, ambulance instead of fire brigade
What is your location?	So that the emergency service can find you quickly and does not waste valuable time
What is the telephone number from which you are calling?	So that they can telephone you back if you are disconnected or if they want more details about something
What is your name?	So the emergency crew can identify you on arrival
What injuries do the casualties have?	In case any special equipment is needed or if they need to instruct you on an action to take
Is the casualty conscious or unconscious?	They may need to give you a first-aid procedure to carry out
What first aid have you carried out?	To help them think about anything else you need to do and so that the emergency service knows what has been done prior to their arrival

ACTIVITY Role play

Try to obtain two telephones (they do not need to be connected or working). With a partner, practise a telephone call to the emergency services. Make sure you speak clearly and are accurate in the replies you give.

Reverse the roles and role play calling the emergency service again.

Exchange information with the person you did the role play with to give them some feedback about how well they answered the questions and points that could be improved.

Remember to answer the questions that are asked by the operator and do not attempt to interrupt them once they have started.

ASSESSMENT PRACTICE

Thomas and his friend Philip are walking down the street when, unexpectedly, Philip trips over and falls badly, damaging his knee. Philip is clearly in a lot of pain and is very distressed.

1. List the actions that Thomas should take to show he understands the responsibilities of the first aider. [5]
2. Explain what is meant by the term, 'the principles of first aid'. Use examples to illustrate the points made. [10]
3. If there were three casualties, how would the first aider prioritize needs? [10]
4. List **five** facts that should be given when calling the emergency service. Give a reason for each fact given. [15]
5. Identify who is at risk of having minor accidents in a residential home, explaining the types of accidents that could occur and the reasons why they might happen. [10]

HOW TO DEAL WITH DIFFERENT TYPES OF HEALTH CARE EMERGENCIES

Being able to recognize the key signs of common health emergencies and knowing how to carry out the procedures for dealing with them is important to every first aider and to every professional worker who is likely to have to deal with such situations.

Burns and scalds

When treating burns and scalds, it is important to understand the difference between these two injuries:

- a burn is usually caused by a flame or heat
- a scald is caused by hot liquids on the skin.

The table below gives the symptoms, treatment and reasons for the actions when providing first aid for burns and scalds.

Symptoms	First aid procedure	Reason
Redness or tenderness of the skin	Try to cool down the burn using lots of cold running water for at least ten minutes	This will stop the burn from getting any worse, for example, other tissues being affected, and also reduce the pain for the casualty
Blistered skin	Cover the burn, if possible with a lint-free dressing or a plastic bag	To protect it from infection
Swollen areas around the injury	Provide support if needed, to the appropriate area, for example, arm or leg	To prevent further damage
Pain depending on the severity of the burn	Call for professional help or an ambulance	To have the burn examined by a professional person
Feeling faint or dizzy	Treat for shock	To prevent the casualty from falling into unconsciousness

Note:

- For major burns, medical assistance should be sought immediately.
- Any jewellery, watches or clothing should be removed from the burn, provided they are not sticking to the wound.
- Never attempt to remove clothing that has been on fire from a person, as it will most likely be stuck to the wound and cause further damage if removed.

CASE STUDY Robert

Robert works in a care home for young people with learning disabilities. He is supporting one of the clients to prepare and cook a meal as part of his support plan. Unfortunately, whilst reaching for a saucepan on the hob, the client burns himself on the naked flame.

1. What steps should Robert take first, bearing in mind that the individual may be distressed.
2. What first aid should be given by Robert?
3. Research three different types of chemicals used within care homes that could cause burns to the skin. Try to find out the first aid required if this happens.

Wounds and bleeding

Wounds are caused by many different factors. These could be as a result of a fall causing breakage to the skin or as a result of a cut from a sharp object, such as glass or a knife. These wounds can lead to damage such as gashes in the skin that may bleed, and, in some cases, bleed **profusely** and for long periods of time.

When treating wounds and bleeding it is important to always make sure that you aim to do the following:

- Try to stop the bleeding if there are no objects within the wound.
- Limit the amount of infection that comes into contact with the wound.

With such wounds usually comes the presence of blood. This will be in lesser or greater amounts depending on the type of wound, where the wound is and how deep the wound is. The wound could also be quite painful. The casualty could be genuinely distressed as even a small amount of blood can be very frightening to both the casualty and the first aider. It is always important not to panic and to encourage the casualty not to panic either.

When dealing with blood it is important to realize that this is a bodily fluid and both the first aider and the casualty could be at risk from cross-infection. It is therefore important that the first aider maintains **aseptic technique** at all times. This involves washing the hands in antibacterial soap and, if possible, wearing disposable gloves when dealing with the casualty.

The action to be taken when providing first aid to a wound is:

- If there is nothing obstructing the wound, then the first aider should apply direct pressure, using a sterile dressing, directly over the wound.
- If, however, there is an obstruction in the wound, such as glass, then this should never be removed under any circumstances, as this may cause the casualty to bleed further. Therefore, indirect pressure should be applied to the wound. The first aider should make sure that the sterile dressing is applied around the object rather than over it.

...WORD CHECK

profusely – abundantly/a lot.

aseptic techniques – observing all recommended hygiene processes.

- It may also be necessary to ask the casualty to lie down on the ground and raise the affected part. This could reduce the amount of blood that reaches the wound and therefore reduce the bleeding.
- Summon the emergency services if the wound is serious.
- For minor wounds, clean the area and cover with a sterile dressing.

CASE STUDY Wendy

Wendy is a care assistant working in a residential care home for older adults. Wendy is performing her hourly check on the residents and some are alone in their bedrooms, which is normal practice. When checking on one of the female clients, Wendy finds a hand mirror has been broken and there is a large shard of glass protruding from the wound in the client's arm. There is quite a lot of blood coming from the wound and the individual is very distressed.

1. Why should Wendy never attempt to remove the glass from the wound?
2. What first aid should Wendy give?
3. Why is it important to make sure that the wound is covered with a sterile dressing?
4. This accident was most likely preventable. With a partner you will need to access the Internet in your centre. Look at the Health and Safety Executive's (HSE) website, www.hse.gov.uk, and research 'risk assessment'. Then, with your partner, look back at the case study scenario, apply the risk assessment guidelines, draw up your own risk assessment and state how you would use it to protect clients from cutting themselves on broken glass.

Fractures

A fracture is a break or a crack in a bone. This is usually caused by slips, trips and falls that result in the casualty landing in a particular way on the area, which causes the bone to fracture.

Symptoms can be hard to see but could include:

- bones protruding from the injury
- swelling around the injury
- discoloration around the area of the injury
- joints may be in very strange positions
- the client will almost certainly be in lots of pain.

When treating fractures it is always important to make sure that you do the following:

- Make the casualty as comfortable as is possible by supporting the affected area and allowing the casualty to maintain the most comfortable position possible.
- Comfort the casualty by talking to them and explaining what you think could have happened. Reassure the casualty and tell them what you intend to do.
- Support the affected limb using plenty of padding, such as towels or any clothing that is available.
- Seek medical advice immediately. Any fracture will require medical treatment by a qualified practitioner.
- Never try to make any sort of bandage or splint for the affected area.

CASE STUDY Stephen

Stephen is a support worker in a residential unit for people with mental health needs. He is accompanying an individual on a walk around the gardens of the residential home, when suddenly, without warning, the person trips over a branch and falls to the ground. The individual is distressed and in great pain. Stephen can see that the leg is bent awkwardly and that a piece of bone is pushing up beneath the trouser leg.

1. What sort of verbal support could Stephen give the casualty?
2. Why should Stephen never attempt to move the client while providing support for him?
3. Who must Stephen contact? Why?
4. Carry out research to find out about the different types of fractures that may occur. What treatment should be given to the different types of fracture?
5. Look at the two pictures of fractures given below.

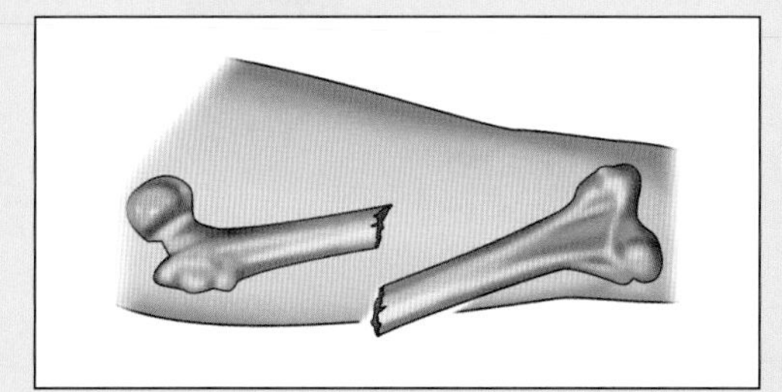

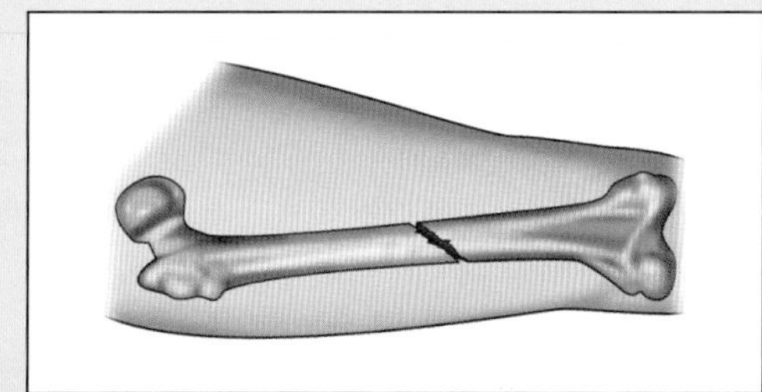

Can you identify which is a simple fracture and which is a compound fracture, and explain the differences?

Loss of consciousness

Loss of consciousness can take place for many different reasons. The usual reasons are because of an illness or injury.

The symptoms of loss of conscious are reduced reactions to **stimulus**. The casualty may not be able to respond to you or questions that you ask. The casualty may just be a little woozy or they may be totally unconscious.

> **...WORD CHECK**
> **stimulus** – to cause a reaction/to make interested.

The first aider should:

- Summon medical help immediately.
- Find out what may have caused the casualty to become unconscious. Try to look for any wounds that may have caused the person to become unconscious. Perhaps a person has a condition, such as diabetes, that has resulted in the unconscious state.
- Keep the airway open and clear. This should be done by lifting the chin and tilting the head backwards.
- If the person does not come to consciousness after a short time, then the first aider should put them in the recovery position.

This is done by:

- Kneeling by the side of the casualty at their waist.
- Opening the casualty's airway by tilting their head back. The casualty then needs to be on their back, with their limbs out straight.
- The casualty's arm that is nearest to you should be bent so it is at right angles to their body. The arm on the far side of you should be placed over their chest with the back of their hand against their opposite cheek.
- The first aider should then use their other hand to roll the casualty towards them by pulling on the far-side leg, just above the knee. This should then put the casualty on their side.
- When the casualty is rolled over, their legs should be bent at right angles to their body. Then, the first aider will need to make sure the casualty's head is tilted right back to keep the airway open.

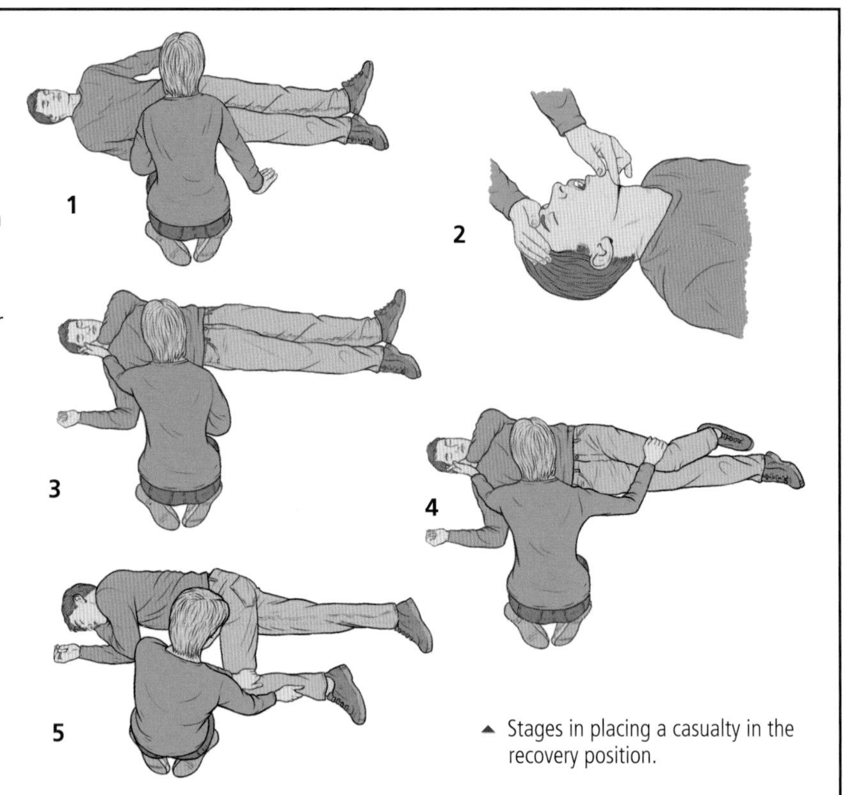

▲ Stages in placing a casualty in the recovery position.

ACTIVITY Jenny

Jenny has been out clubbing and begins walking the short way home. It is about 3:00am. When she turns a corner, she discovers a girl of about 17 years, lying on the pavement. She bends over to look closer and to speak to her. When she gets no reply, Jenny suspects the girl is unconscious but is unsure why or what has happened. Jenny gets out her mobile phone to call the emergency services.

1. What information should Jenny give to the emergency services?
2. What actions should Jenny take next?
3. Ask your teacher to supervise this activity: with a partner take turns at putting each other in the recovery position.
4. Research different types of injury and illness that could cause somebody to become unconscious.

Breathing difficulties

Breathing difficulties could be caused by an obstruction stuck at the back of the throat, because the person is having an asthma attack or for other medical reasons.

Symptoms

- choking
- difficulty breathing
- red face that may later turn grey
- being unable to speak
- the person will quite often be pointing at their throat or mouth in a state of panic.

Action for an obstruction

Make the casualty cough and if this does not work:

- Bend the casualty forwards and slap them sharply on the back between the shoulder blades up to five times.

If this does not work:

- Stand behind the casualty and place your arms around them, connecting each hand just below the breastbone. One of your hands should be in the shape of a fist and the other should be holding it.
- The hand wrapped round the fist should then be sharply pulled upwards and into the casualty's body at the same time. This is known as abdominal thrusts or the 'Heimlich manoeuvre'. This action should expel the obstruction.

▲ 'Try to bring it up!'

Action for asthma

The casualty will need access to their inhaler. The first aider will need to find this and make sure that it is administered to the casualty immediately. If the attack is a particularly bad one then it will be necessary to call for medical assistance.

Action for anaphylactic shock

For anaphylactic shock, which is usually caused by a severe allergic reaction to something, such as a bee sting, then medical help should be sought immediately. The casualty will need to be administered a dose of adrenalin by a medical professional.

CASE STUDY Rebecca

Rebecca is a care assistant and is supervising clients at lunchtime in the residential care home where she works. Rebecca notices a commotion coming from one of the tables where one of the elderly clients is sitting. One client is pointing at his own throat and looks very red, and another client is calling out and pointing at the other client. Both appear to be very distressed indeed.

1. What should Rebecca do in this situation?
2. How should Rebecca support other people who have been affected by the situation?
3. What should Rebecca do after she has dealt with the first-aid emergency? Why?
4. How could Rebecca and her manager make sure that the risks are minimized around eating and drinking within the residential home?

PREVENTING THE SPREAD OF INFECTION

When dealing with any minor emergencies it is important that whoever gives and receives first aid is protected from infection at all times. This means adopting **universal precautions**. These are:

- Thoroughly washing hands with antibacterial soap or hand wash before administering first aid. This will remove any bacteria from the hands before selecting appropriate latex gloves.
- Wearing latex or, if allergic, non-latex protective gloves when dealing with the casualty. This will prevent cross-infection taking place between the first aider and the casualty.
- Wearing protective clothing, such as an apron, to cover the first aider's clothes. This will protect the first aider from getting blood from the casualty on their clothes.

...WORD CHECK

universal precautions – recognized, world-wide hygiene practices.

- It may also be appropriate to wear protective coverings on the shoes. This may be appropriate when there are bodily fluids that the first aider is likely to step into.
- A protective face mask will also be necessary to prevent cross-infection taking place whilst giving breaths of life during the CPR process.

If it is possible, then the casualty should be informed as to why the first aider is using universal precautions. This is common practice and common courtesy to the client.

CASE STUDY Tim

Whilst on duty at a day-care centre Tim is confronted with a situation where a client is bleeding profusely from an open wound on their arm. Another client races up to him and tells him that he must give first aid straightaway.

Tim informs the client that he does not have any protective clothing with him and must go and get this before dealing with the accident. The client tells him not to be silly and that he should act immediately.

1. What do you think Tim should do in this situation?
2. What are the implications for Tim and the client if he does not apply universal precautions?
3. Carry out research to find out what type of infections Tim is leaving himself and the client open to if he does not adopt universal precautions.

ASSESSMENT PRACTICE

Ruben is a first aider who has to deal with a variety of emergency procedures. Explain how each should be carried out.

1. Basil has an asthma attack. Describe the first-aid procedure to be followed. [3]
2. Give **three** symptoms of a burn. [3]
3. Ruben is required to give first aid for a burn. Give the actions he should take. Make sure they are given in the correct order. [4]
4. At the pub, Ruben's friend chokes on some chips. He is turning red in the face. What first-aid procedure should Ruben follow? [5]
5. On his way home from work, Ruben finds a man lying on the side of the road clutching his leg. He has fallen off the pavement. Ruben thinks the man has fractured his leg. List **three** reasons why Ruben may think this. [6]
6. Explain how Ruben could protect himself from infection while carrying out first-aid procedures. [5]
7. Ruben has to deal with two different types of bleeding. These are:
   - a minor cut
   - severe bleeding of the leg.

   Describe the first-aid procedure for each.
   Explain why each is treated differently. [10]
8. Ruben needs to call the emergency services. List the information Ruben needs to give. For each point made, state why the information is required. [10]
9. Explain how the casualties given below would be prioritized when giving first aid, giving reasons for doing this:
   - a minor cut
   - an unconscious casualty
   - a burnt finger. [10]
10. Explain the correct order of steps for placing a casualty in the recovery position. You can use drawings to help you. [10]

LEGISLATION

Legislation affects the way that all workers do their job whilst in the workplace. All legislation should be followed at all times as failure to do so can result in disciplinary action being taken by the employer and also legal action by the government. Legislation is there to make sure that everyone in the workplace knows what is expected of them and keeps everyone in the workplace safe and legal.

The Health and Safety (First Aid) Regulations 1981 state that every workplace and home environment for clients should have:

> *'Adequate and appropriate equipment, facilities and personnel to enable first aid to be given to people if they are injured or become ill in the workplace.'*

The provision depends on various factors, such as:

- the number of people employed
- whether those people are working with hazardous substances
- the level or categories of risks, for example, lower – shops; medium – care homes.

A risk assessment should be carried out to determine the level of first-aid provision required. The minimum required is a suitably stocked first-aid kit and an 'appointed person'. That is someone with specific duties relating to first aid. First aid is essential, as it will prevent the injury from becoming worse and could save lives.

Every employee in the workplace must be made aware of first-aid procedures. They should have access to a first-aid box, which should be easily identifiable and well stocked. There should be a clearly visible notice stating where the first-aid box is located and who the appointed person is. A trained first aider and a first-aid room should be made available if the workplace gives rise to special hazards.

▾ Minimum requirements for a first-aid box.

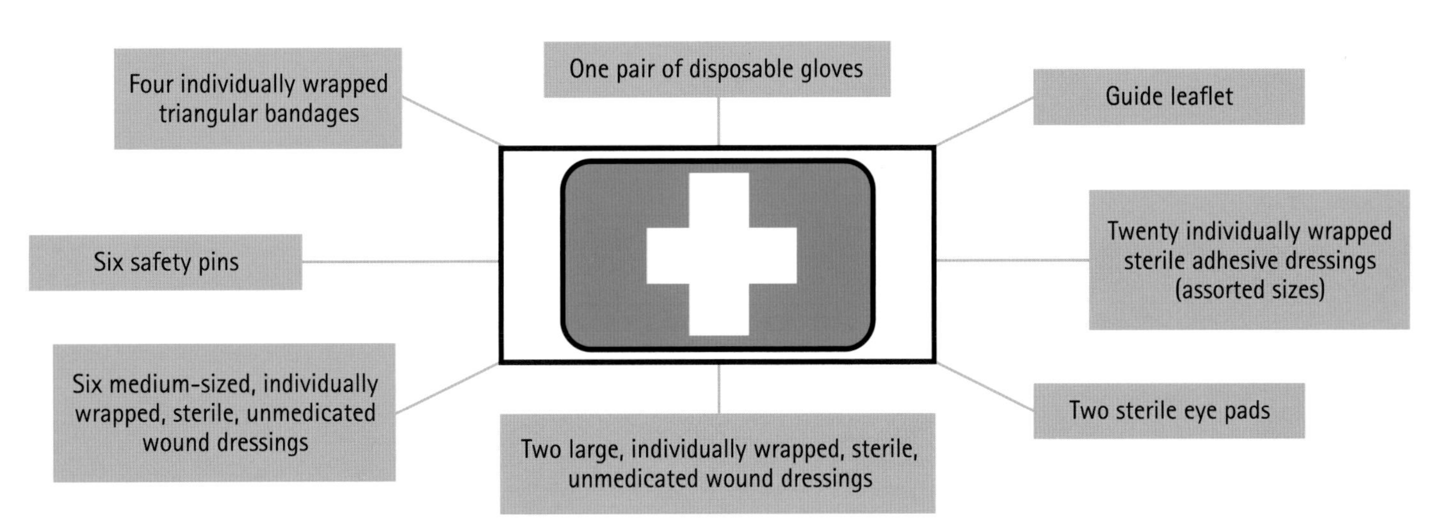

All first-aid cases dealt with must be recorded by the appointed person. Records should include the name of the casualty, date, time, circumstances of accident, details of injury and treatment given. These records should be retained.

An employer must have a policy/procedure in place for recording accidents, either an accident book or report form. RIDDOR requires the recording of an accident and so do the Registered Homes Inspectors, if the accident occurs in a residential or nursing home. Employees should know the location of the accident book and how to fill it in. If an accident happens, complete an accident report ensuring any witnesses to the accident also complete a report. The report must contain:

- date, time and place of accident
- details of what you saw
- condition of person after accident.
- people involved
- comments from any persons involved

ASSESSMENT PRACTICE

Jay is the named person responsible for health and safety at Buzzing Bees Nursery School. He is also the named first aider responsible for all first aid at the nursery.

1. List **eight** items that should be in the first-aid box kept at the nursery. [8]
2. Name the regulations that require a first-aid box to be available at the nursery. [1]
3. Explain how the regulations affect Buzzing Bees Nursery. [5]
4. List **four** pieces of information that should be kept for each accident that occurs at the nursery, and explain why each must be included. [10]
5. What are the likely effects of not following the regulations on Buzzing Bees Nursery? [5]
6. Explain how the regulations are likely to have a beneficial effect on:
   - clients
   - care workers. [10]

How to recognize potential risks to safety and how to reduce risks in settings

How to recognize potential risks to people who use services and care workers and how to provide protection for those using the settings

Getting started

For the external assessment you will need to know how to recognize potential risks to individual clients and care workers and how to provide protection for those using the setting. This will include:

- fire
- electricity
- unsafe equipment
- unsafe electrical fittings and fixtures
- flood
- gas leaks
- unsafe furnishings and fittings
- unsafe storage of hazardous substances.

You will also need to understand where risks often occur within the care setting:

- community rooms and lounges
- kitchens
- play areas
- bedrooms
- community areas, such as hallways, entrances and stairs
- bathrooms.

You will also need to understand how safety features can help to reduce risks, how to follow safety procedures, and how to use safety equipment, including:

- firefighting equipment, such as extinguishers and blankets
- emergency procedures, such as evacuation in the event of a fire
- smoke alarms
- fire exits
- staff training
- security fixtures, for example, electronic pads on doors, window guards, handles placed at a high level on doors
- safety/warning signs, such as first aid, exits, prohibited areas and no smoking.

You should recognize how and when these safety features are used and be able to give reasons about why their use helps to keep individuals safe.

You need to know how to conduct a risk assessment and the reasons why this action will help to protect individuals. To conduct a risk assessment within your workplace you need to consider:

- the five key stages and the associated purpose of each
- how to keep records of a risk assessment
- how to conduct a risk assessment
- the reasons for conducting a risk assessment.

Helping individuals to feel safe and protected is an important part of a care worker's role. You should know how to evacuate a building in the case of fire or other emergency.

You will need to understand the importance of protecting individuals against intruders such as:

- burglars
- unwanted visitors.

You should also consider:

- safety of possessions
- privacy.

You need to understand how to apply the following legislation:

- The Health and Safety at Work Act 1974
- Control of Substances Hazardous to Health (COSHH) Regulations 1994 and 2005.

You should also understand the role and responsibilities of the Health and Safety Executive (HSE).

POTENTIAL RISKS IN CARE SETTINGS

All settings, whether they are health, social care, early years, voluntary or private organizations, need to have regular maintenance checks to make sure that they are not at risk from any of the following:

Fire: Fire and smoke alarms should be checked regularly. Fire exits should be kept clear. Firefighting equipment, such as extinguishers and fire blankets, must be regularly maintained.

Flood: Could be caused by burst pipes, washing machines, dishwashers, water storage tanks, overflowing baths or leaking showers.

Electricity: Poor wiring could cause fires or lights to fail, or the loss of power. Overloading sockets or not having protected sockets, particularly where children are present, can be a risk.

Gas leaks: Boilers that are not regularly checked and cookers that are not maintained correctly could cause explosions. Gas fires that are not correctly ventilated can cause death.

Unsafe equipment: Large equipment that could be dangerous should have guards attached, for example, cutting equipment, laundry gadgets. Small equipment, such as mixers, should be regularly checked.

Unsafe furnishings: Broken chairs should be removed. Furniture that is unbalanced or could tip over should be repaired.

Hazardous substances: These should be kept in a locked cupboard or high enough so that they cannot be reached easily.

Unsafe electrical fittings: Frayed wires should be taped, broken sockets and covers mended.

Floor coverings: Frayed or worn carpets should be removed or taped to prevent slips and falls.

Not having regular checks could lead to the setting:

- being sued by care workers and clients if accidents occur
- being fined by local inspectors/local authorities
- having a poor reputation in the area
- finding it difficult to recruit professional workers
- being closed by local inspectors/local authorities.

Risks can occur in any part of a building or in any individual room. Areas that are most at risk are:

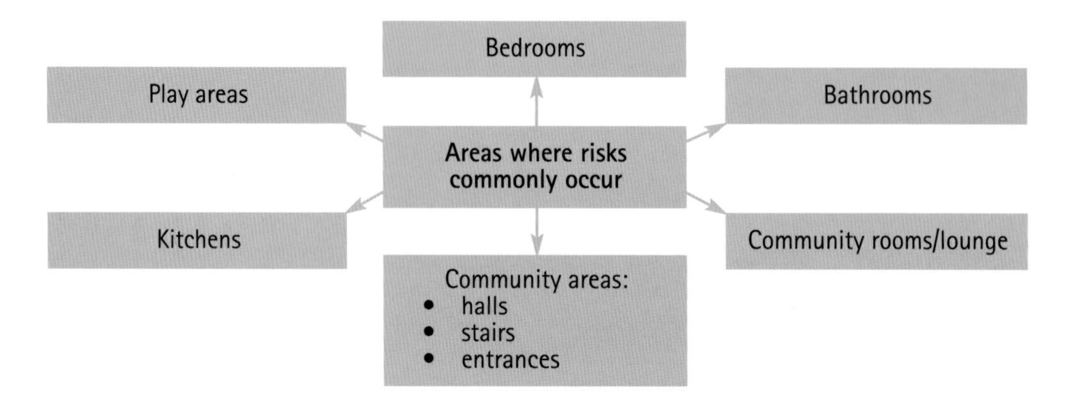

Bedrooms

Bedrooms are **solitary** places and more often than not clients will want to be left on their own. For most clients this is perfectly acceptable and normal, but for others, who are more vulnerable, supervision will be needed. Certain individuals may break the rules and smoke in their bedrooms and this could cause fire. Other clients may be at risk of abuse from less vulnerable residents, or they may be **susceptible** to epileptic seizures, which could cause them to fall to the floor and injure themselves. If this is the case then a risk assessment should be conducted as a high priority. This will usually result in regular checks needing to be made by staff members or having listening devices placed in the room so that the person can be monitored for their own safety.

...WORD CHECK

solitary – alone.

susceptible – open to/prone to (illness/ideas).

There are also dangers to the staff when involving themselves in the personal care of clients. These could be dangers caused by moving and handling clients, especially when using lifting equipment, such as hoists. These should always be used according to staff training and the manufacturer's instructions. There should always be two people involved in any moving and handling task with any individual.

Kitchens

In most medium to large care settings the kitchen will be 'off limits' to all but a few well-trained staff members. This is because in busy periods the kitchen will be a danger area for all non-trained staff. There should be a serving hatch in place where the waiting staff will collect and return plates of food and so on for clients. For those who enter the kitchen, protective clothing, such as hats, aprons or whites, shoes and protective gloves, should be worn to prevent cross-infection. All staff working in the kitchen should have basic food hygiene training to include dealing with hazards in the kitchen, preparation and storage of food, and correct cleaning and hygiene methods.

A kitchen in a hospital could be dangerous if care is not taken.

Community rooms and lounges

All community areas should be well lit and have clearly marked fire exits. It is also important that there are chairs for people to sit on, in case they need to rest whilst transferring from one room to another. Chairs must be in good condition and not broken in any way or this could cause an individual to fall and hurt themselves.

Play areas

These areas are more often used by children or adults with learning disabilities, where play is an integral part of human development. There should be round-the-clock supervision by trained staff members who will know what to do if there is a first-aid emergency. All equipment and play areas should be regularly serviced to prevent any equipment malfunction that could cause injury to a client. Regular risk assessments should take place on all people using the play area and the tasks that they are involved in.

All staff working with therapeutic play equipment should have training in its use. This equipment could include items such as gym equipment or sensory rooms that include lights and oils, which all need specialist training to use.

Bathrooms

Bathrooms can be dangerous places for clients and staff. There may be specialist equipment within the bathroom that clients and staff will need training to use. This includes hoists, ceiling tract hoists, bath chairs and showering equipment. No staff member should attempt to use a hoist on their own or without specialist training. Risks such as slips, trips and falls will be a danger while clients are bathing and using the bathroom facilities. All floors and bathrooms should be non-slip and if not, non-slip mats should be made available. There should also be non-slip mats in the bath to prevent clients from slipping whilst getting in and out of the bath. Vulnerable clients should never be left alone in the bathroom and this should be decided through a comprehensive risk assessment. All clients who are not supervised whilst in the bathroom should be regularly checked on by staff members.

Entrances, halls and stairs

These areas will get a lot of use and, therefore, wear and tear will take place on carpets, banisters, doors and entrances. Worn carpets are one of the main causes of slips, trips and falls within hallways and entrances in the home. It is important that these are regularly serviced and replaced as necessary. On the stairs, loose carpets can cause a very nasty accident!

Poor lighting is often a major risk in these areas. When staff or clients cannot see clearly, accidents will often happen. Sometimes packages can be left in the hall, such as boxes from deliveries, that people could fall over.

CASE STUDY Jane

Jane is a care worker at Manor Side Residential Home for people with learning disabilities. She has recently become worried about a new client who has come to live at the home. The home's management have not been keeping up to date with risk assessments recently due to short staffing. Most of the clients like to spend their time in the lounge but the new client spends a lot of time in his bedroom making model aeroplanes. This involves using glue. Jane has had experience with risk assessments before coming to Manor Side and decides to do the risk assessment for the client with her manager's permission.

1. Write a list of ten checks that Jane could make when conducting a risk assessment of the client's bedroom.
2. What dangers may face a client whilst alone in their bedroom, if a risk assessment is not carried out?

CASE STUDY Mary

Mary works at Tall Trees Home for people with learning disabilities. One day, one of the clients approaches her and asks if she may shower on her own. Mary has wondered for quite some time why the client has not been able to use the bathroom on her own before, as she is very capable. Mary tells her client that she will take the matter to her manager. The manager tells her to do a risk assessment so they can see what the risks are.

1. If you were Mary, what factors would you take into consideration when writing a risk assessment for the bathroom?
2. List the dangers that could occur in a bathroom if a risk assessment was not carried out.

ASSESSMENT PRACTICE

Barti has been asked to identify potential risks in specific areas of a hospice for children and young people.

1. Below is a picture of the play area at the hospice. Identify **five** risks. State why each is a risk. [10]

2. How should hazardous substances be stored at the hospice? [4]
3. Unsafe equipment can be a risk. The following items of equipment are used at the hospice. State why each could be a risk and how the risk could be reduced:
   - hoist
   - meat-slicing machine in the kitchen
   - a wheelchair
   - a kettle with a frayed lead. [8]
4. Explain why halls and stairs could be areas in the hospice where accidents could occur. [5]
5. Explain why it is beneficial to the hospice to have regular risk assessments. [5]

SAFETY FEATURES

Fire

▲ Safety features can save lives.

...WORD CHECK

devastating – shattering/very upsetting.

sustain – be affected by something.

arson – to set fire deliberately.

A fire in the workplace can be **devastating** to all those involved, be they staff members, clients or their families. A fire in a care setting could cause those involved to lose property, **sustain** injuries, such as burns, or even die. This is especially so in a care setting where more often than not the clients are vulnerable adults and children. This may mean that they will have difficulties in evacuating the care setting in the event of a fire.

Fires in the workplace may start for many different reasons. Examples include:

- Failure to follow health and safety policies and procedures in the workplace, such as smoking in non-designated areas, leaving kitchen areas whilst cooking food, overloading cupboards with flammable items, not regularly servicing firefighting equipment and smoke alarms, staff not being properly trained in the use of firefighting equipment, policies and procedures, and so on.
- Fires can also be set deliberately; this is called **arson**.
- Faulty equipment can also create the risk of fire.

There are many different forms of firefighting equipment and when fighting a fire, the correct equipment should always be used. If this is not the case then the equipment may make the situation and fire a lot worse. The different types of equipment are:

Extinguishers

Water

This is red in colour and contains water. This should be used on cloth, paper, plastics, coal, and so on. It will mainly be used on solid objects. It should never be used on burning oil or fat, or on anything electrical.

Standard dry powder

This is blue in colour and contains standard dry powder. It should be used on liquids such as petrol, paint, fats or oil, grease, and so on. It is safe to use this extinguisher on live electrical equipment. It should not, however, be used on chip or fat pan fires.

Multi-purpose dry powder

This is blue in colour and contains multi-purpose dry powder. This can be used on live electrical equipment but should never be used on chip or fat pan fires. It can be used on liquids such as grease, paint, petrol, oil and fats.

AFF (Aqueous film-forming foam)

This is a cream colour and can be used on liquids, cloth, paper, plastics, coal and so on. It can be used on fires involving solid objects. It should never be used on chip pan fires.

Carbon dioxide (CO_2)

This is black in colour and contains carbon dioxide. It may be used on liquids such as grease, fats or oil, paint, petrol, and so on. It must never be used on chip pan fires. The fumes from this extinguisher can also be harmful if used in confined spaces. Always make sure that the area is well ventilated when using this extinguisher.

Fire blankets

Can be used for fires involving liquids and solids. It can be used on chip pan fires and also fires involving clothing. It is thrown over the fire to exclude oxygen and so put out the fire.

Group Activity

Arrange a visit from your local fire safety officer (with your tutor's permission). Ask him or her about the most common causes of fire in care settings and how each should be dealt with.

In pairs, organize a quiz to test others in the group about safety features to reduce the risk of fire.

Take part in the quiz.

ASSESSMENT PRACTICE

Aub is the health and safety officer at a hospital. It is his responsibility to make sure that all firefighting equipment is well maintained and in working order so that it can be used effectively whenever needed.

1. Identify what types of fire Aub would use the following equipment on:
   - water fire extinguisher
   - standard dry powder fire extinguisher
   - fire blanket
   - multi-purpose dry powder. [4]
2. Identify the type of fire where a fire blanket would be used. Describe how a fire blanket would help when fighting a fire. [4]
3. Explain how the quality of clients' lives might be improved when they feel protected. [5]

Emergency procedures

If a fire does occur in the workplace, the worker must then be prepared to act immediately following the basic safety procedures:

- The workers should go to and break the glass point and sound the fire alarm.
- Dial 999 or make sure that 999 has been dialled by another person.
- All people in the setting should be removed from danger, for example, evacuated from the setting.
- Windows and doors should be closed if at all possible, to prevent the fire from spreading.
- If it is a small fire and it is safe to do so, two people could fight the fire with the appropriate fire extinguisher.
- Everyone who has evacuated the building should be asked to go to or be taken to the fire assembly points, which will be stated on the fire-procedure notice. Checks that everyone is present should be made by the named person.
- Never return to the building for any reason whatsoever until the 'all clear' is given by the fire brigade.

▲ This fire assembly point is clearly signposted.

Smoke/fire alarms

Smoke or fire alarms are in place to make sure that there is an early warning of any fire within the building. This hopefully allows the clients and staff to leave the building in good time. These either work on the detection of smoke or heat. Whichever system is used, the devices will be connected to the main fire-alarm panel within the setting. This panel will act as an early warning system for any fire in any area or zone within the building. As with any life-saving equipment, the smoke alarm should be tested on a weekly basis by a designated person to make sure it is **functioning** correctly. It should also be serviced by a professional on an annual basis.

...WORD CHECK

functioning – something that is active or working.

Fire exits

Group Activity

As a group, imagine a fire has broken out in the setting. Work in pairs to organize correctly evacuating the building, telephoning the emergency services and checking those present at the assembly point.

When everyone has had the opportunity to do the role play, discuss any issues that were found as a whole group. How difficult was it? Would you do anything differently?

Fire exits are the main means of escape from a setting in the event of a fire. There should be more than one fire exit in case one becomes blocked during a fire. All fire exits should be clearly marked with a fire exit sign, which will usually light up in the event of a fire. This will be directly linked to the fire-alarm panel. Fire exits should never be blocked and there should be a clear escape route in the event of a fire. The fire exits should be inspected on a daily basis to make sure that they are free from any obstruction that would be likely to prevent exit.

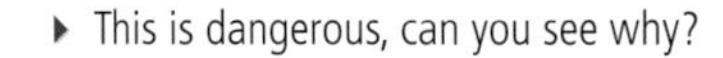

This is dangerous, can you see why?

ASSESSMENT PRACTICE

Jugjit is the manager of a training centre for adults who have learning disabilities. He is also responsible for health and safety. Every Monday, before the clients arrive, Jugjit checks some of the safety features in the centre.

1. Complete the table to show:
   - the purpose of the safety feature
   - how the safety feature could reduce the risk. [9]

Safety feature	Purpose	How it would reduce the risk
Fire exit		
Smoke alarm		
Fire alarm		

2. On one occasion a small fire starts in the kitchen of the training centre. What should Jugjit and the staff do? [6]
3. Some of the rooms at the training centre are on the second floor. How could Jugjit protect the clients when they are working upstairs? [5]

Staff training

Staff need to be correctly trained in how to deal with a fire and any other emergency that could arise in a setting, and this can only be done by training. Training should be taking place with all the staff, management and, where appropriate, clients on an annual basis.

Training should include:

- How to recognize dangers associated with the risk of fire, for example, where is the highest risk of a fire occurring and how can the risk be reduced?
- How to use firefighting equipment.
- How and where to access policies and procedures regarding fire safety within the care setting.
- Where the evacuation points are around the care setting.
- What to do in the event of a fire or other emergency.
- Making reference to written instructions of what to do in the event of an emergency, for example, instructions in bedrooms.
- Identification of the named first aider and the person who will check at the assembly point that everyone has left the building.

Additionally, staff will need to be trained in basic first-aid procedures so that they can help if an emergency should arise.

Group Activity

Arrange to visit a setting or invite a professional care worker to your centre (with your tutor's permission) to find out what happens at their setting in the case of a fire or other emergency. What staff training do they carry out? What policies do they have in place to deal with emergencies? What is the impact of these policies on the setting?

CASE STUDY Peter

It is Peter's first day at Sunnydale, a residential care home for the elderly. Peter has been assigned a **mentor** in order that he may complete his induction period within the home. Peter has already had it explained to him that it is part of his training package that he will complete a full induction, to include how to deal with the risk of fire in the home.

Jonathan has been assigned as Peter's mentor and he will be responsible for making sure that Peter receives training in how to deal with the risk of fires. Jonathan is an experienced member of staff and is a senior carer within the home.

1. Think about how you would plan the training that Peter is to receive about how to reduce the risk of fire. Describe what you think are the most important areas of training to cover with Peter.
2. Draft a health and safety checklist that you would use with a new member of staff when inducting them. Consider the following:
   - knowledge of policies and procedures
   - knowledge of fire exits and evacuation procedures
   - knowledge of legislation that impacts on the setting
   - use of firefighting equipment.
3. In pairs, take turns at being Jonathan and Peter and cover some of the important induction points surrounding fire and fire prevention.

Security fixtures

In order to maintain the safety of clients within the setting, it may be necessary to have certain security fixtures in place. The security fixtures need to be serviced on a regular basis to make sure that they are safe and effective. It should also be stated that in no way must security fixtures **inhibit** the freedom of a client. Some of the security fixtures that may be used in the building could be as follows:

...WORD CHECK

mentor – someone who is experienced in a skill or subject.

inhibit – to discourage.

Electronic pads on doors

Electronic pads are used to monitor the opening and closing of doors. They are also used in early years settings to prevent unwanted callers entering the building. Electronic pads will be alarmed and can be heard by people monitoring them, who are usually based in an office. Once the alarm is sounded, then the person will come and investigate.

Window guards

Window guards are a safety measure that stop windows from opening too far. This could potentially save somebody's life as it will stop them from falling out, and can also stop people from getting in through the window and frightening or attacking clients. They can also help to prevent burglary.

CASE STUDY **Millie**

Millie lives at Princes Residential Home because she is unable to look after herself as she has mobility problems. Her room at the residential home is on the first floor.

Millie used to live in the country and always left her window open. She has been asked not to do this at the residential home, but she always does.

One night, Millie wakes up to find a man wandering around her bedroom. She immediately pulls the alarm cord but it is several minutes before someone comes to see what is wrong. As the care worker enters the room she is pushed aside roughly by the man.

The care worker tries to calm Millie down and blames her for not having the window closed. Millie is even more upset about this. She then discovers that all her necklaces and rings have been stolen and the police are called.

The police, however, point out to the residential home that window catches should be in place and that staff should be checking residents every hour!

Handles placed at a high level on doors

High-level door handles are another safety feature used within many settings where people are at risk from entering rooms and where there could be significant danger, such as kitchens and bathrooms. This is especially necessary when dealing with vulnerable adults and children.

Safety and warning signs

...WORD CHECK

corrosive – capable of destroying or eating away solid materials.

The main categories of safety signs are as follows:

Warning signs

These are triangular in shape, with a black picture on a yellow background with black edging. These signs are for hazards, for example: flammable material, toxic, corrosive, radioactive, general danger, danger electricity, and laser beam.

Flammable material or high temperature

Explosive material

Toxic material

Corrosive material

Radioactive material

Overhead load

Prohibition signs

These are round in shape, with a black picture on a white background, red edging and diagonal line. These signs prohibit certain actions, such as smoking.

No smoking

Smoking and naked flames forbidden

No access for pedestrians

Do not extinguish with water

Not drinkable

No access for unauthorised persons

Mandatory signs

These signs tell people they must do something, such as wear safety goggles.

Eye protection must be worn

Safety helmet must be worn

Ear protection must be worn

Respiratory equipment must be worn

Safety boots must be worn

Safety gloves must be worn

Safe-condition signs

These are rectangular or square, with a white picture on a green background. These signs give information about safety features, such as fire exits.

First aid post

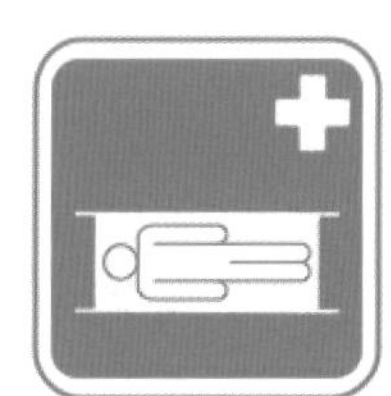
Stretcher

Safety shower

Eyewash

Emergency telephone for first aid or escape

Signs must be clearly displayed and kept in good condition. Safety features such as safety and warning signs can be of very great help to both clients and care workers because they will inform them about:

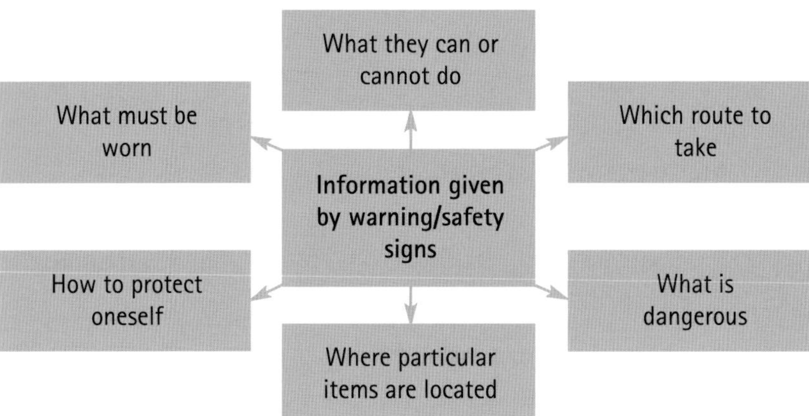

ASSESSMENT PRACTICE

Christine is a new trainee health care assistant on the ward of a hospital. She has been told that she must make herself familiar with the safety features that are in place.

1. For each of the signs above, state:
   - what their meaning is
   - how they help to protect clients and staff. [6]
2. Explain why high-placed door handles protect:
   - children in a playgroup
   - clients who are forgetful or wander. [10]
3. Explain the purpose of an electronic pad attached to a front door or an office. [5]
4. How does having window guards on windows protect clients and staff? [5]

RISK ASSESSMENT

Group Activity

Arrange to visit a setting or while you are on work experience (with your tutor's and the setting's permission), do a risk assessment of one area of the setting. You should not find actual risks as legislation protects clients but make a note of potential risks for the area.

Produce a drawing of the area examined and show where you would place any safety features. Explain how this would protect both clients and staff.

...WORD CHECK

potential – with a possibility of happening.

A risk assessment is one of the main safety procedures within a care setting. There should be a risk assessment in place for all clients, staff members and visitors to the care setting. It is often said that prevention is better than cure, so it is important to get the risk assessment right and that it is followed by all staff members and clients within the setting.

When conducting a risk assessment there are five key stages. These are:

Step 1: Look for hazards

This is where hazards are identified. The person carrying out the risk assessment should walk around the premises or examine the emergency health situation and look at things that could cause serious harm or could affect several people. It could be the equipment, physical environment, people's behaviour or tasks that are **potential** hazards.

Step 2: Assess who may be harmed

All employees including maintenance, full- and part-time staff must be taken into account when making a risk assessment. Clients and visitors, too, must be considered.

Step 3: Consider the risk – are precautions adequate?

The aim at this stage is to make risks small. More needs to be done if the risk remains medium or high. Priority should be given to any risk that remains high or affects most people. If the hazard can be removed or got rid of then do it! For example, wires trailing across a floor or electric sockets that children could push their fingers into. If the hazard cannot be removed, the risk from it needs to be controlled by taking extra precautions, for example:

- prevent access to hazard
- provide personal protective clothing, for example, disposable plastic aprons and latex-free gloves.

Once measures to control risks are found, they must then be implemented. Not all precautions need to be expensive; some could be a change of working practice.

Step 4: Document the findings

If there are five or more employees, then **significant** findings (hazards and conditions) from the risk assessments must be recorded or documented. Staff must be told about the findings. An example of a major finding could be a 'badly worn carpet in the residents' lounge due to be replaced in three months' time'. This would need to be covered with tape to prevent anyone tripping over it and would need to be checked on a regular basis until the carpet was replaced.

Step 5: Review the assessment and revise if necessary

Records to demonstrate that all necessary aspects have been covered are very useful. They make a useful reference point for when assessments need to be reviewed.

A risk assessment should be in place for every client who lives within or attends any type of care service. The risk assessment is an **integral** document that looks at how to keep people safe in any given environment and in any given situation, for example, when assisting a client to have a bath. A risk assessment is all about the **probability** of harm coming to an individual, practitioner or visitor to care services. It is, therefore, important to make sure that all activities that the client involves themselves in are assessed.

A risk is the likelihood of a hazard (something that has the potential to cause harm) becoming a danger to a person or property. Risks are classified as low, medium and high.

...WORD CHECK

significant – having a major part/having a major contribution.

integral – an essential part.

probability – likelihood.

ASSESSMENT PRACTICE

Look at the drawing of a community sitting room in a residential home.

1. Explain the five stages of the risk assessment that would be carried out by the warden on this lounge. [20]
2. Select five risks shown in the drawing.
   - Explain why each is a risk.
   - Explain how each risk could be reduced. [20]
3. Explain how carrying out a risk assessment could improve the quality of life for clients. [5]

PROTECTING INDIVIDUALS AGAINST INTRUDERS

How to prevent access of unwanted callers and burglars

▲ I need to swipe through my card!

There are ways to prevent access by unwanted callers. The main method is to keep all outside doors locked and have a doorbell. This can be done as long as the door locks comply with the fire regulations. Most care settings use a range of methods against unwanted callers. If the establishment is big enough, they may have a reception so that everyone entering and leaving signs in and out. This has two benefits; it allows the monitoring of visitors and supports the fire procedure by listing everyone in the building.

To help maintain the security in the building, doors that are not in regular use should be alarmed. This will identify if anyone is coming in or out unannounced. Closed-circuit television may also be used to monitor the coming and going of all staff and visitors. It is important that everyone who works in a building is aware of and follows the security procedures, as this benefits the safety of all.

To help maintain security, the number of keys issued should be limited. There should be a list of the people who hold keys and the access that they have. Such people are called 'key holders'. By doing this, the safety of the building is increased. Keys should always be looked after and not left lying about for anyone to pick up.

Some care environments will not have keys. Access can be obtained by having door code entry systems where the visitor puts in a secret combination of numbers. The other option is an electronic card entry system. In this system, a magnetic card is used that is similar to a bank card. This is swiped through the lock and the door releases. These can often be combined with a personal identity card. They will be produced with a picture of the individual on them, and will also contain their name and details about where they work or who they are.

Temporary cards could be issued to people who are visiting, or who have come to make repairs or service equipment. These cards will often not have a picture of the individual on them. If they come from an outside company then they should have an identity card of their own to support their identity. This allows the registration of all people moving about the building and helps to identify who they are. Many employers identify their staff by giving them a uniform and a name badge. This, together with an identity card, makes identification immediate.

Unaccompanied packages can often be a risk due to the heightened state of alert that has been caused by terrorism. It is, therefore, important to immediately explore where the luggage, packages, boxes or other unexpected containers that appear come from.

A suspicious package that cannot be identified should not be moved or opened until it has been identified. Most of these objects will prove to be harmless but if a suspicious package is discovered, care workers and clients should evacuate the building immediately.

Group Activity

Arrange to visit a residential home or a day-care centre to find out how safety and security are promoted. Remember to ask questions about:

- safety risks
- security measures
- how unwanted callers are dealt with
- how burglaries are prevented
- security of buildings
- security of people.

Possessions

Any valuables owned by the clients should be kept in a safe. This can be one that is in the client's own room or a central safe in an office, or similar room, that is kept locked when not being used.

Care workers must also respect that a client's possessions belong to the client. They are not for loan to others without the client having given permission. This applies to the client's own clothing. Just because their own clothing is being laundered, it does not mean that they have to wear garments that belong to someone else!

Privacy

All care workers and visitors should knock on a client's door and wait for their permission before entering the room. This shows respect and allows the client to choose whether they want someone else in their room or not. Care workers must also remember that anything they are told by the client must remain in confidence unless the client is likely to:

- harm themselves
- harm others
- commit a crime (or already has).

CASE STUDY Puddle Duck Nursery

Security is very good at Puddle Duck Nursery. There is a key pad on the front door, door handles are placed at a high level so that children cannot escape, window catches are in place so that the windows cannot be fully opened and supervision levels for the children are high.

Janice, a nursery nurse, has to help move some toys outside for the maintenance man to collect. While she is doing this she leaves the door open. She forgets that she has done this and goes off to look after her group.

Later, it is discovered that two purses are missing from staff handbags and one of the children cannot be found. The police are alerted immediately.

The child who is missing is called Jonah and is four years old. He lives about a mile-and-a-half from the nursery school. His parents are alerted and hurry to the school, but Jonah cannot be found anywhere.

Half-an-hour later a policeman telephones the nursery school to say that he has found Jonah outside the house where he lives. Everyone is very relieved! No harm has come to him.

Discuss:

1. What should have happened to protect Jonah?
2. What should staff do with personal possessions when at work?

ASSESSMENT PRACTICE

1. Donna is responsible for safety and security at Sunny View Nursery School. She needs to make sure that all those using the nursery school are protected from harm.

   Identify the possible safety risks to the clients, care workers and visitors that could exist in the nursery school, explaining how these could be reduced. [10]
2. Explain how Donna could prevent unwanted visitors from accessing the nursery. [10]
3. Explain how a residential home could make sure that a client has privacy. [5]
4. Explain how a client's possessions could be made safe. [5]

LEGISLATION AND REGULATIONS

The Health and Safety at Work Act 1974

Legislation and regulations are passed by the government in order to protect people. This includes clients and workers. One piece of legislation that is relevant to this unit is the Health and Safety at Work Act 1974. This Act was discussed earlier in this unit on page 292. Look back and remind yourself of the main points relating to this Act and how it impacts on settings.

Control of Substances Hazardous to Health (COSHH) Regulations 1994, revised 2002

▲ Cleaning products, such as bleach, should be kept in a locked cupboard when not in use.

This regulation requires employers to control exposure to hazardous substances at work. Employers must meet essential requirements for the storage and use of hazardous substances. Care settings must have a COSHH file, which is kept up to date, listing all the hazardous substances stored on their premises. Hazardous substances used in care settings include some cleaning materials, disinfectants, and micro-organisms from soiled laundry and clinical waste.

Employers must assess the health risk faced by their employees, clients and visitors and decide on the action needed to control exposure to hazardous substances. The assessment results should be recorded in the COSHH file.

The file must:

- identify and name each hazardous substance
- state where each hazardous substance is kept
- state how the hazardous substances are labelled
- describe the effects of the hazardous substances
- state the maximum amount of time it is safe to be exposed to them
- describe how to deal with an emergency involving the hazardous substances.

COSHH assessments should be relatively easy in a setting. Firstly, find out which products and biological hazards (for example, soiled linen) are in the setting. Identify whether less harmful products could decrease the risk. If the product cannot be replaced, then staff and clients must be subjected to minimum exposure by providing precautions such as good ventilation.

All cleaning materials, for example, bleach, should be kept out of the reach of vulnerable clients. This can be achieved by keeping the substances in a locked cupboard when not in use. There have been deaths in care homes where clients have swallowed hazardous substances through mistaking them for soft drinks.

When working with any hazardous substances, the care worker should ensure precautions listed in the COSHH file are followed. Storage details of hazardous substances are also given in the COSHH file. Containers should be correctly labelled and have safety lids. Always follow manufacturers' instructions.

COSHH Regulations updated 2005

From 6 April 2005 the Control of Substances Hazardous to Health Regulations 2002 were significantly updated. There is now a new focus on good practice to help employers prevent their employees' health being harmed by workplace chemicals, and a change to the way limits are set for exposure to chemicals in the workplace.

Employers' COSHH duties

To comply with COSHH, employers currently need to follow these eight steps:

Step 1 – Assess the risks.
Step 2 – Decide what precautions are needed.
Step 3 – Prevent or adequately control exposure.
Step 4 – Ensure that control measures are used and maintained.
Step 5 – Monitor the exposure.
Step 6 – Carry out appropriate health surveillance.
Step 7 – Prepare plans and procedures to deal with accidents, incidents and emergencies.
Step 8 – Ensure employees are properly informed, trained and supervised.

Principles of good practice for the control of exposure to substances hazardous to health

Employers already have a clear responsibility to manage and minimize the risks from work activities. They must develop suitable and sufficient control measures, and ways of maintaining them. They should:

- identify hazards and potentially significant risks
- take action to prevent and control risks
- keep control measures under regular review.

To be effective in the long term, control measures must be practical, workable and sustainable. Employers who do not follow these principles will not be properly protecting their employees. They are to:

1. Design and operate processes and activities to minimize emission, release and spread of substances hazardous to health.
2. Take into account all relevant routes of exposure.
3. Control exposure by measures that are proportionate to the health risk.
4. Choose the most effective and reliable control options, which minimize the escape and spread of substances hazardous to health.
5. Where adequate control of exposure cannot be achieved by other means, provide, in combination with other control measures, suitable personal protective equipment.
6. Check and review, regularly, all elements of control measures for their continuing effectiveness.
7. Inform and train all employees on the hazards and risks from the substances with which they work, and the use of control measures developed to minimize the risks.
8. Ensure that the introduction of control measures does not increase the overall risk to health and safety.

See the Health and Safety Executive's COSHH website: http://www.hse.gov.uk/coshh/index.htm.

What should employers do?

- Ensure they involve their safety representatives in the COSHH assessment, so that no substance is used without having first been fully assessed.
- Take copies of COSHH assessments and records of monitoring, including the results of local exhaust-ventilation tests.
- Check that measures to first prevent and then control exposure are introduced.
- Ensure that they provide information and training in the risks and alternative means of working with substances hazardous to health.

The Health and Safety Executive (HSE)

The Health and Safety Executive (HSE) is the main body for the UK responsible for making sure that legislation is followed and for providing guidance on health and safety in the workplace. HSE covers offices, factories, building sites, mines, quarries, fairgrounds, railways, chemical plants, offshore and nuclear installations, schools and hospitals.

The HSE employs health and safety enforcement officers who can:

- enter premises
- conduct investigations
- take samples and photographs
- ask questions
- give advice
- issue instructions that must be carried out by law
- initiate a prosecution
- inspect documents
- take measurements
- issue 'Improvement and Prohibition Notices'.

Until the formation of the Health and Safety Executive for Northern Ireland in 1999, enforcement in the province was undertaken by the Health and Safety Inspectorate and the Health and Safety Agency.

ASSESSMENT PRACTICE

1. Describe the work of the Health and Safety Executive (HSE). Give two examples of how they could impact on care settings. [5]
2. Explain how The Control of Substances Hazardous to Health (COSHH) Regulations 1994, revised in 2002 and 2005, would impact on a residential home. [5]
3. Identify **three** ways of preventing unwanted callers from entering a residential home. For each method, explain how it helps to keep the clients safe. [10]
4. Explain how to maintain safety and security for children and staff of a playgroup. [10]
5. Explain **three** ways that the Health and Safety at Work Act can protect employees in the workplace. [6]

Appendix 1 – Calorie counter

Food	Measure	Calories	Food	Measure	Calories
All bran	1/3 cup	113	Dried apricots	5–6	80
Almonds	25–30	170	Eggs (large)	67g	100
Apple (medium)	1	65	Fanta	375ml	195
Apricots (medium)	1	15	Fillet steak	100g	196
Asparagus spears (medium)	3	10	Fish (white fish, low fat)	100g	100
Bacon (grilled)	1 rasher	112	Flake	30g	177
Baked beans	220g	205	Grapefruit (medium)	1/2	20
Banana (medium)	1	87	Grapes (medium)	125g	125
Banana chips	1/4 cup	155	Hazelnuts	30g	185
Bean sprouts	100g	30	Ice cream single flavour	1 scoop	90
Beans	1/2	13	Kit Kat	2 wafers	104
Biscuit (chocolate)	1	98	Kiwifruit (medium)	1	40
Biscuit (chocolate chip cookie)	1	35	Leg of roast lamb	2 slices	170
Biscuit (ginger nut)	1	42	Lemon	1	23
Bread (wholemeal)	1 slice	62	Lemonade	375ml	160
Bread (white plain)	1 slice	66	Lentils (cooked)	100g	260
Broccoli	2 florets	11	Lettuce	3 leaves	2
Butter	1 tsp	36	M&Ms	1 pkt	238
Cabbage	1/2	7	Mango	1	102
Carrots	1 small	23	Margarine	1 tsp	36
Cashews	12–16	180	Mars bar	60g	265
Cauliflower	1/2 cup	20	Melon (medium)	1/2	135
Cheese	30g	120	Milk (full cream)	1 cup	167
Chicken (roasted breast)	100g	110	Milk (skim)	1 cup	88
Chicken (leg/thigh)	100g	210	Milk (soy)	1 cup	160
Chocolate (plain/nuts/fruit)	5–6 rows	160	Mince (beef)	100g	210
Cola	375ml can	154	Mushrooms	1/2 cup	15
Coco pops	3/4 cup	115	Oil (vegetable)	1 tbsp	176
Corn flakes	1 and 1/3 cups	113	Onions	medium	30
Corned beef	100g	210	Oranges (medium)	1	80
Cream soda	375ml	170	Peach	1	40
Crunchie	80g	413	Peanuts (raw)	30g	120
Cucumber	150g	12	Pear	1	69
Dates	4–5	83	Peas	1/4 cup	20
Diet coke/Pepsi	375ml can	1.5	Picnic	55g	290
Dr Pepper	375ml	157	Pineapple	1 slice	33
Dried apple rings	10 rings	75	Plums	1	33

Continued on next page

Food	Measure	Calories	Food	Measure	Calories
Potatoes	medium	105	Sultanas	2 tbsp	92
Prunes (moist)	2–3	70	T-bone steak	100g	135
Rice (white, cooked)	1/2 cup	92	Tomato (medium)	1	20
Rice (brown, cooked)	1/2 cup	93	Tonic water	375	135
Rump steak	100g	190	Walnuts	15–20	185
Shredded Wheat	1/2 cup	240	Yogurt (flavoured)	200g	190
Smarties	25g	116	Yogurt (low fat)	200g	120
Snickers	60g	283	Yogurt (natural)	200g	160
Strawberries (medium)	6	10			

Appendix 2 – Exercise planner (for a person weighing 160 pounds)

Activity	Exercise time	Calories used	Activity	Exercise time	Calories used
Aerobics	30	214	Playing piano	30	89
Basketball	30	286	Reading	30	64
Biking (leisurely)	30	214	Riding	30	143
Boating	30	89	Rock climbing	30	393
Bowling	30	107	Running (5mph)	30	286
Canoeing	30	143	Running on the spot	30	286
Cooking	30	89	Running up stairs	30	537
Cross country	30	322	Shopping	30	82
Dancing	30	161	Skiing	30	250
Driving	30	71	Sleeping	30	32
Exercise bike	30	214	Squash	30	358
Fishing	30	143	Swimming	30	286
Football	30	250	Talking on the phone	30	35
Gardening	30	179	Tennis	30	250
Golf	30	161	Volleyball	30	107
Hiking	30	214	Walking (4mph)	30	125
House cleaning	30	89	Watching TV	30	35
Jogging	30	250	Weightlifting	30	107
Mountain biking	30	125	Writing	30	35
Playing guitar	30	107	Yoga	30	143

Index